Somerset Atlas
of breeding and
wintering birds
2007–2012

David Ballance
Rob Grimmond
Stephen Moss
Julian Thomas
and
Eve Tigwell

Somerset Atlas of breeding and wintering birds 2007–2012

The publisher gratefully acknowledges the permission granted by the British Trust for Ornithology to utilise data submitted to them via the national Atlas website http://www.bto.org/volunteer-surveys/birdatlas. Maps produced using DMAP software © Dr Alan Morton.

All illustrations © Mike Langman, including many reproduced by kind permission of Tim Davis and Tim Jones.

ISBN: 978-0-9931205-0-3

British Library Cataloguing in Publication Data
A catalogue record for this book is available from the British Library.

Published by Somerset Ornithological Society
www.somersetbirds.net

Layout and image editing by Tim Davis, DJ Environmental, Harpers Mill, Berrynarbor, Ilfracombe EX34 9TB
www.djenvironmental.com

Printed and bound in Great Britain by Short Run Press Ltd, Bittern Road, Sowton Industrial Estate, Exeter EX2 7LW
www.shortrunpress.co.uk

MIX
Paper from responsible sources
FSC
www.fsc.org
FSC® C014540

Contents

Acknowledgements

Cover artwork and all illustrations by Mike Langman, including many from *The Birds of Lundy* (2007), courtesy of Tim Davis and Tim Jones. Topographical and other interpretative maps produced by Chris Dee of Garganey Consulting. Species maps generated by Rob Grimmond using DMAP mapping software (produced by Dr Alan Morton – www.dmap.co.uk), from data provided by BTO and validated by BTO, Rob Grimmond, Eve Tigwell and Julian Thomas, including additional data provided by SOS and reviewed by Dave Chown. Photographs as individually credited – many thanks to all for permission to use them. Lead author of the species texts is David Ballance with input from all other authors, Dick Best, Dave Chown, Brian Gibbs, Tony Parsons, Geoff Suter and others. Tim Davis of DJEnvironmental produced the layout.

    Many thanks to the various SOS members who acted as 'Collectors' (coordinators for one or more 10-km squares) and to all the observers who provided records – a full list is on pages 327–330. And last but certainly not least, many thanks to all those individuals and organisations that contributed towards the costs of producing this book by sponsoring one or more species.

Foreword

Change is inevitable. The weather, the seasons, the light, the way we appear in the mirror. Even mighty mountains and the oceans are all changing each and every day, sometimes so slowly we can not register the shifting forms and sometimes with mercurial speed.

The significant changes that take place in the natural world generally occur over hundreds, if not thousands or millions of years. Creatures evolve and adapt as conditions shift and, but for cataclysmic sudden events such as a giant meteor hitting Earth, every living thing has had time to embrace the differences the planet presents before it. Until now.

Now we have a 'new' player in town. Us. The Earth has never seen anything like us. Never has there been a creature with the capacity to adapt to different environments as we do. A creature that can mould its environment to ensure not only its survival, but its proliferation. We managed to achieve astonishing advances in relative harmony on Earth for tens of thousands of years. Only in the past few hundred years, the blink of a geological eye, has our astonishing success started to seriously threaten the lives of millions of living things, including ourselves.

What has all this to do with a County Bird Atlas? Everything really. Forty years ago when I was roaming the Somerset Levels as an enthusiastic budding birdwatcher, I would often visit Tealham and Tadham Moors in spring to marvel at the drumming Snipe and tumbling display flights of the Lapwing. I waited eagerly for the silver-bell voices of the Yellow Wagtails arriving to breed on the moor from Africa, and sought out the pollarded willows that offered nesting refuge to Redstarts. Barn Owls quartered many of the hay meadows to swoop on the season's vole bounty and Turtle Doves and Cuckoos coo'd and cuckoo'd from seemingly every copse, spinney, and hedgerow. And where are they now? Most have gone or have been squeezed into the margins of existence in our county or even the country as a whole. So many events have affected their misfortunes, and many, if not all, have undoubtedly been because of the actions of Man, particularly the way we use the land. As agricultural practices grew ever more mechanised and intensive, so the opportunity for bird and other wildlife to adapt to changes were snuffed out. Wetlands have been drained, grasslands have been cut two or three times a year for silage where once they were harvested only once as hay in the mid to late summer. Hedges have been removed and woodlands felled to make way for bigger fields. Lowland heath was once a key part of the Somerset Levels ecosystem but today only minute fragments remain. On the surrounding high ground, herbicides have destroyed the food plants of butterflies and bees. Pesticides decimated the staple diet of legions of birds and other small creatures. And a changing climate, accelerated by our ever growing greenhouse-gas emissions, increases the pressure for birds and other creatures to change along with it. Some will adapt. Some cannot.

The Bird Atlas is a snapshot, a slice of what we have with us today against which we can compare records from the past. We know already that nationally there has been a decline in 60% of our natural neighbours, 10% of which are threatened with extinction in the UK.

But there is good news. Just as we can change the world around us to the detriment of every living thing, including ourselves, so we have it in our gift to achieve the opposite. Our intellect, industry, and ingenuity can work together to bring about change for the better, change for good for all living things. We have seen hints of this with the recovery of key species, many of which have been facilitated by the work of various conservation organisations (including the Somerset Wildlife Trust) and of course with your continued care and support. Bittern, Marsh Harrier, Red Kite, Goldfinch, and Siskin – all birds that have done well over the past few decades in our county (not to mention mammals like Otter and Polecat) thanks to focused conservation initiatives or the simple act of providing a ready food stuff.

On my own modest patch of typical Somerset farmland, I have witnessed a phenomenal increase in biomass and biodiversity in three short years due entirely to the way the ground has been managed. The resilience and capacity for the wild world to bounce back from the brink is remarkable, if we give it half a chance.

This volume is an important overview of where we are today, and whilst there is room to celebrate a little and reflect sombrely a lot on its content, there is no room for complacency. We can, we must, make a positive difference to the future fortunes of birds and all other life in Somerset and the country as a whole.

Simon King
Wildlife broadcaster and Somerset Wildlife Trust patron

Introduction

"An account of the nature and habits of the various birds belonging to a county... cannot help being interesting to the inhabitants... for Ornithology, and indeed all Natural History, begins, like Charity, at home."

Cecil Smith, *The Birds of Somersetshire*, 1869

The county of Somerset – the gateway to the West Country – is famed for many things: King Arthur and King Alfred, cloudy cider and Cheddar cheese, Wells Cathedral and the Wurzels, the Battle of Sedgemoor and Glastonbury (both the Tor and the Festival), and of course its birds.

For although Somerset may not attract the same quantity of rare visitors as the neighbouring counties of Devon or Dorset, the variety of habitats found in the county – from the high tops of Exmoor to the low marshes of the Levels – means that we host a wide range of breeding birds, and a respectable number of non-breeding visitors, especially during the winter months.

The presence of such a diversity of habitats ensures that there are plenty of opportunities for birds of farmland, woodland, coast, moorland, heathland, and especially wetland. Starting from Exmoor, the Quantocks and Bridgwater Bay in the west, through the Blackdown, Mendip and Polden Hills, via the flatlands of the Moors and Levels in the centre, to Selwood Forest in the east, there is plenty to keep birders and more serious ornithologists interested and entertained.

The recent events on the Avalon Marshes – an ambitious scheme to 'rewild' much of the landscape in order to attract a wide range of wetland birds and other wildlife – have added to the county's attraction; not just for birds, but for those of us who watch and enjoy them too.

The history of ornithology in Somerset is a long one. In 1869, at the mid-point of Queen Victoria's 64-year reign, Cecil Smith published *The Birds of Somersetshire*, a hefty tome detailing what was then known about the county's avifauna. This was the first real attempt to chart the status of Somerset birds, though two decades earlier, William Baker of Bridgwater had produced a brief list of species found here.

In 1893, the Rev. Murray Mathew produced a 'Revised List', and was followed by another man of the cloth, the Rev. Francis Linley Blathwayt, who compiled a list of Somerset birds in 1901 (eventually published in 1906). He was also the driving force behind the founding of the Ornithological Section of the Somerset Archaeological and Natural History Society in 1911. Bird reports were produced from 1912 (annually from 1918), and in 1974 the birdwatchers left the parent organisation to form the Somerset Ornithological Society – one of the two organisations, together with the BTO, behind this *Atlas*.

In the meantime, in 1955 *The Breeding Birds of Somerset and Their Eggs* was posthumously published by Stanley Lewis (who had died in 1949), and in 1968 Eileen Palmer and David Ballance wrote a full county avifauna, *The Birds of Somerset*. Twenty years later, in 1988, the SOS published *Birds of Somerset*. By then the reorganisation of the county boundaries in 1974 meant that records from the area known as Avon (including those from such well-known sites as Chew Valley Lake and Blagdon Lake) were no longer considered for either the annual report or county avifaunas.

Records of breeding, wintering, passage and vagrant birds continued to be detailed in the annual report *Somerset Birds*, while in 2006 the doyen of county ornithology, David Ballance, published his magisterial avifauna *History of the Birds of Somerset*. This not only showed the current status of the county's birds, but also charted the rises and falls in their fortunes over recorded history. He revealed, for example, that until the 1920s the Lesser Spotted Woodpecker was the commonest member of its family in the county – less than a century later it has almost disappeared.

Meanwhile, during the 20th century, birdwatching had grown from a minority pastime pursued by a few to a mass-participation activity involving tens of thousands of people; if you include those who feed birds in their garden, millions.

In the late 1960s, the presence of thousands of keen and knowledgeable 'citizen scientists' led the British Trust for Ornithology to launch their first national *Atlas* project, which ran from 1968 to 1972, and was published in 1976. Since then there have been three more national surveys of breeding and/or wintering birds (1981–1984, 1988–1991 and the latest, 2007–2011) a *Migration Atlas* (2002), and a host of county-based surveys: about two-thirds of English counties have published their own Atlas.

Until now, Somerset has been a notable absentee from this roll of honour, perhaps because the county's large size (11th of English counties in terms of land area) combined with a relatively small number of keen birders, has deterred local ornithologists from initiating such a project. Now, though, thanks to sterling efforts from more than 600 volunteers, the *Somerset Atlas of breeding and wintering birds* is before you.

So why have we decided to produce a county Atlas, why now, and what does it reveal? One reason is that we were already doing the fieldwork for the national *Bird Atlas 2007–11*, which meant that we already had a wealth of data about the latest status of our county's birds. With one extra year's fieldwork, and a lot of extra effort from the steering committee and many others, it was possible to produce this *Somerset Atlas.*

Even before we embarked on the national and county surveys we were well aware that Britain's birdlife is currently at a crossroads. After a long period of decline for many species – especially those that depend on farmland and woodland habitats – we are at last seeing a concentrated effort being made to improve and restore habitats for a wide range of birds and other wildlife.

This process began around the turn of the millennium, when conservation organisations realised that the traditional approach of fencing off small parcels of land as nature reserves would not serve our wildlife well in the rapidly changing environment of the 21st century.

Concepts such as 'rewilding', 'landscape-scale conservation' and the Wildlife Trusts' 'Living Landscapes' initiative began to be implemented: taking large swathes of the countryside and joining them up to provide extensive areas of habitat, linked by corridors to allow wildlife to move between them. This works better in some habitats than others, and is especially effective when restoring and recreating wetlands. Here in Somerset we have been fortunate to have the ideal location to attempt this brave experiment: the former peat diggings of the low-lying Somerset Moors and Levels.

The results of this are already bearing fruit. In a single decade, from 2002 to 2012, Somerset went from having two species of breeding heron (Grey Heron and Little Egret), to an astonishing six (adding Bittern, Little Bittern, Cattle Egret and Great White Egret to the list). With the addition of the reintroduced flock of Cranes on West Sedge Moor, and regular sightings of White Stork and Glossy Ibis, the Somerset Levels is rapidly becoming the best place in Britain to see a range of scarce waterbirds.

The *Somerset Atlas* also reveals the recent boom in birds of prey: from the 1950s and 1960s when (except in the West) seeing any raptor apart from a Kestrel was an event, to today, when perhaps nine species breed in the county. Buzzards, once fairly scarce away from the western uplands, are now by far the commonest bird of prey in Somerset, and indeed have overtaken Kestrel and Sparrowhawk as the commonest raptor in the UK.

Of course, it is not all good news. Some species, which would have been regular breeders just a few decades ago, have now vanished from the county: these include Turtle Dove and Corn Bunting. And although we are all well aware that many farmland species are in decline, it also now appears that woodland species are suffering too: the Willow Tit is now on the brink of disappearing from Somerset, as it has indeed from most of southern Britain, while even Marsh Tits – once widespread and fairly common – have almost gone.

This book is also appearing at a time when not just Somerset and the UK, but the whole world, is under the greatest threat to biodiversity since the last Ice Age: the rapid and potentially unstoppable onset of global climate change. This is likely to bring excitement for local birders and naturalists in the short to medium term: the arrival of even more heron species from the south, together with various species of songbird such as Great Reed and Melodious Warblers and Zitting Cisticola, and exotics such as Bee-eater. But in the longer term there is certainly the potential for major declines of a suite of currently widespread breeding species, including our commonest summer migrant, the Willow Warbler. Therefore at a time of change – whether for better or worse – it is crucial that we have robust evidence of the status of breeding and wintering birds here in Somerset; evidence which has been provided by the *Somerset Atlas.*

So in one sense the work starts here. Now that we have a baseline for the county's birds, we need to continue to monitor their populations and distribution at regular intervals in order to contribute to greater understanding of changes on a local, regional and national scale.

If we do so, we can hope to influence future environmental and conservation policies for the better, and ensure that we maintain the status of Somerset as a place where breeding, passage and wintering birds continue to thrive, and that we as birders can continue to enjoy watching them.

Stephen Moss

Mark, Somerset

December 2013

Somerset and its habitats

omerset is a greatly diverse county topographically. Its habitats reflect that – everything from heather and grass moorland on the highest hills, through a variety of woodland and coastal types, to lowland farmland, and wetland areas that barely scrape above sea level though miles inland. Here, compiled with the help of reports from the various Collectors who took responsibility for one or more 10-km squares during the fieldwork phase, is a detailed look at the range of landscapes across the county. Following usual practice in the annual *Somerset Birds*, the areas are arranged (approximately) from east to west.

The South-East

This is a very much underwatched area, little visited by birders. It is for the most part a mixture of unremarkable agricultural land, primarily used for cattle grazing and silage crops, and small blocks of mostly broadleaved woodland, many no more than copses or game coverts. Wincanton, Bruton, and Castle Cary are the main towns, the rest of the area's population being thinly scattered in small villages and outlying farms.

In the southeasternmost corner are the mixed escarpment woodland of Hanover Wood and the Somerset part of the Blackmoor Vale, which extends south from Wincanton into North Dorset. It is still 'an engirdled and secluded region', as Hardy called it in 1895 when he placed his heroine Tess in the Vale of the Little Dairies, and dairy farming still predominates on its improved grassland. However, there are a number of features which alleviate what might otherwise be a sterile landscape for birds. Firstly, the land is in places poorly drained, and in wet weather the River Cale and its tributary, the Bow Brook, readily flood a number of fields. These attract significant numbers of wildfowl and the sight is spectacular when they are put up by a Peregrine and mix with the huge numbers of Lapwings, Fieldfares, Redwings, and Starlings that winter here. Secondly, a number of farms are in various levels of stewardship

Typical grass pasture, a widespread but relatively unproductive farmland habitat (Rob Grimmond)

schemes, including organic, and the grass margins in particular support a small population of Barn Owls, and breeding Skylarks. Thirdly, although there are only a few woods, there are many copses and mature trees, mainly oaks. There are also miles of thick hedgerows and these, together with overgrown ditches, help to support a good variety of farmland birds. The stony bottom of the Cale attracts Dippers and Grey Wagtails until it flows out of Wincanton and meets the clay of the Blackmoor Vale. Kingfishers are present throughout its course, and Sedge Warblers breed nearby.

One of the most interesting features of the area, from both topographical and biological points of view, is the small intrusion of the North Dorset Downs into the county, including the outlier of Cadbury Castle, popularly believed locally to be the site of Camelot. Here sheep replace the cattle, and the tops of the downs are close-cropped and windswept. The continued presence of thick elm hedges in some areas is very welcome, providing feeding and breeding habitat for a healthy population of Yellowhammers and other finches.

The River Brue crosses the north of the area, flowing through the middle of Bruton and skirting the north side of Castle Cary. Together with those of its tributaries, the Alham and the Pitt, its overgrown banks provide a welcome respite from the fields of improved grassland, and there is a good spread of Kingfishers and Dippers.

To the west of Castle Cary is Cary Marsh Nature Reserve, where a range of habitats has been created on a hundred acres (50 ha) of capped landfill. There is now rough grassland, meadow, scrub, woodland, ponds, ditches, and a reedbed, which has attracted breeding Reed and Sedge Warblers.

The planting of winter forage crops and supplementary feeding attract large flocks of farmland birds (most notably Tree Sparrows), hunting Barn Owls, and even occasionally quartering Hen Harriers.

As with a number of other areas of the county, there is an almost total lack of bodies of standing water of any size in this wide area, apart from the ornamental lakes in the entirely private grounds of Compton Castle and Redlynch. Unsurprisingly, water birds are at a premium in many tetrads, though careful searching found a number of ponds, mostly artificial and some of them quite new, which offer nesting opportunities for the likes of Little Grebe, Canada Goose, Tufted Duck, and Coot, as well as the ubiquitous Mallards. Reed Buntings are very sparse and seem as much associated with oilseed rape crops as with reed-filled ditches in this area.

Some of the broadleaved woodlands are relatively old, with a mixture of tree species, though oak and ash predominate; hazel and holly feature in the

Oak woodland is well distributed across the county, with bluebell displays in the spring (John Rivoire)

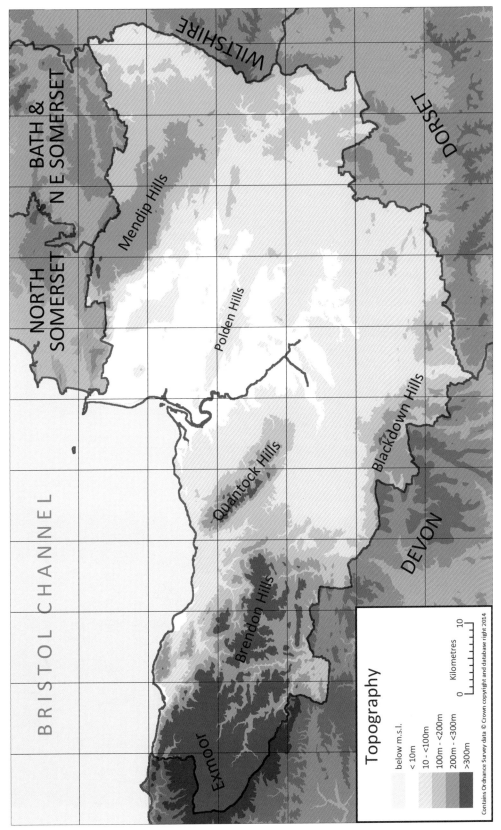

Map 1. Topographical map of Somerset

WILTSHIRE

BATH & N E SOMERSET

NORTH SOMERSET

DORSET

Mendip Hills

Polden Hills

Blackdown Hills

BRISTOL CHANNEL

Quantock Hills

Brendon Hills

DEVON

Exmoor

Topography

below m.s.l.
<10m
10 - <100m
100m - <200m
200m - <300m
>300m

Kilometres

0   10

Contains Ordnance Survey data © Crown copyright and database right 2014

understorey. All of the expected woodland species are well represented, with most suitable woods appearing to contain at least a pair or two of Marsh Tits. The few records of Lesser Spotted Woodpeckers offer hope that more may lurk unfound – the most extensive woods in the area tend to be private and difficult if not impossible to access. Sparkford Wood SSSI in ST62 is a notable exception: though it too is private, the owners welcome a limited number of visitors and readily granted access for the *Atlas*. While not the biggest it is one of the best, with a carpet of bluebells in spring.

The North-East

The north-east of the county is dominated by two main features: the ancient woodland of Selwood Forest and the River Frome with its tributaries. This is a predominantly rural area, with a scattering of small towns, villages and hamlets: the largest population centre being Frome. A high proportion of gardens in all these urban areas offer feeding stations, boosting species records for those tetrads.

The spine of higher ground that runs through the Selwood Forest area peaks at 258 m at the striking King Alfred's Tower on the Wiltshire border, and is the source of many streams and rivers that flow westwards across the county – most form tributaries to the River Frome and the River Brue. The Mells River runs through the Vallis Vale area and provides unintensively managed habitats that attract species such as Dipper. There are also many small springs scattered throughout the area: some create interesting features such as tufa-streams. Little Egrets are an increasingly common sight alongside many of these watercourses where they run through agricultural areas.

Whilst mainly heavily managed, the woodland areas nevertheless provide a unique habitat in this part of Somerset. Most are within large estates; extensive areas are conifer plantations with patches of both planted and natural broadleaf species. The largest contiguous area is along the Wiltshire border and is made up of parts of the Longleat and Duke of Somerset's estates. To the north of Frome the Orchardleigh Estate includes a large tract of woodland, a lake and a disused quarry. A few of the woods, for example Postlebury, remain in reasonably original condition and some areas are designated as SSSIs. Some of these estates also provide less usual habitats, for instance the planted gardens of Marston Park. The areas of woodland, whether native or exotic, provide a complex of habitats for a wide range of birds from the widespread and generalist woodland-edge species to the deep woodland specialists.

Priddy Pools, Mendip: acid heathland and bog, with Stockhill plantation in the background (Rob Chace)

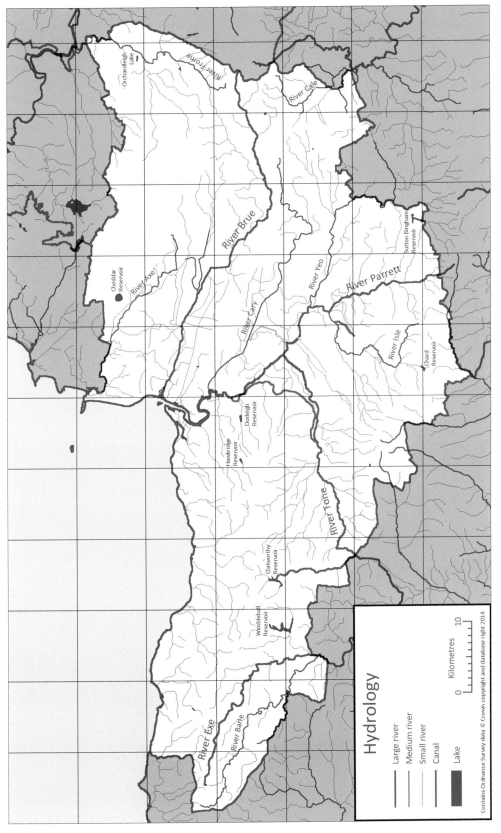

Map 2. Somerset's main lakes and rivers

Hydrology

Large river
Medium river
Small river
Canal
Lake

0   10
Kilometres

River Frome
Orchardleigh Lake
River Cale
Sutton Bingham Reservoir
River Brue
River Yeo
River Parrett
Cheddar Reservoir
River Axe
River Cary
River Isle
Chard Reservoir
Dunleigh Reservoir
Hawkridge Reservoir
River Tone
Clatworthy Reservoir
Wimbleball Reservoir
River Exe
River Barle

Beyond forestry, the main land use is relatively intensive dairy farming: silage and maize are grown along with small amounts of wheat and oilseed rape. This industry could have led to areas with few bird species, but the majority of fields remain small, separated by the thick hedges which are characteristic of the area. Although the latter are mainly tightly managed, there are sufficient lengths cut on more flexible regimes to provide habitats for a range of species, a key factor in the numbers of Whitethroats, finches and Yellowhammers. Lapwings attempt to breed but are ruthlessly targeted by Carrion Crows, so successes are few and far between. There are also some areas of rough grassland, which clearly benefit species such as Barn Owl.

There are several sizeable bodies of standing water: these include Marston and Orchardleigh Lakes, and the Witham Friary fishing ponds. The much newer pools created as part of the Frome Flood Relief Scheme, now known as Rodden Nature Reserve, account for many of the wetland-related species recorded in 10-km square ST74. West of Frome is perhaps the best-known, and certainly best-watched, of East Somerset's waters – Torr Works Reservoir. Patient and diligent coverage of the site has produced records of a variety of waders, including some that are unusual so far inland, and an impressive list of rarities and scarcities in the winter gull roost. The general area also holds a few pairs of Tree Sparrows, and the only regular breeding Little Ringed Plovers in the county.

There is further parkland at Ammerdown and Farleigh Hungerford, and small woods scattered across the area hold Stock Doves and Marsh Tits. In line with national trends, Blackcaps and Chiffchaffs are widespread, but species such as Turtle Dove have been lost in recent years. As in other areas, there is much rearing of Pheasants and of smaller numbers of Red-legged Partridges, for which the provision of winter feed is a clear advantage for passerines.

Mendip

Mendip is characterised by a limestone plateau some 250 m above sea level, with only one area of lowland in the extreme north-east where the River Chew flows near Litton. Much of the plateau is primarily semi-improved grassland and rough pasture, reclaimed by the application of lime and enclosed by dry stone walls for sheep and cattle grazing. There are also pigs and some arable. Much of the area lies within the Mendip Hills Area of Outstanding Natural Beauty (AONB), but has suffered from increasing disturbance, walkers and riders now being easily outnumbered by mountain bikers; the area has also been discovered by users of off-road motorbikes.

View from Draycott Sleights, western Mendip, with Cheddar Reservoir in the background (Rob Chace)

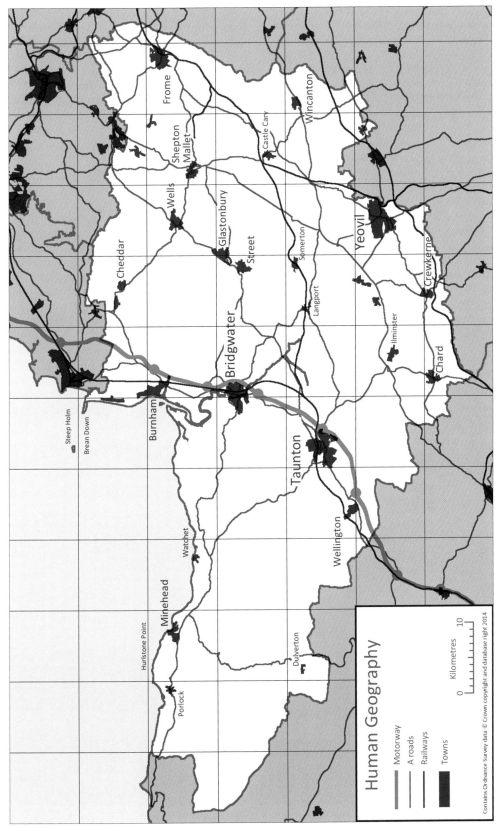

Map 3. Main towns and transport routes in Somerset

Human Geography

— Motorway
— A roads
— Railways
▮ Towns

0   10
Kilometres

Contains Ordnance Survey data © Crown copyright and database right 2014

The avifauna of the plateau is comparatively sparse, and the landscape can appear birdless at times. Typical upland species are there at low densities, however. Regulars include Kestrel, Buzzard, Woodpigeon, Carrion Crow, Magpie, Wren, Blackbird, Robin and Chaffinch; in summer there are Whitethroats, and there is often a croaking Raven overhead. There are few hedges in this part of Mendip, but most farms have shelter belts planted around them, which often provide sites for rookeries. In winter, Starlings, winter thrushes and gulls feed on the pastures and ground turned for arable crops. Farm buildings attract small colonies of House Martin, Swallow and House Sparrow.

There are patches of rough grassland and heath on Chancellor's Farm and Yoxter Ranges, and at Priddy Mineries, where lead mining activities have left their mark on the landscape, and Tree and Meadow Pipits breed. These hilltop roughets can be attractive to passage Wheatears, especially in the spring, and occasionally they stay to breed. Where scrub has been allowed to develop, Willow Warblers, Whitethroats, Linnets and Stonechats still thrive. Scattered pairs of Redstarts nest too. Short-eared Owls and Great Grey Shrikes sporadically winter on the hills.

The most significant areas of woodland are coniferous forestry plantations at Stockhill, East Harptree Woods and Rowberrow Warren; at the last there has recently been much felling, which may have benefited the small numbers of Nightjars and Tree Pipits. Siskins breed, and occasionally Crossbills. Wood Warblers are irregular on spring passage. Broadleaved woodland is scarce, but a new plantation of over 200 hectares planted by the Wills Woodlands Trust may provide useful habitat in future. Of the owls, Tawny and Barn are the more common, while Long-eared and Little Owls have become decidedly scarce in recent years.

There are ponds at Charterhouse and Priddy, but the only areas of open water of any size are Litton Upper Reservoir, where Great Crested Grebes nest, and Emborough Pond, which has limited public access. Herons fly up to the hilltop ponds to hunt for small fish and amphibians while Snipe, winter visitors hereabouts, feed in the damper areas. There are a few other specialities that attract birders on to the hill, not least breeding Nightjars in the conifer plantations and a colony of Tree Sparrows around Green Ore. Quail and Crossbill are worth searching for during irruption years.

The western end of the Mendip massif, culminating in the noticeable landmark of Crook Peak, is narrower and steeper-sided than the rest, and is also higher: Beacon Batch on Black Down, at 325 m, is the highest point. Black Down, with its cap of Devonian

Shapwick Moor: typical lowland grass moor with rhynes, with Glastonbury Tor in the distance (Rob Chace)

Ham Wall RSPB reserve, with reedbed and pools – part of the Avalon Marshes wetlands created from old peat diggings (John Rivoire)

sandstone over limestone, is frequently wet, and holds a small number of breeding Mallard, Grasshopper Warblers and Reed Buntings. In winter there are Common Snipe and occasional Golden Plover. The mix of heather, gorse, bracken and rough grass attracts good numbers of breeding Skylarks and Meadow Pipits and a few pairs of Stonechats, but Whinchats and Wheatears appear now only as passage migrants, and the Arctic weather of February 2009 wiped out the small Dartford Warbler population. The southern slopes, steep in many places, are a mix of woodland and open grassland, with a handful of small nature reserves. Two quarries remain in operation, at Callow Hill and Batt's Combe. Cheddar Gorge and its caves continue to be a major tourist attraction; the implications of plans, announced early in 2012, to build a cable car, with a visitor centre or viewing area above the Gorge, are as yet unknown.

The Levels north of the Polden Hills

This large area includes all of the great wetland reserves created in the last thirty years, except West Sedge Moor and Greylake further south, and is bounded to the north by Mendip and to the south by the long ridge of the Poldens. Although not strictly part of the Levels, also included here are Wells and Glastonbury and the land surrounding them, some of which forms a natural transition between Mendip and the Levels.

In the north-west, at the foot of the Mendip escarpment, lies Cheddar Reservoir, one of the county's major birding sites. A concrete bowl completed in 1937, it holds important numbers of diving duck and Coots in winter, together with grebes, the occasional diver, and an impressive gull roost; passage waders are dependent on low water levels. This is another area where disturbance has markedly increased, from sailing, fishing, jogging, and walking. South of this and of the A371 the farmland is flat, drained by the Cheddar Yeo and the Axe. In the coming decade, a second reservoir will be built here, with the potential to become an important area for wildlife. The Cheddar Moors, and other moors along the Axe valley, were once much wetter than they are today, being now mostly improved pasture drained by a network of ditches, locally called rhynes (pronounced 'reens'), but they still have some interest for breeding Lapwings, though perhaps with little success. The land around Chapel Allerton is a little higher, but unremarkable. A low ridge carries the road from Wells through Wedmore to Mark, through mixed farmland once famous for its cider production.

15

South of this is the Lower Brue Valley. Peat has been extracted from here for centuries, latterly by heavy mechanisation. As the beds were worked out, the opportunity arose to create a series of wetland reserves – some still expanding – managed variously by the RSPB, Natural England, the Somerset Wildlife Trust, and the Hawk and Owl Trust. The resulting area is generally known as the Avalon Marshes, a term which can be used to cover all the land from Glastonbury Heath west to Catcott Heath and north to Westhay Moor, and including the flagship reserves of Shapwick Heath and Ham Wall. The development of these reserves has been one of the most significant changes to the county's landscape since the last national *Atlas*, and the rewards for all the hard work put in by the various conservation organisations, aided by bands of dedicated volunteers, are now there for all to see. This has become a centre for 'ecotourism' to rival the North Norfolk coast, and rightly so.

Management of the drainage along the River Brue and the parallel North Drain has enabled water levels to be maintained as high or low as required in different compartments through the summer. There are hides to view the many wintering and passage waders and wildfowl, and ever-extending reedbeds that have at last enabled a regular breeding population of Bitterns to become established. Pochard, Gadwall, and a few Garganey nest, as do Lapwing, Redshank, Snipe, and Yellow Wagtails. Marsh Harriers have again become regular breeders after a brief absence. The area is famous for its huge winter Starling roosts and for the spectacular spring gatherings of Hobbies. There is a huge population of Reed Warblers (and thus, a lot of Cuckoos), and also many Cetti's Warblers; Bearded Tits have also colonised in recent years. Just to the north-west, Tealham and Tadham Moors are sometimes included in the Avalon Marshes, but more often considered a separate area. Once of great interest, they have suffered from 'improvement', but they still hold breeding waders and Yellow Wagtails, and, in some years, Quail.

In addition to the Bitterns, five other heron species bred in the area during our period, of which two (Cattle Egret and Great White Egret) bred for the first time in Britain, and Little Bittern for only the second time ever. On the other hand, some species formerly characteristic of the area have vanished or become very scarce, partly because they need drier ground: these include Nightjar, Willow Tit, Nightingale, and Tree Pipit. Of these, Willow Tit is of particular concern across the county, but in the Mid Levels at least, the gains outweigh the losses.

The north-eastern portion of this area is dominated by the City of Wells, backed by the steep slopes of the Mendip Hills. Its large walled gardens with their trees and bushes can provide an abundance of habitat for owls, woodpeckers, Treecreepers, and Bullfinches. To the south is the eastern outlier of the Levels, the flat expanse of Queen's Sedge Moor. Between these extremes is the small but significant high ground of Launcherley and Worminster. Another low ridge to the south carries the town of Glastonbury, with its spectacular Tor that provides the signature backdrop to many views around the Avalon Marshes reserves, and the villages towards Shepton Mallet, of which Pilton (of Glastonbury Festival fame) is perhaps the best known.

South and east of Street and Glastonbury is mainly a country of low-lying fields, but with some distinctive features on its boundaries. The River Brue sets its character: benign in the summer, but winter flooding may drive the resident Kingfishers on to the ornamental ponds of Baltonsborough and Butleigh. Kennard Moor seems to be either better reported or genuinely richer in species than other local moors; it is favoured by Mute Swans, waders, hirundines and partridges, and in winter occasionally by Short-eared Owls or even a stray Great Bustard from the reintroduction project on Salisbury Plain. There are Barn Owls, and to the east, Pennard Hill attracts Tawnies. The low-lying pastures to the west of Kennard Moor are often poorly managed and rarely considered in conservation terms.

Away from the flood plains, where grazing for cattle and sheep predominates, this is cider country: the former orchards are now reduced to much smaller stands of older apple and pear trees, which still attract Green Woodpeckers, Little Owls and Bullfinches, and hold a few remaining Lesser Spotted Woodpeckers. Fields of oilseed rape attract migrating warblers and Hobbies may hunt over the wetter fields. The more productive non-orchard areas east of Baltonsborough are in regular farming rotation, which provides an annual but local change in species densities, and the farmers seem to be more sympathetic to the requirements of local wildlife.

In contrast are the heights of Great Breach Wood and Copley Wood, at the south-east tip of the Poldens; these attract raptors and owls, as well as Ravens and Crossbills. Marsh Tits are still present though less common than before; once they were the dominant tit in Copley Wood. Collard Hill to the west is the acknowledged haunt of the Large Blue butterfly, and the close-cropped sward and plentiful ants attract Green Woodpeckers. The main ridge of the Poldens is narrow and dominated by the busy A39, but there is some woodland on the shallow northern slope, and arable farming here supports pockets of Yellowhammers as far west as Shapwick village.

The Levels south of the Polden Hills

The Levels immediately south of the Poldens are traditionally known as King's Sedge Moor. This name strictly refers to the central area immediately east of the A361 between Othery and Greinton, but in more general contexts it covers all the low ground from Somerton Moor and Butleigh Moor in the east to Bawdrip Level in the west. This lies on both sides of the King's Sedgemoor Drain, completed in 1940, which is in effect a canalisation of the River Cary, emptying into the Parrett through the sluice at Dunball. Parts of the central section of King's Sedge Moor are managed as Areas of Raised Water Level, and the RSPB has recently developed an excellent reserve at Greylake, where much attention has been given to maintaining and improving populations of breeding waders.

The isolated Dundon Hill protrudes between Butleigh and Somerton Moors, but a larger area of higher ground runs south-east from Turn Hill past Langport to Somerton, including the substantial woodland of Breach Wood and the escarpment from Turn Hill to Aller Hill. To the south lie the most southerly of the Somerset Levels: from east to west, King's Moor, Wet Moor and West Moor. These are crossed by three of the county's major rivers: the Parrett, the Yeo and the Isle, which finally become a single river outside Langport, which itself is low-lying.

Before the installation of efficient pumping stations, the South Levels were the wettest places in the county, since the only way for the water of the three rivers to escape is under the bridge at Langport. These Levels can still afford great interest to observers, especially in the winter. Since 1987 they have been protected as part of the Somerset Levels and Moors Environmentally Sensitive Area, and include several SSSIs. This protection allows the creation of Areas of Raised Water Level, so good numbers of wildfowl and waders are present, especially in times of high flooding. There have recently been large assemblies of Little Egrets. Despite this habitat protection, breeding birds have yet to respond with similar success, and their numbers are still far below those of fifty years ago. Snipe and Redshank, once common, are now scarce breeders, and few Lapwings try to breed. However, Curlew and Yellow Wagtails have defied this trend and continue to maintain viable populations. The surrounding countryside still has widespread Skylarks and Yellowhammers, but Grey Partridges, once common, have vanished.

Heading south-west from Langport along the A378 the land rises as one reaches Curry Rivel and Fivehead. From vantage points here one can look

Meare Heath scrape, Shapwick Heath NNR – each spring and autumn this pool attracts passage waders and waterbirds (John Rivoire)

down over the escarpment, blanketed in deciduous woodland including the famous Swell Wood with its large heronry. Below is the vast expanse of West Sedge Moor, an RSPB reserve, with a history of rarities going back two hundred years. This has many breeding waders and in winter attracts huge numbers of Lapwings and Golden Plover, together with many thousand Teal and other duck, and accompanying predators. The ongoing reintroduction programme means that the trumpeting of Cranes can now be heard again in the area.

A low ridge carrying a string of villages from North Curry to Stathe separates West Sedge Moor from the Tone Levels: Hay Moor/Curry Moor – regularly flooded and the scene of a recent attempt at breeding by Black-winged Stilts – and Stan Moor, beyond which the Tone meets the Parrett at Burrowbridge. The area round this confluence is rich in birdlife, and is good for Yellow Wagtails and Skylarks.

South Somerset

This is an extensive area, mostly of rolling farmland and hedgerows and many small villages, and much of it is often overlooked by birdwatchers. With two or three notable exceptions, there is little in the way of extensive bodies of standing water.

Woodlands tend to be small in extent, mostly deciduous, and often private, though there are some very good and even ancient ones tucked away, and some are reserves. Coniferous woodland is found in Somerton Wood/The Sleights near Somerton in the north-east of the area, around Yeovil, and on the edge of the Blackdown Hills, and these areas have produced a number of sightings of Siskin and Crossbill, both in summer and winter. Most woodlands feature occasional conifers in their mix of species, and these and ornamental conifers in village gardens offer extra habitat for the likes of Coal Tits and Goldcrests.

The Cary and Yeo flow through the north-east portion of this area, and Reed and Sedge Warblers occur along the banks, though at low densities. Nine Springs, on the south side of Yeovil, has many breeding woodland species, and Mandarin Ducks have nested successfully in the past few years. Like other towns in the area, Herring Gulls and a smaller number of Lesser Black-backed Gulls have found industrial units to their liking for breeding.

To the south of Yeovil is Sutton Bingham Reservoir, completed in 1953. It is well watched, and at least 226 species have been recorded. However, its value as a wintering area for duck has declined considerably; it now holds only a few hundred at most, mainly Wigeon, Mallard and Teal, whereas in the 1970s there were sometimes thousands. The main

River Tone, Taunton – a wetland corridor running through the heart of the county town (Rob Grimmond)

18

losses are of diving duck (Pochard, Tufted Duck and Goldeneye), but Shoveler and Pintail have also gone, perhaps attracted by the new reserves on the Levels. Sometimes the reservoir can now seem devoid in winter of any sort of bird life. In summer, there are still four or five pairs of Reed Buntings, and since the mid 1990s there have been regular Reed Warblers.

To the north-west of Yeovil the castle-like promontory of Hamdon Hill towers over the A303. This is the source of the lovely yellow limestone ('Ham stone') of the villages, and it has been used in the past for migration watches. There is a variety of habitats around it and in the parks and grounds of the stately houses of Tintinhull, Montacute and Brympton D'Evercy.

Further west, the birds of Crewkerne have been intensively studied for many years by Tony Parsons. Most common species have steadily declined as the town expanded, and the monocultures of the surrounding countryside, with its shaven hedges, have lost much of their interest. On the north side of the town, Millwater has long been a ringing site, and its records have been a barometer for the fortunes of migrants and residents alike.

Chard Reservoir, originally built for the short-lived Chard Canal, has a good mixture of habitats – open water, reed-beds, meadow and woodland – and is managed by South Somerset District Council as a public open space and for its coarse fishing, not as a water source. It has breeding Great Crested Grebes, Moorhen and Coot, and these are joined in winter by numerous other waterfowl. Because of its closeness to Chard, several local birders have worked the reservoir regularly and have provided a good number of county records. The only other significant body of water is the lake at Cricket St Thomas, though a few smaller ponds south of Chard have proved attractive to Mandarins.

East of Chard, the higher ground slopes down from the Windwhistle ridge. It is mostly a patchwork of fields, farmed largely for dairy; in many tetrads species are concentrated in the villages, though the farmland still holds reasonable numbers of Yellowhammers, and Whitethroat and Spotted Flycatcher are doing quite well. There are a number of small sewage treatment works, among which Pudleigh in particular has proved a very good place to find wintering Chiffchaffs.

North of the expanding town of Ilminster, the landscape is somewhat gentler along the Isle valley. The overgrown courses of the former Chard–Taunton railway and canal are important features and birds are in general less reliant on villages for winter feeding and for breeding sites than they are further south. South Somerset is a stronghold for Nightingales, at the western edge of their breeding range: the MOD-

Low tide at Stolford, where the mud of Bridgwater Bay meets the rocky shore to the west (Rob Chace)

protected scrub around Merryfield, a satellite airfield to RNAS Yeovilton, is the most important site.

The tributaries of the Isle still hold breeding Dippers, but the most significant river in the area is the Axe, which runs along the county border. Some tetrads that it bisects are only partly in Somerset, but have been included because of the river's presence and contribution to the county's avifauna: both Chard Reservoir and the Axe have produced records of several species that are not common in other parts of South Somerset.

The Blackdown Hills

The Somerset section of the Blackdown Hills runs from Curland in the east to Wrangway in the west, and south to Churchinford and Wambrook. It consists of a flat-topped plateau with ridges and spring-lined valleys. Staple Hill, at 315 m, is the highest point. The area is sparsely populated and settlements are generally small.

The northern scarp is steep and well wooded, both deciduous and coniferous, with small hedged fields lower down and north towards the M5. The geology of the Blackdowns is almost unique in Great Britain: underlying the steep slopes of the northern scarp there is a layer of porous sandstone, called Upper Greensand, overlaid by chert. Beech is the most significant tree on the plateau and lines many roads. The undulating upland plateau dips away to the south, cut by valleys in which there is rough grassland and peaty bog; roads there are lined with hedges and the odd, isolated, mature tree. Sheep and dairy cattle are grazed on the rough pastures, but many fields are now horse paddocks. There are also several pig farms, which are attractive to gulls and corvids, especially Ravens.

The Blackdowns generally lack the heathland of the Quantocks and the moorland of Exmoor. The only large, open area of gorse and heather moorland is at Sampford Point, at the extreme western end of the area. The largest water bodies are Otterhead Lakes, near Churchinford, and Leigh, Luxhay, and Blagdon Reservoirs, above Angersleigh – the latter three are not easy to access. There are three main rivers in the Blackdowns, though none are large – the Yarty, Otter and Culm.

Forestry Commission plantations and semi-natural broadleaved woods along the ridge between Staple Hill and Castle Neroche are good sites for Nightjar, Redstart, Wood Warbler, Tree Pipit, Crossbill and wintering Woodcock. The Somerset Wildlife Trust has a small number of reserves in the area, of which perhaps the most significant for birds is Dommett Wood; during the Atlas period it was notable as the only confirmed breeding site for Pied Flycatchers in the county outside Exmoor and the Quantocks. Here they use nest-boxes.

The South-West

This area, between the two uplands of the Blackdowns and the Brendons, contains much pleasant but unsensational countryside either side of the River Tone. To the east lies the Vale of Taunton Deane, which is watered also by the Tone's northern tributaries, Halse Water and the Hillfarrance Brook. The farming is mixed, but mainly arable, and there has been some hedge removal, but many large oaks remain to help the spread of Buzzards. There are only three towns, of which much the largest is Wellington, which has greatly expanded in recent years. Further north, Wiveliscombe has also grown outwards from its Swift-haunted brewery tower, but nearby Milverton remains compact. Bishops Lydeard and Norton Fitzwarren have become Taunton dormitories, and there has been much elegant gentrification by barn conversions along the twisting lanes of ancient countryside. The new village of Cotford St Luke was built around the old Tonedale mental hospital, with large numbers of House Martins under the broad eaves of its post-modern housing.

To the south, the railway, the A38 and the M5 pass over or under the watershed of White Ball Hill into Devon. The sandpit here holds the largest Sand Martin colony in Somerset. This north-east/south-west line is also a marked migration route between the Bristol and English Channels, as has become apparent from many years' records from Wellington. There are still orchards and fruit farms, but no large tracts of woodland, apart from the interesting survival of Langford Heathfield. Now managed by SWT, its 226 hectares of ancient woodland, heathland and ponds make it an unusual and fascinating place; until recently it held Willow Tits and may still do. Ash Priors Common is a Local Nature Reserve; Pied Flycatchers were unexpectedly found there, but it is much used by dog walkers. There are no lakes of any size, but there are old and new waters for fishing or irrigation, of which the largest are those between Halse and Milverton and on Oake Golf Course. The Tone has some Dippers and Grey Wagtails, but they are probably under-recorded, partly because of a lack of footpaths.

Apart from a brief stretch along the Tone and its tributary the Marcombe Lake, the border with Devon is not aligned with natural features, though at Venn Cross it does mark the obvious watershed between the Tone and the Batherm. This is a remote and little-visited part of Somerset – before the Atlas fieldwork, very few records were published from here. Even the B3227, connecting Taunton to Bampton, is seldom busy, and away from this one finds broken signposts and grass growing along the middle of the narrow, high-hedged lanes. Most of the little woodland is concentrated along the Tone, where some is accessible. There is less arable farming than in Taunton Deane, but enough to ensure a fairly high Yellowhammer population along the broad-based hedges, and walls which are topped with beech on the higher ground.

Taunton and Bridgwater

This lowland area is dominated by its two large towns and the M5 motorway which joins them. The county town of Taunton has some ornithological interest beyond its many bird-feeders: during the *Atlas* period it hosted wintering Peregrines (which found the Feral Pigeon population much to their liking), Black Redstarts, and, occasionally, flocks of Waxwings. The small Council-owned nature reserve on Hankridge retail estate, between the town and the M5, has a good selection of breeding birds, including Kingfishers, Reed and Sedge Warblers, Blackcaps and even occasional Nightingales. Herring and Lesser Black-backed Gulls still attempt to breed on town roofs, but are strongly controlled.

Taunton is surrounded by farmland, and the centre of the town is connected to open country on the south through Vivary Park, and to the west via Longrun Meadows. To the south and south-east are several areas of interest – in particular, Thurlbear Wood, in ST22Q, is known for its Nightingales, and others were found nearby during the 2012 BTO Survey. Hobbies presumably breed in the area, as they are sometimes seen over the town. To the east, the old Bridgwater and Taunton Canal has a good variety of breeding species, and Ham Sewage Treatment Works, now being extensively rebuilt, have been regularly surveyed in winter and hold an important population of Shoveler.

To the east of Taunton is a land of contrasts. In the south, the gentle lowlands of the Isle valley continue northward and rise westward to the eastern foot of the Blackdowns. This is a land of many lanes, hedgerows and ancient cattle droves; some flooding occurs regularly along the Isle, but there is no permanent open water except the old decoy at Earnshill. Many summer visitors are numerous: Spotted Flycatcher, both Whitethroats, Blackcap, Garden Warbler and even Nightingale seem to be flourishing. Skylarks have declined, but there are plenty of other farmland birds, such as Linnet, Bullfinch and Yellowhammer. Woodland is thin and patchy and is found mainly along the escarpment that forms an abrupt divide

Looking east from Lilstock towards Hinkley Point, showing low cliffs and shingle beach typical of this area (John Rivoire)

between the south and the north of the area. However, the many mature gardens act as wildlife corridors. Four species of tit breed commonly, but Marsh Tits were apparently hard to find.

Much of the district is only just above sea level, but north of Taunton the land rises towards the Quantocks. Here the prominent villages are West Monkton and Kingston St Mary, both with varied habitats. Lesser Spotted Woodpeckers were still present in 2008. Further north, the tetrads from North Petherton west to Broomfield Hill are mainly undulating farmland, penetrated by a confusing tangle of very narrow and high-hedged lanes. There is much woodland here, both deciduous and coniferous, with reasonable access, and useful vantage points, such as Kingston Beacon (197 m). The area round Fyne Court has been much studied and is one of the few places in Somerset where there is some hope of seeing a Hawfinch.

Bridgwater is a growing town with a long history as a port and industrial centre, and as the lowest point where the Parrett is bridged. The manufacture of bricks and tiles has left a legacy of clay-pits, to the north (at Chilton Trinity) and to the east (at Dunwear), which now provide a network of ponds and reedbeds, some managed as reserves, others used for angling.

Perhaps the most productive for wildlife are Screech Owl Pits, just the other side of the M5 to the southeast. The closeness of the motorway has led to a rapid growth of warehousing for light industry and distribution centres, which provide sites for expanding gull colonies. On the western edge of the town is Durleigh Reservoir, formerly an important roosting site for Bewick's Swans. Now Canada Geese are the most numerous wildfowl, though it still provides a haven for a variety of species, and attracts migrant waders when water levels are low.

The older housing estates of the town, originally housing workers for the now defunct cellophane works, stretch out over the railway and towards the M5, where they have engulfed some of the brick pits. Beyond the motorway lies the western end of King's Sedgemoor. There are smaller levels on both sides of the Parrett and the canal above Huntworth, some not wholly drained, with tussocks and rushes, others converted to arable and orchard. Between the Parrett and King's Sedgemoor Drain the 'island' of Sowy lifts the villages of Othery, Middlezoy, and Westonzoyland above the floods. The last of these villages has for many years housed a busy ringing station operated by Doug Miller.

Porlock Bay, from Bossington Hill, showing classic heather and gorse of Exmoor (John Rivoire)

At the northernmost point of the Somerset coast the limestone peninsula of Brean Down, an outlier of the Mendip ridge, extends westward into the Bristol Channel. Interesting botanically and geologically as well as being probably the premier migration watchpoint in the county, it is almost an island, its eastern end attached only by a narrow pedicle of flat farmland. The mouth of the Axe is at its eastern base – the river is tidal well inland and brings some waders upriver. Southward, Brean Sands and Berrow Flats stretch to the mouth of the Parrett; they are over seven kilometres long and at lowest tides three kilometres wide. These are backed by a broad dune system, which contains scrub (including large stands of sea buckthorn), a sizeable reedbed, a golf course and caravan parks.

A low hinterland comprises arable and improved pasture. These Levels are on average very slightly higher than the 'Moors' further inland, and north of the Parrett mouth are protected by the dune-line. In consequence, the farmland is largely enclosed by good hedges, as well as ditches, as it remains rather flat except for the striking flat-topped cone of Brent Knoll (137 m). This is the country visible from the main transport arteries which run noisily across the area: the main Bristol to Exeter railway line, the A38, and the M5. By the railway bridges there are 'borrow pits', offering habitat for the likes of Moorhens and Reed Warblers across the land. The village of Lympsham boasts a small heronry in the garden of its Gothick manor, but the lack of woodland larger than a copse makes for an impoverished avifauna.

The linked towns of Burnham-on-Sea and Highbridge lie at the mouths of the Parrett and the Brue. The estuary of the latter provides high-tide roosts for waders and waterfowl, and the promenade at Burnham is a regular watchpoint for storm-driven seabirds. At Highbridge, gulls breed on the warehouse roofs, and Walrow Pits attract wildfowl, including Great Crested Grebes.

On the west side of the Parrett Estuary, and in the corner of Bridgwater Bay, lies the Steart peninsula. The effects of wind and tide cause continuous changes in its topography. The tidal range here is famously the second-largest in the world, and the intertidal Stert Flats are extensive; they combine with the Berrow Flats and the Parrett/Brue estuaries to provide feeding grounds for thousands of wintering and passage waterfowl, waders and gulls. A coastal reedbed extends the length of the peninsula from Stert Point to Wall Common. Offshore is Stert Island; uninhabited and largely undisturbed, it provides an important wader roost site. The hinterland of the peninsula is a mosaic of pasture, permanent and resown, and arable. At the time of writing the creation of a new, large area of intertidal habitat by managed retreat of the sea defences is nearing completion. There are two schemes for creating breaches: one, by the Environment Agency, through the west bank of the Estuary, which includes the new Steart Marshes reserve, managed by the Wildfowl and Wetlands Trust (WWT); the other, by the Bristol Port Company, through the coast. Archaeological findings during the preliminary works confirm a long history of agriculture and fishing.

Between Steart and the hamlet of Stolford are the rough coastal pastures of Wall Common and Catsford Common, the latter becoming intertidal at high spring tides; both commons have reed-fringed borrow pits. The coast and its hinterland resemble the Steart Peninsula apart from the gradual increase in size and height of the shingle ridge towards Stolford. West of this, a concrete sea wall extends to the nuclear power stations at Hinkley Point. The cooling-water outfall attracts gulls, and, in season, terns; the offshore structure of its inlet provides a wader roost, especially for Purple Sandpipers in winter.

This entire stretch of coast is included in the Severn Estuary SSSI. This includes Pawlett Hams, Combwich Common, Wick Moor and part of the Steart Peninsula. The coast and intertidal areas from Stert Island to Lilstock and up the Estuary to Combwich form Bridgwater Bay National Nature Reserve. There are also four Local Nature Reserves: Brean Down, Berrow Dunes, Pawlett Hams, and Hinkley Point.

West of Lilstock the character of the coastline changes, and becomes one of crumbling, fossil-rich Lias cliffs above beaches of mud and ribbed ledges, as far as the ancient port of Watchet and beyond to Doniford, although this area is little-watched. It is of limited interest, though Rock Pipits breed, and in winter Wigeon, Turnstones and occasional Purple Sandpipers visit. Coastal copses at Lilstock and Kilve sometimes hold passerine migrants. Behind the coast between Bridgwater and Lilstock is the area commonly referred to in *Somerset Birds* as 'Quantock farmland', which is mainly pasture inland, though arable nearer the coast, with scattered villages and small copses. This was once prime Grey Partridge country. Reservoirs at Ashford and Hawkridge provide freshwater habitat for wildfowl; the first has one of the few regular Sand Martin colonies in Somerset. The new fishing lake east of Nether Stowey is also of interest. As in other urban areas Herring Gulls have colonised the roofs of Williton and the paper mill at Watchet.

The low coast of Minehead Bay, from Blue Anchor to Minehead itself, is a mixture of sand and shingle beaches. Concentrations of gulls at Blue Anchor have received much attention in recent years, documenting the increase in Mediterranean Gulls in particular, while the coastline from the Avill overspill channel to Warren Point has been regularly watched since the 1930s, and has often yielded rarities; Dunster Hawn hosts one of the largest rookeries in the county.

The much expanded town of Minehead is full of bird feeders. Its eastward extension of Butlin's, which was developed from the 1960s, substituted resident Canada Geese for wintering White-fronts, but attracts a large colony of Herring Gulls, who exchanged their draughty cliffs for the comfortable roofs of a restaurant. The offshore waters hold regular Gannets and Manx Shearwaters on summer feeding forays from colonies elsewhere, and seawatching has become a more popular pursuit both here and at Hurlstone Point to the west. In between the two the coast rises again, with steep grassy and bracken-covered slopes on the flank of the North Hill massif.

Porlock Marsh has shown much reduced interest for wildlife following the breaching of the shingle ridge in 1996. It has lost most of its wintering duck and nearly all its attraction for migrants, but it has gained a pair of Oystercatchers. The warm fields of the Porlock Vale are still a refuge for birds escaping frozen conditions elsewhere and much wintering stubble is usually available for finches and Skylarks. The coast west of Porlock Weir is mostly covered in steep woodland and cliffs, and its beach is accessible only in two places near the Devon border.

The Quantock Hills

The long whaleback of the Quantock Hills forms the western side of the Lower Parrett Basin. Its block of red Devonian sandstone is capped with a moorland and heathland ridge extending north-west from the highest point, on Wills Neck at 384 m. This carries many ancient tracks, but is crossed by only two minor roads from the east, joining to become one at Robin Upright's Hill before descending to Crowcombe on the west side. The eastern valleys are long and twisting: these are Aisholt Combe, Cockercombe, Quantock Combe, Rams Combe, and the many-combed catchments of Holford Combe and Hodder's Combe. Also on the eastern side are the little town of Nether Stowey, strong in Swifts, and the fine parks of Alfoxden and Quantock Lodge.

Until the 1920s, the eastern combes south of the Nether Stowey to Crowcombe road were largely heathland. There are remains of this on Aisholt Common. The heathlands were then planted up with conifers by the Forestry Commission. In their maturity, and in later fellings and replanting, they have acquired Nightjars, Crossbills and Siskins. North of the road, most of the woodland is ancient sessile oak; the adjacent heathland has scattered thorns and hollies. There are flourishing populations of Pied Flycatchers, mainly in nest-boxes, some Redstarts and a few Wood Warblers; Lesser Spotted Woodpeckers still maintain a foothold.

By contrast, the western slopes are very steep, indented by a number of combes which are often no more than wide gullies. Most of these have agricultural intakes in their lower sections; some of these extend up to the ridge, but others have been abandoned and are crowned by moorland or scrub. Two abandoned quarries have tall faces, at West Quantoxhead and Triscombe; the huge cliff of the latter appears as a raw scar under Wills Neck.

The open tops are basically heather moorland, with variable amounts of bracken and gorse. This is a land of Skylarks, Stonechats and Meadow Pipits, but it has seldom or never attracted Ring Ouzels (except on passage), and it is too dry for waders or Reed Buntings. Northward, heathland or woodland descends in places to the A39. The Quantocks look small on the map, where only five tetrads are at least half moorland, but they always look much bigger on the ground.

Between the western escarpment and the A358 from Bishops Lydeard to Williton, there is a long series of affluent villages and hamlets, from Cothelstone in the south-east to Bicknoller and Weacombe in the north-west. These have fine manor houses, some with parks and steep, largely private, woodland, especially Crowcombe Park, with its splendid beeches. West of the A358, along the lowest ground taken by the West Somerset Railway, is a deep, tangled country of muddy lanes around Crowcombe Heathfield, a partly-enclosed birch heath with overgrown beech-hedges, some of which has recently been taken over by commercial forestry. Above this, the ground rises into the East Brendons.

In all this area there are hardly any waters larger than a farm pond. The biggest are the park lake of the vanished Cothelstone House and the ponds of Cedar Falls, near Bishops Lydeard.

The Brendon Hills

Away from the coastal strip, the ground rises ever higher as one moves west in Somerset, and the Brendon Hills, while not as high as Exmoor, are truly upland in character, wind-swept and sometimes snow-covered in winter. They fall easily into two

Oak and beech dominate the upland woods, as here at Castle Neroche, Blackdown Hills (Rob Grimmond)

main sections, south and north of the B3224, the ancient ridge track and droving way from North Devon towards Taunton. This was once a busy industrial landscape, with iron mines and slate quarries.

In the southern portion, north of the B3227 and the hamlet of Waterrow, is Heydon Hill, which was heathland until the last century. It is now planted with conifers, and there are strong sporting interests, especially in the Batherm Valley, where access was limited. A small SWT reserve on Huish Moor is an outpost for Pied Flycatchers. Raddington has a large conifer plantation and an interesting shallow lake; all other waters are very small.

Deep combes have been formed by the headwaters of the Tone, which rises in Beverton Pond, by the B3190 west of Ralegh's Cross. The river was dammed in 1962 to create Clatworthy Reservoir. Its deep waters are of limited attraction to birds, other than roosting Canada Geese, but the shallower southwest end is of some interest. The farmland to the west and north of the reservoir is mainly pasture with enclosing beech hedges, replacing earlier heathland. Most species are concentrated around the farm buildings, especially in winter. Eastward of Clatworthy the land falls steeply away to the village of Brompton Ralph and the remarkable forested knoll of Willett Hill, crowned by a folly tower; the new plantation

has been colonised by Nightjars. The farmland along the eastern side of the Brendons has a high proportion of arable and probably carries the greatest concentrations of Yellowhammers in Somerset.

West of Clatworthy is the high plateau of the Brendons, perhaps the least interesting part of the area ornithologically. For the past two hundred years this has been mainly enclosed farmland, mostly as pasture. The fields are fairly large and are divided by beech hedges. Most birdlife is concentrated around the farms, especially in winter, when with their shelter belts and huge new sheds they form oases. An especially large enclosure is that round Venne Cottage, on the south-east corner of the plateau. The deep, narrow valleys leading off the high ground can be more interesting, but there are few footpaths. The remote hamlet of Withiel Florey includes some fish ponds.

Most valleys drain southwards, and a large reservoir, Wimbleball Lake, was created in the 1970s behind a spectacularly high dam, impounding the water of the Haddeo and Bessom streams. At the north end, in the Bessom valley above the road bridge, the 20-hectare Hurscombe Nature Reserve was formed from woodland, scrub, marsh and rough grassland. It is now managed by the South West Lakes Trust. In winter the lake attracts a variety of wildfowl, including Wigeon, Teal, Tufted Duck, Pochard and Goldeneye, as well as the occasional rarity. It is also an important roost for wintering Goosanders, which fly in at dusk over the dam, as do some Cormorants, presumably from a wide area of southern Exmoor and Mid Devon, and large numbers of gulls, including Common Gulls, which are in fact rather scarce over lowland Somerset. The numbers of breeding species depend on water levels: in some years Canada Geese, Tufted Duck, Little and Great Crested Grebes and Coot may nest. Along the southern shores of the lake deciduous woodland prevails; some conifer plantations have recently been removed. There are Redstarts, Pied Flycatchers, and Wood Warblers. To the south, Haddon Hill forms a backdrop along the skyline, with heather, birch scrub, gorse and whortleberry; here, too, the removal of Hadborough Plantation has brought about the regeneration of moorland. Stonechats breed regularly, and there are Tree Pipits, Linnets and Lesser Redpolls. Below the dam the Haddeo is joined by the Pulham River from the north. This runs down a marshy valley from its source near Heathpoult Cross and through the village of Brompton Regis. Dippers breed here.

To the west, Dulverton is the commercial and social centre for a wide area, and the only place with more than one shop. It also houses the headquarters of the National Park. The little town stands on the Barle, the largest Exmoor river. This flows south to join the Exe at the Meeting of the Waters and to lose its identity to the much smaller stream. Below this, at Exebridge, a large trout farm can readily be visited. It has regular Kingfishers and various duck. Between the Exe and the Barle is the high and potentially interesting promontory of Pixton Park, to which there is no public access.

Northward from Hele Bridge on the east of Dulverton, the Brendons are divided from Exmoor by the deep and largely wooded cleft of the Exe and Quarme Valleys. These steep and generally inaccessible woods, some ancient, have been little explored, even for the Atlas, but there is good territory in Barlynch Wood, owned by the League Against Cruel Sports, where the erection of nest-boxes has achieved the highest concentration of Pied Flycatchers in Somerset. There is a heronry near Coppleham Cross.

On the northern slope of the Brendons, north of the B3224 between Elworthy and Wheddon Cross, is a steep-sided and complicated landscape of deep and twisting valleys formed by the Washford and Monksilver streams and the Doniford Brook. Much of the woodland is coniferous and some was opened up during the *Atlas* period by emergency felling to counter the spread of *Phytophthora ramorum*, a fungal disease which has recently started to attack larch in addition to its more usual hosts. Before 1914, this was iron-mining country, but like much of the area its chief industry now is the rearing and shooting of thousands of Pheasants and Red-legged Partridges. The feed provided for them attracts large numbers of wintering finches, and the available carrion has led to the greatest gatherings of Ravens ever seen in Somerset. There are now established populations of Siskins and Crossbills. There is attractive parkland, with ponds, at Chargot House and the Combe Sydenham estate, near Monksilver, has a chain of lakes and good deciduous woodland on Bird's Hill, including some spectacularly overgrown beech hedges. The finest ancient timber is in Nettlecombe Park, with its huge stag-headed oaks. There are a number of small waters created for fisheries or irrigation, notably the lake at Rowdon Farm, near Stogumber. A study of the farmland around Rodhuish and Withycombe (Townend 2010) was helpful for the Atlas.

Exmoor

The Somerset part of Exmoor National Park covers a great variety of landscape, including many well-watched areas popular with local and visiting observers. Much countryside here is under the control of the National Trust, the Forestry Commission or the Crown Estates.

The Exmoor Plateau is a high sandstone block; at 519 m (1708 ft), Dunkery Beacon is the highest point on Exmoor (and indeed in the county). Much of the country over 300 m is still open moorland, and the high Dunkery ridge is largely cloaked in heather. The Beacon itself is flanked on the west by Rowbarrows (almost as high, at 510 m) and on the east by Robin How, at 428 m. From Robin How one can look down at the extensive deciduous woodland of Horner Wood, and the rich farmland of the upper part of the Porlock Vale, with its villages. To the north-east across the A39 in the Headon Col the view is filled by the long ridge from North Hill above Minehead to its sharp western end at Hurlstone Point, where much seawatching has taken place in recent years. Below the heathery summits are the old planted woodlands of Selworthy, with their ilex and silver firs. To the east the view is down the Avill valley to Dunster and the sea. Either side of the Avill, and south of Minehead, are the massif of Croydon Hill and its northern outlier of Bat's Castle above Dunster Park, and the ridge running west from Dunster to Tivington Common. All are heavily forested with planted conifers, and Nutcombe Bottom at the base of Croydon Hill boasts the tallest tree in England, a 60 m-tall Douglas Fir. Most of the Nightjars, Siskins and Crossbills west of the Quantocks live within this view from Robin How; Woodcock and Long-eared Owl have been noted in recent years too.

West of the Dunkery ridge, moorland is almost continuous over Chetsford, Weir, and Chalk Waters to Badgworthy Water on the Devon border. Winsford Hill is a varied landscape of heather, bog, gorse, and hawthorns, still with breeding Snipe but much disturbed by traffic; Withypool Hill to the west is much degraded. This part of Exmoor is easily reached by road and is much more regularly watched than The Forest to the west, though it has lost some of its most distinctive species since the last national *Atlas*: Red Grouse was last seen in 1996 and Ring Ouzels have only occurred as passage birds since 2002.

Many visitors venture no further west than the road across the moor from the A39 above Porlock Hill to the village of Exford, but west of there Exmoor takes on a different character. Before the 19th century, the south-west section was a Royal Forest (a game reserve, not a wood), heavily grazed by the adjacent parishes in summer, but in winter an almost uninhabited and treeless wilderness. In the 19th century mining was developed (but later abandoned), and much of the lower ground was enclosed as farmland. The resulting large fields and their dividing beech hedges remain the general pattern today, and the big farmhouses such as Warren, Emmett's Grange, Cornham and Wintershead, with their yards, barns and shelter belts, form oases for such birdlife as there is, especially in winter, when visits to the moorland produce only the briefest of lists, mainly of corvids. The unenclosed land of The Forest, as it is still called, is almost entirely covered in coarse *Molinia* grassland, where in summer Skylarks and Meadow Pipits are by far the commonest birds. In the wetter bottoms and along the upper reaches of rivers Whinchats and Reed Buntings flourish. The area is notorious for its bogs, though much drainage took place as recently as the 1950s and it would now be hard to find one deep enough to absorb R.D. Blackmore's villainous Carver Doone. South West Water have recently sponsored the restoration of a number of mires, to offset possible flash flooding; these have yet to show much of an effect on birdlife (restoring plant and invertebrate communities is the primary conservation aim), but Snipe have benefited, and some wintering Teal have appeared.

River Barle, near Simonsbath, Exmoor – a typical upland stream running through rough grass moorland (John Rivoire)

Winters can be harsh on the hills – North Hill, Exmoor, in the snow (John Rivoire)

The few villages provide winter shelter, nest sites for Swifts and hirundines, and abundant feeders, which attract Nuthatches, Coal Tits and Greenfinches in winter. Most of the enclosed farmland is pasture. More roots were formerly grown but anyone seeking winter finches will do well to seek out game-rearing estates: their scale is now extraordinary, but the shelter crops do provide some variety in the upland valleys, even if the carrion encourages an excess of corvids.

The only open waters of any size are Nutscale Reservoir, Pinkworthy Pond at the source of the Barle, and the ponds at Litton and on the Great Bradley Estate. As expected, they are oligotrophic and attract relatively few birds.

Across Exmoor, much of the ornithological interest lies in the steep valleys. The Forest is drained to the east by the Exe and the Barle, both of which have boggy upper reaches and ancient woodland lower down, mainly of oak and ash. The Barle woodlands, some of which are now National Nature Reserves, have not been well studied, partly because of difficult access and complicated private ownership. However, Dippers and Grey Wagtails have recently been joined by Goosanders, and in the summer there are Pied Flycatchers, Redstarts and Wood Warblers. For these passerines, the greatest concentrations are in the more accessible Horner Wood, where many nest-boxes are provided.

About this Atlas

Geographical scope

The area covered by this Atlas is the present-day county of Somerset, within the boundaries adopted in 1974. The distribution maps for each species are based on the surveys organised by the BTO for the period from 1 November 2007 to 31 July 2011 and extended by SOS to 31 July 2012.

The recording unit for this Atlas is the tetrad, a 2 × 2 kilometre square, each allocated a letter A–Z (except O); there are 25 tetrads in each 10-km square. The 10-km squares covered wholly or in part in this Atlas are shown below (Map 4).

Included are almost all the 973 tetrads which are within the county boundary or contain Somerset territory, including some coastal tetrads which contain only small portions of land. There are, however, some 26 tetrads along the borders with other counties where the land within the Somerset boundary is insignificant, usually less than one quarter of the tetrad; these have been omitted.

Where tetrads are shared with neighbouring counties, some records of scarcer or colonial species have also been omitted where it is certain that their breeding sites were not in Somerset. Examples of these include Grey Heron, Willow Tit, Sand Martin and Tree Sparrow.

Methodology

Timing
Fieldwork ran from 1 November 2007 to 31 July 2012: covering five winters and five breeding seasons.

Fieldwork methods
There were two complementary methods. They had equal priority for observers and contributed differently to the final Atlas.

- **Roving Records.** The aim was to compile a comprehensive list of all the species of birds in each tetrad in Somerset during both the winter and breeding seasons. For the latter, and in other seasons, observers were asked to note any evidence of breeding (using BTO standard codes – see page 32). These records were the main source of information for the distribution maps and related statistics and texts. The level of breeding evidence recorded determines the shade of red of the dot on the distribution maps (see 'Map key' on page 32). Over the course of the five years, observers gathered records from all the tetrads in Somerset, roving far and wide across the county.

Map 4. Somerset 10-km squares

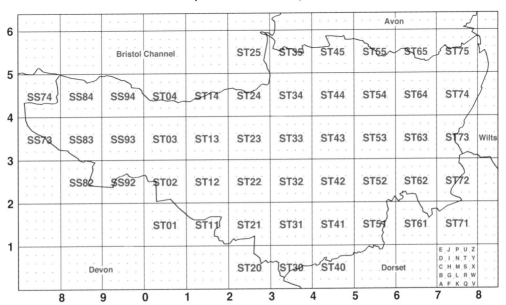

- **Timed Tetrad Visits.** These were timed counts in tetrads. There were two counts in the winter (early and late visits) and two in the breeding season (early and late visits); each visit was for a minimum of one hour (a second hour was optional, though recommended and often done). Volunteers were asked to walk around the main habitats in the tetrad to record all the species encountered and to make an estimate of numbers. TTVs are used by the BTO to provide information on relative abundance of species in each 10-km square. While not so important for the Somerset Atlas as the Roving Records, these records have added some extra species to the tetrad lists, and breeding status information where this did not already exist.

Data submission and validation
This was through the BTO Atlas website or on paper forms; data from the latter were entered into the website, mainly by volunteers. All records were checked and, where necessary, queried with the person who submitted the record. This validation meant that all records were checked before being included in the Atlas.

Extra records
The BTO included in the Atlas website records from a wide range of other surveys including: Breeding Birds Survey; Heronries Census; BirdTrack; and all ringing data. In particular these added some very useful breeding status information. Searches were also made of the SOS database for records of particular

species that were likely to be under-recorded because of detectability issues or the main breeding season falling outside Atlas recording months, and these too were included.

Coverage

The initial aim of SOS was to fulfil its responsibility to ensure that there was at least minimum coverage for the national Atlas, but soon it was apparent that the opportunity was there to produce a tetrad-level Atlas for Somerset. A network of 'Collectors' was established, each responsible for coordinating efforts within one or more 10-km squares and ensuring that the tetrads within them received adequate coverage for both Roving Records (RRs) and Timed Tetrad Visits (TTVs). This worked well, and some observers took to the task particularly enthusiastically, spending many hours in the field. With hindsight more fieldwork could have been done in the first pair of seasons, and two prolonged periods of cold weather in the winters of 2009–10 and 2010–11 impaired the ability of even the keenest observers to get out into the field in some areas, so the decision was taken to extend the county Atlas fieldwork for a further year beyond the end of the fieldwork phase for the national project. This allowed not only for an assessment of the areas and species that needed further targeted effort, but also the opportunity to include the data from an extra year's surveys, including the 2012 national BTO Nightingale survey.

As noted in the Methodology section, the vast majority of records came via the two routes of TTVs

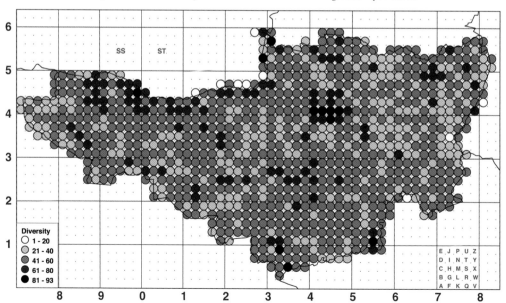

Map 5. The number of species recorded in the breeding season per tetrad

and RRs. In the end nearly all tetrads received TTVs in both seasons, though as the county Atlas is primarily concerned with distribution rather than abundance, RRs were vital.

The tetrad species-richness maps for both the breeding season (Map 5, page 30) and the winter season (Map 6, below) show the number of species recorded in each tetrad, within bands which are similar (though not identical) to those used on the BTO Atlas website. As can be seen, inevitably, there are variations in the bands into which tetrads fall. The reasons for these variations fall into two broad categories: landscape and people.

As explored in detail on pages 7–28 and shown in the topographical map on page 9, Somerset is a highly diverse county. As one would expect, the presence of wildfowl and wader species means that coastal tetrads tend to score highly, as do tetrads that contain significant water bodies (or parts of them); this is evident at both seasons, though particularly so in winter. By contrast, the higher areas of uplands such as Exmoor and Mendip are often largely deserted in winter, resulting in much lower species lists in those areas, again entirely as expected. Both areas have much richer avifaunas in spring and summer, though comments were received from observers that in some tetrads steep gradients presented an extra challenge.

On the Levels, the general lack of any significant areas of woodland is one factor depressing species lists, especially where the prevalent land use is a grassland monoculture for pasture. An obvious exception is the Avalon Marshes, where a much more diverse mosaic of wetland and woodland habitats

has provided some of the highest-scoring tetrads in the whole county.

The Avalon Marshes also benefit considerably from the people factor, as the presence of a number of flagship reserves attracts many observers, again in stark contrast to the small number of pairs of eyes providing casual records from some other areas of the Levels or more remote areas in the hills. The east of the county has traditionally been underwatched, and did not always feel the benefit of significant numbers of casual visitors; the same could be said of other areas such as the Vale of Taunton Deane. This shows to a certain extent on the species-richness maps, though a relatively small number of enthusiastic observers did much to make up for this and achieve adequate coverage in these areas.

There are relatively few cases (fewer perhaps than expected) where it is obvious that an otherwise unremarkable tetrad has a resident Atlas observer, boosting the species list for that tetrad compared to similar ones nearby. Rather, this 'resident effect', if present, seems to be spread over a number of tetrads in an area and does not show up well on the species-richness maps; it is more noticeable perhaps at the level of individual species, particularly those under-recorded, such as owls, where a resident observer within the local community can help to track down birds which may not be found by normal survey methods.

Access was no doubt an issue in some places. Some areas in the east have significant areas of mature woodland, but often these are private with no rights of way, frustrating efforts to survey them effectively. The same is likely to be true to a greater or

Map 6. The number of species recorded in winter per tetrad

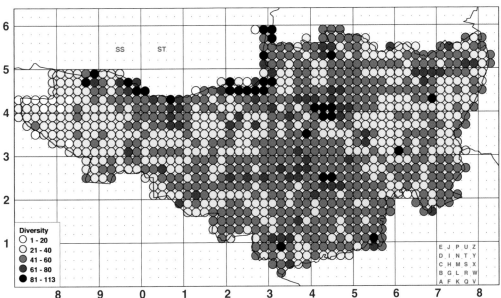

lesser extent in many places across the county, but was particularly noted to be the case by some observers in the west.

Because of all of these factors, species richness is (perhaps inevitably) a rather crude measure of the coverage achieved. However, it is still useful in the absence of detailed records of how long observers spent in each tetrad (which would have been too burdensome for many observers to keep accurately). Some level of variation is inevitable, and the authors know that in a few cases tetrads will have had little more coverage than the allotted TTVs or a couple of *ad hoc* visits in a season to collect RRs; while in others, even in areas rarely if ever visited by birdwatchers outside Atlas times, observers visited tetrads time and time again to find species they suspected to be present or to secure higher levels of breeding evidence. Overall, however, the picture is of at least adequate coverage over the vast majority of tetrads across the county.

The number of species recorded in each 10-km square for each season is given in Table 1 on pages 35–36, together with the number of tetrads involved in each case. For the breeding season the table also includes a breakdown of the number of species for which each of the three levels of breeding evidence was the highest recorded in each 10-km square, as well as those which were recorded as present, but without breeding evidence.

Species maps

The nomenclature of species, both vernacular and scientific, accords with the British List as published by the British Ornithologists' Union (BOU) in 2013, with amendments later recommended by Sangster et al. (2013). As such it does not include the very latest changes, published by the BOU in 2014 while this book was being prepared for publication, placing falcons and parrots just after woodpeckers, for example. The order of species is taken from the 2013 list as far as possible, but has been altered in places where layout constraints have demanded it.

- Species which are largely resident are generally accorded two maps, one for each season, though a small number of scarce resident species require only a single map to cover both seasons.

- Species which are largely restricted to one or other season have one map relevant to that season.

- Seabird species which are common or reasonably frequently recorded as migrants, but which do not breed in Somerset, are not mapped; they are dealt with at the appropriate place within the main

Map key

The **breeding-season maps** illustrate records from 1 April to 31 July over the five years 2008–2012; in a few cases they also include data from other months where it is relevant to the breeding cycle of certain species. The entries fall into four categories, which are represented on the original records submitted to the BTO (electronically or on paper forms) by the letter codes given under each category, and on maps by the symbol on the left.

- **Confirmed breeding** by one or more pairs in at least one season, for which the evidence can be:

NY	Nest with young
NE	Nest with eggs
FF	Adult carrying faecal sac or food
ON	Adults at nest site in circumstances indicating occupied nest
FL	Recently fledged or downy young
UN	Used nest or eggshells
DD	Distraction display or injury-feigning

- **Probable breeding**, for which the evidence can be:

P	Pair present in suitable habitat
T	Permanent territory defended over at least a week (or presence of at least 3 singing males on one visit)
D	Courtship or display
N	Visiting probable nest-site
A	Agitated behaviour
I	Brood patch on bird in hand
B	Nest building or excavation

- **Possible breeding**, for which the evidence can be:

H	Observed in suitable habitat
S	Heard singing in suitable habitat

+ **Presence, but without evidence of breeding**, for which the code could be:

F	Bird flying over
M	Migrant
U	Summering non-breeder

The **winter maps** use blue dots to indicate presence on at least one occasion during November–February in any year between 1 November 2007 and 29 February 2012.

section, with some commentary on their status. In some cases similar species (e.g. the skuas) are grouped together.

- A number of other rare or scarce species occurred on one or more occasions within the county during the Atlas period. Some were vagrants; others were mainly on passage, especially from August to October, and thus outside the months when Atlas work was in progress. Many of these were regular transients, often waterbirds. All such species can be found in a separate section on pages 325–326, after the main species accounts.

Rare and scarce breeding birds

The BTO has a policy on mapping rare and scarce birds which has been agreed by the Rare Breeding Birds Panel (RBBP). It clearly states at what level species can be mapped (10-km square, 100-km square, or sometimes not at all) and all records submitted are treated in confidence. SOS has a similar policy for local rarities and is guided by the SOS Rarities Committee (SOSRC). BTO policy has been followed in most cases, though a few species treated as 'rarities' at a national level on the Atlas website are common enough within Somerset for mapping rules to be relaxed: again, advice has been taken from SOSRC in those cases.

The species accounts

The commentary in the species accounts has three main purposes:

1. To draw attention to patterns (and occasional apparent anomalies) in the maps which relate to the geography and habitats of Somerset.
2. To set the distributions of species in their recent historical and national contexts.
3. To comment on any other matters which could affect the results as displayed in the maps. These may include matters of access, timing, coverage, and weather.

The authors emphasise that this book, like any *Atlas*, represents a snapshot of distribution over (comparatively) a very short period and that an awareness of the past may be vital to understanding the present. Somerset has one of the oldest formal bird-recording systems in England, dating back to 1912, and there have been three county avifaunas in the last forty-five years, the latest (Ballance 2006) covering up to the end of 2004, only three years before the start of the Atlas period. However, this is the first *Somerset Atlas* at tetrad level.

When the question of committing to a county Atlas first arose, the authors, in concert with colleagues on the General Committee of SOS, decided that it would be beyond our capabilities to attempt to map adequately both distribution and abundance of all species at tetrad level. This is therefore primarily a distribution Atlas, and abundance is not commented on routinely. There have, however, been frequent and detailed surveys of many areas within Somerset and of various species over the last forty years, some of which were carried out during the five-year *Atlas* period. The neighbouring recording area of Avon, with much less ground to cover (but with some of their allocation being within Somerset boundaries), have attempted assessments of abundance. They also completed fieldwork and published their local Atlas early, so we have also been able to draw on their results and compare and contrast where relevant. For the national scene, the maps and commentary for *Bird Atlas 2007–11* were made available by the BTO in the period leading up to its publication. The authors of this book have been able (most gratefully) to draw on these and other sources to give some pointers as to trends both within Somerset and nationally, but with the recognition that drawing any specific conclusions at a county level from such data is difficult to do with any precision and may be unwarranted.

Full details of past Atlases for Britain and Ireland are given below and in the Bibliography.

Relationship with Avon

Before the provisions of the Local Government Act 1972 came into force in 1974, Somerset extended north to the edge of Bristol and to the hills north of Bath, and there was an overlap as far south as Cheddar Reservoir between what were then the recording areas of the Ornithological Section of the Somerset Natural History Society and of the Bristol Naturalists' Society (BNS). When the county of Avon was created, the BNS retreated within the new boundary along Mendip, and for the majority of species-recording organisations, including the BTO, the county of Avon became a recording unit. Amongst other matters, this has led to the production of two Atlases for Avon. The first coincided with the BTO's *New Atlas* of 1988–91, and the second, the *New Avon Atlas*, has (as noted above) appeared recently, in advance of both this book and of the national *Bird Atlas 2007–11*.

As a county, Avon existed for 21 years before it was divided into four unitary authorities. It continues as a recording area for birds, and for some other taxa, though for others the Watsonian vice-county system has been retained throughout, regardless of administrative boundary changes. For those more familiar with that system, VC5 is wholly within the area covered by this *Atlas*, but VC6 is roughly equally split (on an approximately east–west axis) between Somerset and Avon.

Differences between the BTO *Bird Atlas 2007–11* and the *Somerset Atlas*

The main difference between these two publications is a matter of resolution, or scale: *BA 2007–11* is, as is usual for a national Atlas, at a 10-km square scale; this *Atlas* is at tetrad level, providing far more detail on a local basis than is possible at national level.

The majority of differences between the maps in this *Atlas* and those in *BA 2007–11* are due to the length of the recording period. In Somerset observers were asked to continue surveying for an extra pair of seasons (2011–12). This assisted greatly in providing extra data for the higher resolution required in a tetrad Atlas, and extra records for under-recorded species such as owls. SOS is very grateful to the BTO for maintaining their computer database and keeping it open for data entry for this extra year. This meant that the majority of the Somerset records submitted in the final year were entered directly into the database, which facilitated production of the maps including data from all five years. Additionally there were a few records of rarer species which were submitted either to SOS or the *British Birds* Rarities Committee and which have been able to be included in this Atlas.

References

A full list of references cited in the species texts, as well as other further reading, may be found in the Bibliography on pages 331–333. The following abbreviations are those commonly used within the text for national and local Atlases and other publications.

AvA 1988–91	Bland, R.L., and Tully, J. (1992). *Atlas of Breeding Birds in Avon, 1988–91*. Bristol. Bristol Ornithological Club (BOC) and Bristol Naturalists' Society (BNS).
BA 1968–72	Sharrock, J.T.R. (comp.) (1976). *The Atlas of Breeding Birds in Britain and Ireland*. Berkhamstead. T. & A.D. Poyser.
BA 2007–11	Balmer, D., Gillings, S., Caffrey, B., Swann, R., Downie, I., and Fuller, R. (2013). *Bird Atlas 2007–11. The Breeding and Wintering Birds of Britain and Ireland*. Thetford. BTO Books.
HBS	Ballance, D.K. (2006). *A History of the Birds of Somerset*. Penryn. Isabelline Books.
NAvA 2007–11	Bland, R.L., and Dadds, M. (2012). *Avon Atlas 2007–11*. Bristol. BOC and BNS.
NBA 1988–91	Gibbons, D.W., Reid, J.B., and Chapman, R.A. 1993. *The New Atlas of Breeding Birds in Britain and Ireland 1988–1991*. London. T. & A.D. Poyser.
SB	*Somerset Birds* (1912–). The annual report on the birds of the county. From 1912 to 1918 it was titled *Notes on Somerset Birds* and from 1919 to 1959 *Report on Somerset Birds*. From 1912 to 1973 it was published by the Ornithological Section of Somerset[shire] Archaeological Society; thereafter by Somerset Ornithological Society. Last issue available for reference for this book was *SB* 2012.
WA 1981–84	Lack, P. (comp.) 1986. *The Atlas of Wintering Birds in Britain and Ireland*. Calton. T. & A.D. Poyser.
WeBS	*The Wetland Bird Survey*. Annual. A joint scheme of BTO, RSPB and the Joint Nature Conservation Committee (JNCC), in association with the Wildfowl and Wetlands Trust (WWT).

Table 1. Number of species recorded in Somerset tetrads in each 10-km square during Atlas seasons 2007–2012

| 10-km square | Number of tetrads (up to 25) | Breeding season | | | | | Winter |
		Confirmed breeding No. *(%)*	Probable breeding No. *(%)*	Possible breeding No. *(%)*	Present (no breeding evidence) No. *(%)*	Total	Total
ST84	3	38 *(60)*	9 *(14)*	13 *(21)*	3 *(5)*	63	63
ST85	6	40 *(56)*	8 *(11)*	14 *(20)*	9 *(13)*	71	62
ST71	2	25 *(56)*	13 *(29)*	6 *(13)*	1 *(2)*	45	50
ST72	15	55 *(63)*	16 *(18)*	5 *(6)*	11 *(13)*	87	88
ST73	18	45 *(54)*	16 *(19)*	15 *(18)*	7 *(9)*	83	69
ST74	25	66 *(67)*	12 *(12)*	8 *(8)*	13 *(13)*	99	96
ST75	17	63 *(69)*	6 *(7)*	11 *(12)*	11 *(12)*	91	93
ST61	4	37 *(60)*	16 *(26)*	7 *(11)*	2 *(3)*	62	82
ST62	24	55 *(69)*	6 *(7)*	11 *(14)*	8 *(10)*	80	78
ST63	25	67 *(70)*	6 *(6)*	12 *(13)*	11 *(11)*	96	108
ST64	25	61 *(62)*	9 *(9)*	10 *(10)*	19 *(19)*	99	108
ST65	13	54 *(66)*	6 *(7)*	16 *(20)*	6 *(7)*	82	79
ST50	4	29 *(38)*	25 *(33)*	13 *(17)*	9 *(12)*	76	71
ST51	22	63 *(64)*	11 *(11)*	6 *(6)*	19 *(19)*	99	109
ST52	25	61 *(70)*	8 *(9)*	7 *(8)*	11 *(13)*	87	81
ST53	25	59 *(66)*	10 *(11)*	9 *(10)*	12 *(13)*	90	95
ST54	25	60 *(66)*	11 *(12)*	11 *(12)*	9 *(10)*	91	89
ST55	16	52 *(58)*	17 *(19)*	13 *(14)*	8 *(9)*	90	89
ST40	10	49 *(70)*	7 *(10)*	10 *(14)*	4 *(6)*	70	71
ST41	25	57 *(63)*	9 *(10)*	13 *(14)*	12 *(13)*	91	86
ST42	25	63 *(61)*	21 *(20)*	9 *(9)*	10 *(10)*	103	117
ST43	25	80 *(71)*	18 *(16)*	4 *(3)*	11 *(10)*	113	125
ST44	25	74 *(66)*	16 *(14)*	8 *(7)*	14 *(13)*	112	124
ST45	22	64 *(60)*	11 *(10)*	11 *(10)*	22 *(20)*	108	122
ST30	16	62 *(60)*	14 *(13)*	11 *(11)*	16 *(16)*	103	106
ST31	25	58 *(61)*	13 *(14)*	11 *(12)*	12 *(13)*	94	95

Table 1 continued. Number of species recorded in Somerset tetrads in each 10-km square during Atlas seasons 2007–2012

| 10-km square | Number of tetrads (up to 25) | Breeding season | | | | | Winter |
		Confirmed breeding No. (%)	Probable breeding No. (%)	Possible breeding No. (%)	Present (no breeding evidence) No. (%)	Total	Total
ST32	25	63 (60)	20 (19)	9 (9)	12 (12)	104	111
ST33	25	67 (63)	19 (18)	10 (9)	11 (10)	107	113
ST34	25	58 (56)	13 (13)	13 (13)	19 (18)	103	124
ST35	18	56 (53)	12 (11)	14 (13)	24 (23)	106	123
ST20	4	25 (42)	22 (37)	8 (13)	5 (8)	60	59
ST21	23	52 (47)	17 (18)	18 (20)	5 (5)	92	86
ST22	25	64 (67)	9 (9)	10 (10)	13 (14)	96	105
ST23	25	60 (63)	12 (13)	15 (16)	8 (8)	95	102
ST24	21	63 (57)	21 (19)	10 (9)	16 (15)	110	147
ST25	6	45 (46)	12 (13)	9 (9)	31 (32)	97	118
ST11	15	50 (60)	14 (16)	14 (16)	7 (8)	85	75
ST12	25	58 (63)	13 (14)	9 (10)	12 (13)	92	88
ST13	25	62 (68)	14 (15)	7 (8)	8 (9)	91	79
ST14	15	65 (69)	14 (15)	7 (7)	8 (9)	94	100
ST01	1	21 (45)	8 (17)	18 (38)	0 (0)	47	63
ST02	23	53 (61)	11 (13)	16 (18)	7 (8)	87	78
ST03	25	58 (64)	15 (17)	9 (10)	8 (9)	90	91
ST04	11	65 (64)	9 (9)	8 (8)	19 (19)	101	124
SS92	12	63 (71)	14 (16)	6 (7)	5 (6)	88	78
SS93	25	63 (69)	10 (11)	9 (10)	9 (10)	91	97
SS94	23	71 (65)	15 (14)	8 (7)	15 (14)	109	140
SS82	6	42 (58)	17 (24)	8 (11)	5 (7)	72	60
SS83	24	61 (68)	17 (19)	7 (8)	4 (5)	89	80
SS84	25	67 (65)	13 (13)	9 (8)	14 (14)	103	116
SS73	12	41 (55)	21 (28)	5 (6)	8 (11)	75	66
SS74	13	45 (59)	21 (27)	5 (6)	6 (8)	77	50

Somerset Atlas

Species
Accounts

MUTE SWAN *Cygnus olor*

Mute Swans are a familiar bird wherever there are water bodies of any size, as comparison of the species' maps with the maps in the introduction will show: the distribution at both seasons (and they are very similar) almost mirrors the Levels and the county's lakes and rivers.

There is no count of breeding pairs from the Atlas years, but in 2002, 102 pairs were found in the county, though these may exclude a few on private waters. More than half were on the Avalon Marshes and 20 on West Sedge Moor; the remainder were on a wide variety of waters, ranging from rhynes on the Levels to the larger flooded pits and park lakes. Occasional pairs are also to be found in some quite out-of-the-way places on small ponds, some recently created as ornamental features or for fishing or irrigation: an increasing trend in areas of the county with otherwise very little standing water. Very few breed west of the Quantocks or on waters over the 100-metre contour.

Many non-breeding birds gather on the Levels in summer, as was first realised when an aerial survey in 1961 found 400 (Eltringham 1963). No recent counts are complete, but samples suggest a slightly higher figure, concentrated mainly on Tealham and Tadham Moors and the Avalon Marshes (especially around Sharpham Deer Park and on Westhay Moor).

In the four winters from 2007/08 to 2010/11, the Levels held either first or second place among British sites for the species, with a mean total of 1,101 birds, slightly more than the Abbotsbury area in Dorset. Most of these are probably Somerset-bred birds, though visitors from Abbotsbury and a few other places have been identified from ringing returns. Counts of over 100 have been made at the above summering sites, and at Cheddar Reservoir (during hard frost), Butleigh Moor, Aller Moor, Curry and Hay Moors, West Sedge Moor, Witcombe Bottom and Wet Moor.

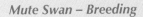

Mute Swan – Breeding

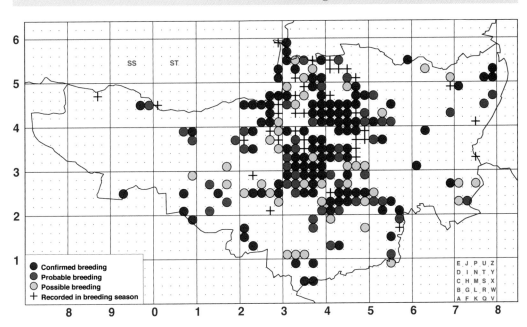

Legend:
- ● Confirmed breeding
- ● Probable breeding
- ○ Possible breeding
- + Recorded in breeding season

Mute Swan – Winter

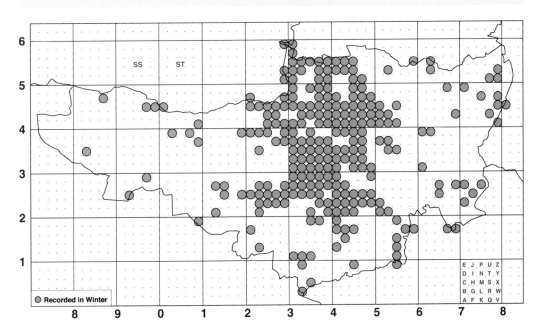

Legend:
- ○ Recorded in Winter

BEWICK'S SWAN *Cygnus columbianus bewickii*

The distribution mapped here is very much what would be expected, with most records coming from the Levels north and south of the Poldens, and from the area south of Bridgwater Bay from the Parrett Estuary west to Lilstock.

Numbers of wintering Bewick's Swans in the county were at their highest during the latter half of the twentieth century, and even as recently as 2000 there was a single herd of over 100 birds on what is now Greylake RSPB reserve. Numbers have fallen dramatically since, however: from 2004/05 to 2009/10, the highest count was of 39, during the hard weather of the last of those years. During the first winter period of 2011 it was suggested that as many as 106 different birds may have been present on the South Levels, though the highest WeBS count was 63; this brief resurgence in numbers was attributed to exceptionally cold weather on the Continent. By contrast, in the winter of 2011/12 there were no records at all from the South Levels, which were exceptionally dry.

The decline of this species has been most marked in Ireland and in western Britain. It has been ascribed to falling productivity in the Siberian breeding stock and to the increased attractions along their south-westerly course in autumn, especially of the Ouse and Nene Washes and the Wildfowl and Wetlands Trust site at Slimbridge, though numbers have been falling there too and in milder winters many birds may remain with the large wintering herds in the Netherlands.

WHOOPER SWAN *Cygnus cygnus*

The difference in fortunes between this species and the previous one could not be more stark. While at the beginning of the Atlas period Bewick's still outnumbered Whoopers and were more widespread, the gap has narrowed markedly in the last few years. Whooper Swans used to be scarce birds in Somerset, and while identification issues may have masked some earlier records, there is no doubt that in the run-up to the Atlas period and during it there has been a real increase in both frequency and numbers. The highest total was 39 in the winter of 2008/09, though some of these may have been duplications. Most have been in small parties, often families, of up to seven. They tend to occur in the same areas as Bewick's, both often also associating with Mute Swans, though it is unusual to see both species of 'wild' swan together. The impression that Whooper is now commoner than Bewick's is probably still erroneous (just), but is fuelled by regular and long-staying parties within the Avalon Marshes, which attract far more visitors than the South Levels, formerly the Bewick's stronghold.

This increasing regularity, though still modest, is in accordance with recent numbers at the main British sites, on the Ouse Washes and at Martin Mere and the Ribble Estuary, and reflects an increase in the Icelandic breeding population.

Bewick's Swan sponsored by Nigel and Elaine Smith

Bewick's Swan – Winter

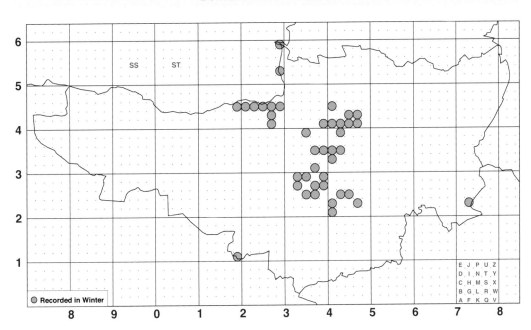

Whooper Swan – Winter

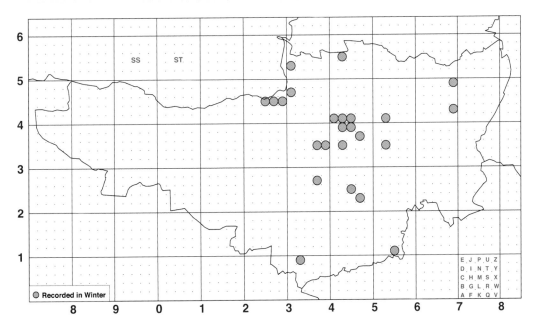

WHITE-FRONTED GOOSE *Anser albifrons*

Among the grey geese, only the White-front has ever been a regular winter visitor to Somerset. The flocks which spent each winter around the Parrett Estuary and on Minehead Marshes disappeared around 40 years before the start of the current Atlas period, however, and now there are only occasional records of small numbers on the Levels. Their decline in Somerset is linked with the general pattern of wintering habits in north-west Europe, where increasing numbers have remained in the Netherlands. The famous flock at Slimbridge, in Gloucestershire, has declined to mere hundreds over the last ten years (Kirk and Phillips 2013).

There were about ten records during the Atlas period, including a flock of 32 in the Shapwick Heath and Sharpham area in December 2010/January 2011; one of these birds had been given a Dutch collar in 2001.

There have been about 11 records of the Greenland race *A. a. flavirostris*, which winters in Ireland and the west of Scotland, but the only one during the Atlas years was in October, and is therefore not mapped.

BEAN GOOSE *Anser fabalis*

There were only two records in the Atlas period: one of the Tundra race *A. f. rossicus*, on Wet Moor in January 2008; and one of the nominate Taiga race *A. f. fabalis*, in fields at Brean in December 2011.

Most of the previous 40–50 Bean Geese recorded in the county were formerly thought to have been of the nominate race, but it is now believed that the majority of records are more likely to have been *rossicus*, which was first officially recorded in 1996 during a national influx of this race. There have been several influxes of Tundra Beans, including one in 2004, when over 30 were seen in Somerset. The Taiga Beans which regularly winter in Britain tend to be site-faithful, so it may well be that in a local context it is the rarer race.

PINK-FOOTED GOOSE *Anser brachyrhynchus*

There were 25 Pink-footed Geese recorded during the Atlas period, including a flock of 19 in November 2008; four others were on passage outside the Atlas months. So far there has been no regular pattern of occurrences, other than them turning up in the same areas where one would expect to see swans and occasional geese: the Levels, the south side of Bridgwater Bay, and the marshes between Minehead and Dunster. The wintering population in the British Isles has quadrupled over the last 30 years, and one might expect some increase in records, though the nearest regular flocks are in Lancashire and in the Fens.

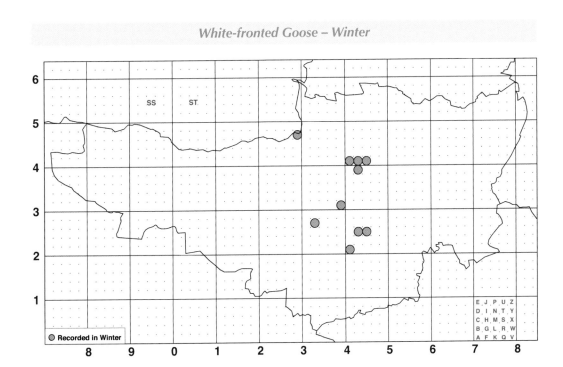

White-fronted Goose – Winter

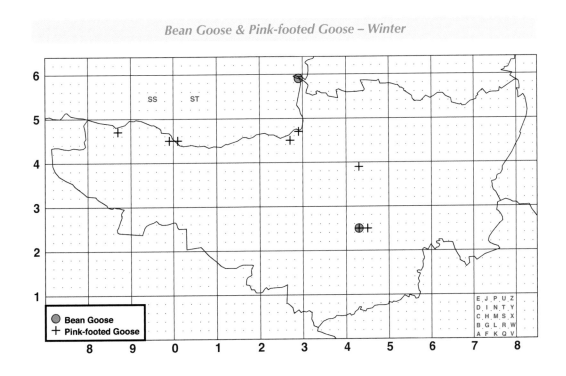

Bean Goose & Pink-footed Goose – Winter

GREYLAG GOOSE *Anser anser*

Somerset's Greylag Goose population is feral in origin, dating back to a release on Chilton Moor in 1982. Since 2000 up to 14 families have been seen annually in the Avalon Marshes, though they have been slow to spread elsewhere. A few records from other sites were noted in the Atlas database, but no confirmation of breeding.

The Avalon Marshes birds are largely sedentary and in winter most remain on the Levels north of the Poldens, forming flocks of 50 to 95 birds, though there is also some dispersal to the South Levels. From 2000 to 2011, there were about 70 records elsewhere, of which 11 were of parties of ten or more, mainly from October to January. Over the Atlas period there was a slight increase in records of small numbers around the coast of Bridgwater Bay, and one on Minehead Marshes. These may also refer to some of the Levels birds, but there are evidently some wanderers from outside the county too, since one colour-ringed at Llanwern (Gwent) in 2007 was seen at Brean in April 2008.

There has also been speculation that some of these records may even have been wild Icelandic birds, especially those seen during periods of hard weather, but there is no evidence for this. The British range has almost doubled over the last 30 years, and a few pairs breed with some regularity in all neighbouring counties.

Greylag Goose – Breeding

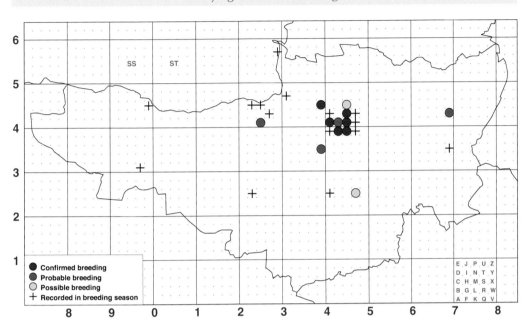

- ● Confirmed breeding
- ● Probable breeding
- ○ Possible breeding
- + Recorded in breeding season

Greylag Goose – Winter

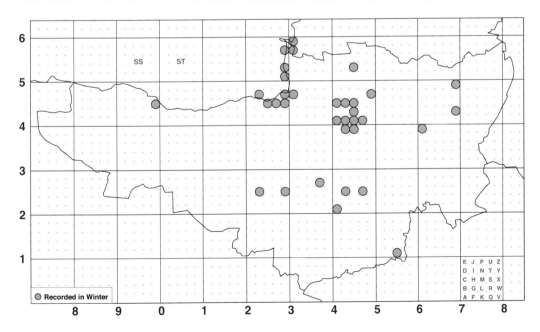

- ● Recorded in Winter

CANADA GOOSE *Branta canadensis*

This North American species is now familiar to all. It first bred in Somerset in 1969 at Clatworthy Reservoir, perhaps spreading from a strong population in Mid Devon, and was later introduced at Butlin's in Minehead. So it is not surprising that one of the most flourishing populations in the county now occupies a range including the Brendon Hills and the coastal lowlands from Watchet to Porlock Weir. There are particular concentrations around Wimbleball Lake, Clatworthy Reservoir and Minehead. This flock and sub-flock structure is typical of Canada Geese, and at least partly explains why sometimes there might be hundreds at a site, and sometimes none. These birds pair off in February or March and disperse to breed by many smaller waters, even on high ground wherever sites are available. They then gather to moult at Wimbleball or Butlin's, where peak concentrations may be of 400 birds; in October 2009 there was a count of 1,124 at Wimbleball, which probably included many from outside the county.

Away from the west, Canada Geese are also a common sight, in all the areas one would expect, with noticeable concentrations on the Avalon Marshes, around the Brue and Parrett Estuaries, the Bridgwater clay-pits, and various reservoirs. Isolated pairs also nest on sometimes very small waters, especially those with islands, including many newly created ponds in areas with little other standing water. Many of these are on private land and may not be viewable from public rights of way, so it is quite likely that some pairs have evaded detection by Atlas observers.

Outside the breeding season and the autumn, flocks of between 200 and 520 have been found since 2007 on Torr Works, Cheddar, Sutton Bingham, and Durleigh Reservoirs, on the Parrett Estuary and adjacent coasts, and on West Sedge Moor, Wet Moor and King's Moor, as well as at the sites already mentioned in the west. From 2006/07 to 2010/11, the mean wintering total on the Levels recorded by WeBS was 627. Wandering parties can now be seen almost anywhere in Somerset at any time of the year, though they are generally scarce on high ground and in the south-east.

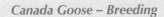

Canada Goose – Breeding

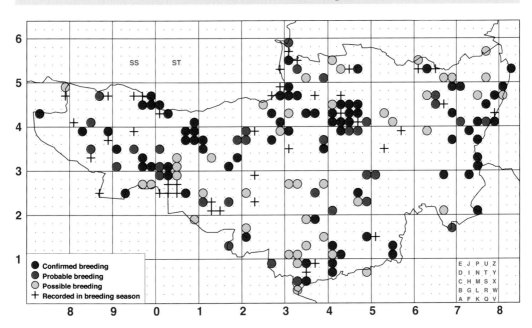

SS   ST.

Confirmed breeding
Probable breeding
Possible breeding
+ Recorded in breeding season

E J P U Z
D I N T Y
C H M S X
B G L R W
A F K Q V

8 9 0 1 2 3 4 5 6 7 8

Canada Goose – Winter

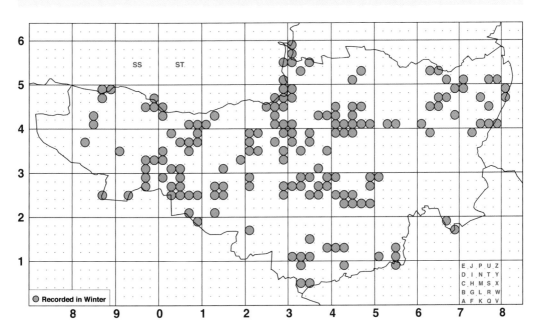

SS   ST.

○ Recorded in Winter

E J P U Z
D I N T Y
C H M S X
B G L R W
A F K Q V

8 9 0 1 2 3 4 5 6 7 8

BARNACLE GOOSE *Branta leucopsis*

Most Barnacle Geese recorded in Somerset are suspected of being of captive origin: a number of captive birds have escaped and joined flocks of Canada Geese, often for extended periods of time: these will account for some of the records mapped. The picture is more interesting than that, though, as there are over 2,000 naturalised birds in the British Isles, some of which are now breeding, so it could happen in Somerset, though it is not known to have occurred yet. A small resident flock has become established, based on Chew Valley and Blagdon Lakes over the Avon border, and one or two pairs successfully bred there in all Atlas years: this flock is the source of regular records during the Atlas period of up to 20 birds at Torr Works Reservoir.

There have been occasional records of birds which at least appeared wild. During the Atlas period, in January 2011, a flock of 56, including a Barnacle × Snow Goose hybrid, frequented Curry Moor and West Sedge Moor for a week or so: enquiries showed that this was in fact the feral flock from the Fleet in Dorset, which later returned there. That November, however, 19 visited the Avalon Marshes that were not traced to a source.

BRENT GOOSE *Branta bernicla*

Dark-bellied Brent Goose *B. b. bernicla*

Light-bellied Brent Goose *B. b. hrota*

The nominate race, from Northern Russia, has traditionally been the commoner in Somerset. The Light-bellied birds, from Canada, formerly scarce, have now become regular; they winter mainly in Ireland, where their numbers have increased greatly.

The first Brent Geese generally appear in late October, and from then to March small numbers can be found anywhere along the coast from the Axe Estuary to Porlock Marsh, though most often along the coast between Steart and Hinkley Point. Winter totals are difficult to determine beyond the WeBS counts, since most birds move around erratically, and the counts are supplemented by occasional migrant flocks. Dark-bellied birds have averaged 40 over the last ten years, but the number present at any one time is much lower than this, because of duplication. Light-bellied birds have become much more frequent since 2003/04, and in some (though not all) Atlas winters they outnumbered Dark-bellied birds.

Inland records are still unusual, and most are of single, short-staying wanderers from the coast. The sites mapped here are a representative scatter, though by no means the only sites at which they have occurred in the past: there is, for instance, a remarkable record of 41 Dark-bellied Brent Geese at Torr Works Reservoir on 31 March 2005.

There was one unusual summer record, an adult of the Dark-bellied race on Brean Down in June 2008, most likely a bird that delayed migration due to illness or injury.

Barnacle Goose – Combined Winter & Breeding

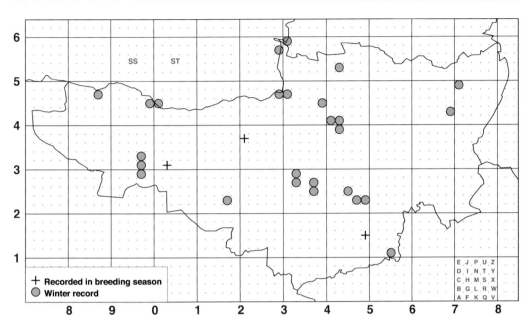

SS   ST

+ Recorded in breeding season
◉ Winter record

	E J P U Z
	D I N T Y
	C H M S X
	B G L R W
	A F K Q V

8   9   0   1   2   3   4   5   6   7   8

Brent Goose – Winter

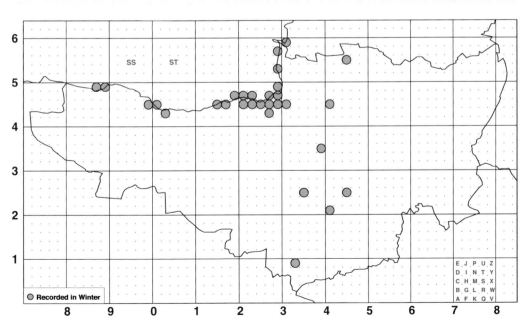

SS   ST

◉ Recorded in Winter

	E J P U Z
	D I N T Y
	C H M S X
	B G L R W
	A F K Q V

8   9   0   1   2   3   4   5   6   7   8

SHELDUCK *Tadorna tadorna*

Shelduck once bred along almost all the coast and in the immediate hinterland, but records declined with the increase in coastal development and the inevitable disturbance that brings. Breeding is now largely restricted to the area round the Axe and Parrett Estuaries, to the coast from Steart to Lilstock, and to woodland and land-slips west of Minehead. Except around Steart, recording has been erratic, and the western sites can usually only be inferred from birds visiting possible places on the dangerous slopes, or from broods which are led down to Porlock Marsh. As the map shows, summer records are frequent along the remainder of the western coast, but breeding is seldom proved. The total of pairs in any one year since 2000 is unlikely to have been more than 15.

Since 2007, pairs have been prospecting sites on or near Greylake RSPB reserve, where as yet there has been no proof of breeding. Before 1997 there was occasional breeding well inland, for example on West Sedge Moor, and that tradition was revived in the exceptional floods of 2012, when a family was seen on Curry Moor in May; the presence of juveniles on Wet Moor in August suggested that breeding had also taken place that summer somewhere on the South Levels.

Bridgwater Bay is an important moulting area from June to November, when waves of Shelduck arrive to pass their flightless weeks drifting with the tide between Stert Point and Kilve (Eltringham and Boyd 1960, 1963). They are thought to come from Ireland, but there is no proof of this. The peak numbers are from July to September: from 2007 to 2012 annual peaks varied between 3,243 and 4,450, the latter, in August 2010, being the highest count.

Winter records present some problems. High November numbers suggest that some moulting birds remain to winter or that their departure overlaps fresh arrivals. The most important area is Steart, where peak numbers, usually in December, averaged 900 from 1987 to 2002. These were continued up to the winter of 2007/08, and even rose to 2,200 in December 2005, but in the following two winters, including part of the Atlas period, the peak fell as low as 192. At the north end of the coast, the Axe Estuary has regularly held up to 170, but there, too, numbers fell below 75. A third site is Dunster Beach, which normally holds up to 80 birds. There are also about 50 wintering regularly on Porlock Marsh, where a slight increase has followed the breach in the shingle ridge in 1996 that has turned it into a tidal saltmarsh.

Flocks of up to 20 are sometimes found inland during the winter, chiefly on flooded Levels, though they also appear sometimes on reservoirs.

Shelduck sponsored by Nigel Milbourne

Shelduck – Breeding

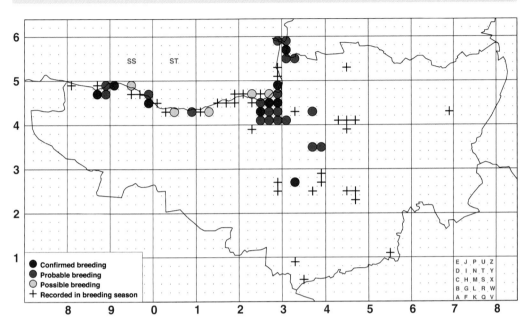

SS   ST.

- ● Confirmed breeding
- ● Probable breeding
- ○ Possible breeding
- + Recorded in breeding season

E	J	P	U	Z
D	I	N	T	Y
C	H	M	S	X
B	G	L	R	W
A	F	K	Q	V

Shelduck – Winter

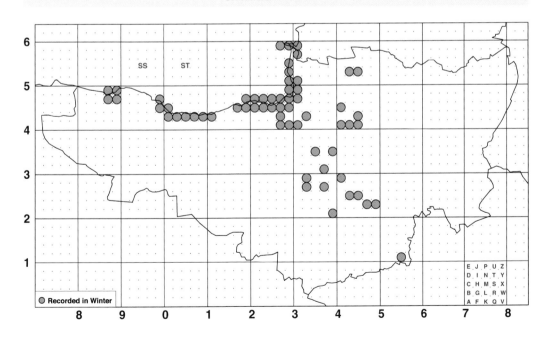

SS   ST.

- ● Recorded in Winter

E	J	P	U	Z
D	I	N	T	Y
C	H	M	S	X
B	G	L	R	W
A	F	K	Q	V

MANDARIN DUCK *Aix galericulata*

Breeding was first recorded in the wild in the east of the county early in the 21st century, at Bruton in 2002 and Orchardleigh Lake in 2003. During the Atlas period most records of confirmed or probable breeding came from the north-east, centred on Orchardleigh Lake, and especially from the Yeovil and Chard areas in the south, which have been only recently colonised but now seem to be the species' stronghold in the county. These three areas now seem to hold relatively small but self-sustaining populations. Numbers are difficult to be sure of, but the highest individual site counts are from the Yeovil area just before and after the Atlas period: 24 at Sutton Bingham Reservoir in September 2007 and 28 at Ninesprings Country Park in January 2013. The breeding-season records from the Mendip and Cheddar area are something of a surprise, and it will be interesting to see if a further population builds up in that area in future years.

The southern strongholds in particular also show up well in the winter distribution map. This endearingly improbable bird is always popular with owners of captive wildfowl, and the records in ST22 (Taunton) and SS94 (Dunster Hawn) relate to single birds which may be recent escapees. A series of records in ST23, centred on Hawkridge Reservoir, relate to wandering individuals from a nearby collection. Nonetheless, there is suitable breeding habitat for them there, so it is possible another feral population could become established.

There are no real clues otherwise about the origins of the Somerset population. Apart from local escapes, there may also be wanderers from the largest British centre for this naturalised species, in the Forest of Dean, where recent autumn counts have found up to 270, but there is no evidence to support this.

Mandarin Duck – Breeding

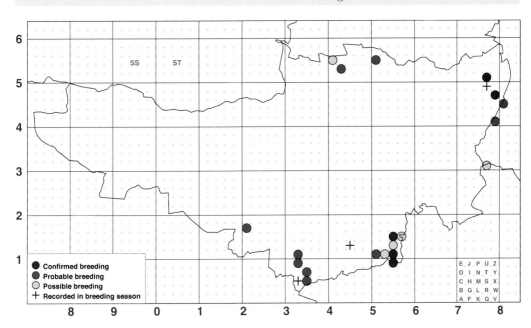

- ● Confirmed breeding
- ● Probable breeding
- ○ Possible breeding
- + Recorded in breeding season

Mandarin Duck – Winter

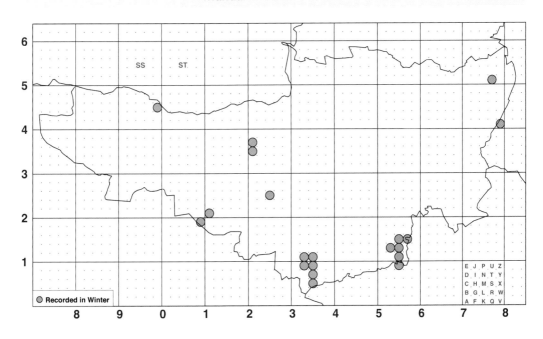

- ● Recorded in Winter

GADWALL *Anas strepera*

The first Somerset pair bred at Durleigh Reservoir in 1968. Numbers continued to build up on the Levels and by 2000 the reedbeds of the Avalon Marshes may have held over 100 birds, though their breeding success and definitive numbers in such dense habitat have always been hard to establish. Published totals in *SB* have recently been lower, but it is unclear how much of this is a real decline, and how much is due to reduced monitoring effort and the difficulty of counting in such habitats. King's Sedge Moor and Greylake form another population centre in summer; as the map shows, there is a scatter of other records. Other sites in the east have been used relatively recently, but there were no records during the Atlas period for Cary Moor, Wells or the Glastonbury Moors. Odd birds can occur on smaller waters throughout the county, but as yet there has been no evidence of breeding in the west or south-west.

As might be expected, the winter map shows a rather wider spread of records, with varying numbers being recorded at nearly all water bodies of any size (see Map 2 on page 11 to compare). The large block of occupied tetrads in ST42 reflects the regular winter flooding of the low-lying South Levels to the south and east of Langport. A few isolated records refer to dispersing birds during the big freeze-ups in the 2009/10 and 2010/11 winters, but these do not distort the overall picture to any noticeable extent.

Wintering numbers in the Avalon Marshes have fallen from a peak of over 1,000 in the winter of 2002/03 to between 320 and 700, a number which still qualifies for recognition as of national importance.

Gadwall sponsored by Richard Devitt

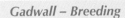

Gadwall – Breeding

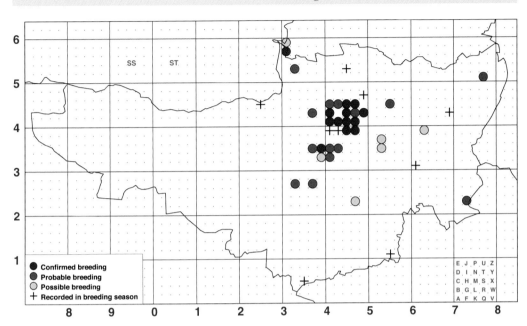

- ● Confirmed breeding
- ● Probable breeding
- ○ Possible breeding
- + Recorded in breeding season

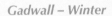

Gadwall – Winter

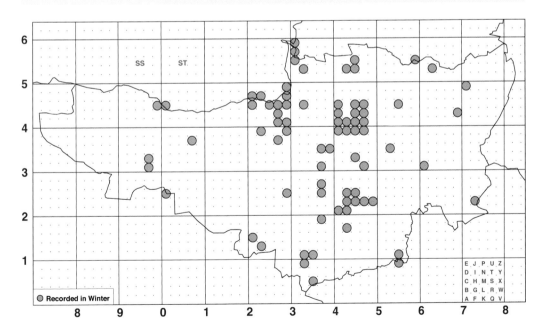

- ○ Recorded in Winter

TEAL *Anas crecca*

As the winter map shows, Teal are widespread in this season in Somerset, utilising water bodies of all sizes. Birds begin to arrive in August or September, but the main influx is from early November. Since the winter of 2006/07, the Somerset Levels have been the most internationally important British site for Teal; counts have been twice as high as those from any other area. In the freeze-up of 2010/11 February numbers rose to 45,000: West Sedge Moor alone held 20,000. Other areas which may have over 1,000 include the Axe Estuary, the Avalon Marshes, Greylake RSPB reserve and Wet Moor, and at times other flooded Levels. Teal are widely distributed over the rest of the county, and the Atlas has revealed that even small ponds on the Exmoor Plateau may be visited by small parties. On the coast, up to 2,000 are sometimes present around Bridgwater Bay. Most leave in late February or early March.

During the Atlas period breeding was only confirmed within the Avalon Marshes, though probable breeding records also came from King's Sedge Moor, West Sedge Moor (both of which have been used as breeding sites in recent pre-Atlas years), Chard Junction gravel pits, Otterhead Lakes in the Blackdown Hills, and on the Parrett Estuary. This seems to indicate a reduction in the number of breeding sites in the county in recent decades or perhaps a shift – before 1965, there were a number of breeding records from Mendip, Exmoor and the larger reservoirs, though this was also well before the development of the Avalon Marshes.

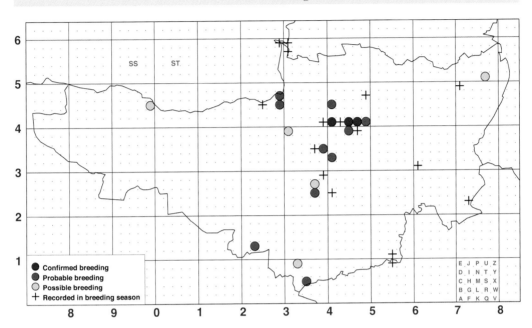

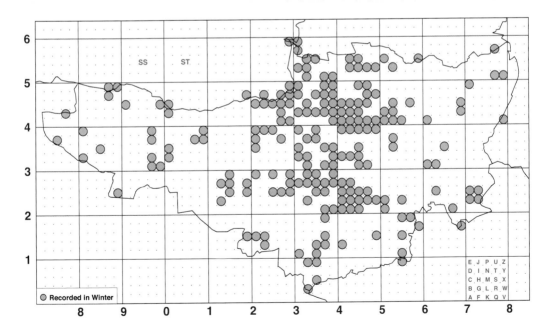

MALLARD *Anas platyrhynchos*

Mallard are familiar birds throughout the county, and the maps for both seasons show them as being unsurprisingly widespread. They are even present, but very thinly distributed, in the uplands of the Quantocks, the Blackdowns, the Brendons and Exmoor Forest. Many small populations centred on farm or village ponds are only half-wild and hybridise with domestic ducks. Observers have seldom taken much interest in Mallard; they appear in WeBS counts, but may be under-recorded in non-Atlas years.

There are few very recent surveys of breeding numbers over a wide area, but the new reserves must have enhanced their local populations: the general Levels Survey by Weaver and Chown (1983) found 404 pairs, of which three-quarters were on King's Sedge Moor; in 2002 there were 306 pairs in the Avalon Marshes alone, and West Sedge Moor showed an increase from 50 pairs in 1990 to 148 in 1995 and 2009. The latest information from these sites, and from the Cheddar Moors, suggests some decline. However, the national stock increased by a fifth from 1998 to 2008 (Baillie *et al.* 2010); the decline may be a reflection of recent cold winters on a sedentary local population.

Wintering counts from WeBS will include immigrant birds, but some of the highest numbers have been from August to October and are likely to include locally-bred birds or shooting releases. Numbers are not particularly high – the most consistently so have been: Cheddar Reservoir, with up to 400, and Chard Reservoir, with up to 220, both mainly in autumn; Westhay Moor and Shapwick/ Meare Heaths, both with up to 420, mainly from August to December; Greylake RSPB reserve, with up to 650 in December/January; and West Sedge Moor, with up to 570 from November to February.

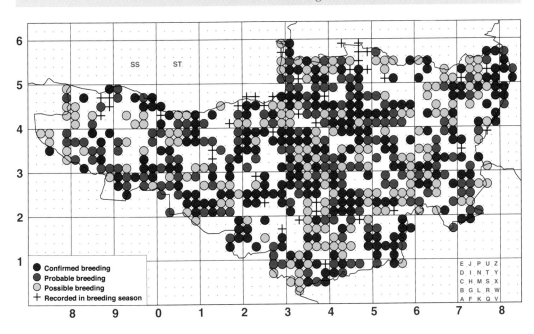

Mallard – Breeding

Confirmed breeding
Probable breeding
Possible breeding
+ Recorded in breeding season

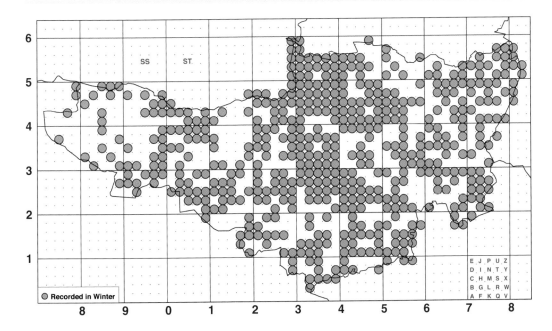

Mallard – Winter

Recorded in Winter

PINTAIL *Anas acuta*

Pintail can and do turn up fairly regularly on most waters of any size within Somerset during the winter; they arrive from late October and depart from late February to mid-March. They are creatures of habit, though, and tend to concentrate at a few favourite places. The map shows the most regularly used sites as being the coast of Bridgwater Bay from the Parrett Estuary to Hinkley Point, the Avalon Marshes (especially Catcott Lows), and the Levels south of the Polden Hills, including King's Sedge Moor, West Sedge Moor, and the Wet Moor to West Moor complex south and east of Langport.

Numbers fluctuate from year to year. The Levels have sometimes qualified as a site of international importance, with counts of up to 1,500, of which two-thirds were on West Sedge Moor, but wintering numbers at the latter site appear to have collapsed during the Atlas period from 613 in February 2008 to just seven in the same month in 2012. This has not been offset by increases at other sites in the county (*SB* 2012): numbers recorded in Bridgwater Bay, for instance, have remained relatively static.

No breeding has been suspected in recent years; the most recent breeding records were single pairs on arable land near Muchelney as far back as 1951 and 1952. There have been a few late-spring and summer records for this Atlas, but without breeding.

GARGANEY *Anas querquedula*

In Somerset the Garganey is at the westerly tip of its wide breeding range. Most seen are passage males and pairs in March or April at reserves on the Levels. There has been, however, a small breeding population in the county for most of the last century, based on the Levels: recent estimates have usually hovered around eight pairs. Given the species' preferred habitat it is difficult to obtain confirmation of breeding. No confirmed breeding records were entered in the Atlas database for Somerset, so none appear on the map opposite, but this is known to be inaccurate. Information from other sources indicates that four pairs bred on the Avalon Marshes in 2009. Regular records of parties of juveniles in August mean that breeding can be reasonably inferred to have also taken place in other years during this period. Garganey is a Schedule 1 species under the Wildlife and Countryside Act 1981, and therefore this Atlas follows the convention of mapping centrally within 10km squares. Birds were recorded in 20 tetrads in total, with probable breeding in seven, possible breeding in four, and presence without evidence of breeding in nine.

Though it is a species regularly recorded on autumn passage, winter records are very rare: one in the Atlas period concerned a female at Catcott Lows on 3 January 2010. With two more records from the Avalon Marshes in January 2013 it remains to be seen whether these are isolated occurrences or the start of a pattern.

Pintail – Winter

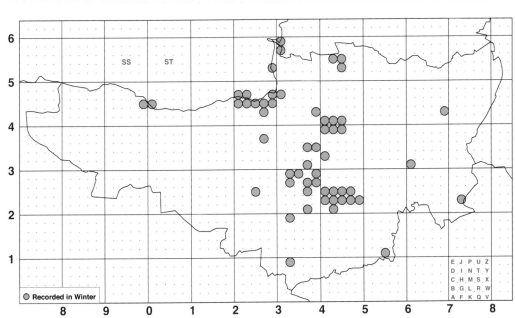

Legend: ⊙ Recorded in Winter

Garganey – Breeding

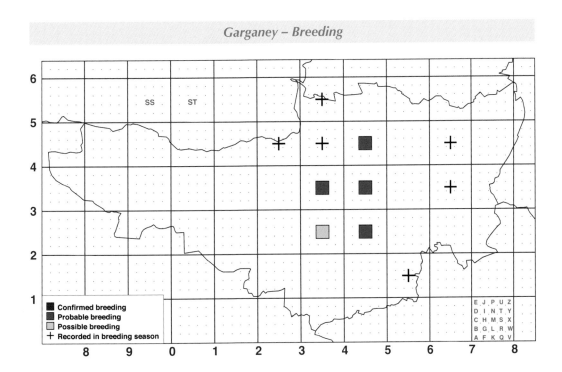

Legend:
- ■ Confirmed breeding
- ■ Probable breeding
- □ Possible breeding
- + Recorded in breeding season

SHOVELER *Anas clypeata*

Breeding was first recorded on the Levels in the late 19th century. From 2008 to 2012, from five to 20 pairs were seen every summer, mostly in the Avalon Marshes and on King's Sedge Moor (particularly at Greylake RSPB reserve), but only about a quarter of these were confirmed as breeding. The area of reserves in the Avalon Marshes continues to grow, providing more suitable habitat for a range of species, although it may also create difficulties in assessing breeding success. Elsewhere, probable breeding was recorded (mostly pairs of birds seen) on West Sedge Moor, in the Blackmoor Vale, at Chard Reservoir (which, though small, covers part of three tetrads), and at Combe Sydenham in the west and Lympsham in the north.

Wintering birds appear from September, but are present mainly from October to early March. During the Atlas period, the Levels were between first and seventh in importance among British sites, with a population of between 400 and 1,800, the lowest figures being in the coldest weather and the highest in the wettest. The leading site has generally been West Sedge Moor, which sometimes has held up to 1,200 Shoveler in January, and accounts for about two-thirds of all records for the county. This is followed by Catcott Heath (up to 375) and Ham Wall (up to 215); other sites with occasional counts of over 100 are Cheddar Reservoir, Shapwick and Meare Heaths, Westhay Moor, and Wet Moor. In February 2012 there was a remarkable count of 243 at Ham Sewage Treatment Works, near Taunton, but that site may now be lost through recent redevelopment. Smaller numbers visit many other parts of the Levels, and there are occasional records from the coast, especially in hard weather, and, more regularly, from other reservoirs and suitable shallow waters. Because of the variety of weather experienced during the Atlas period, the map probably shows a broader range of sites than might be used in any one winter.

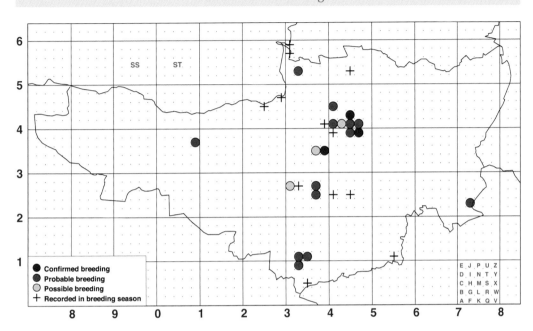

Shoveler – Breeding

- ● Confirmed breeding
- ● Probable breeding
- ● Possible breeding
- + Recorded in breeding season

Shoveler – Winter

- ● Recorded in Winter

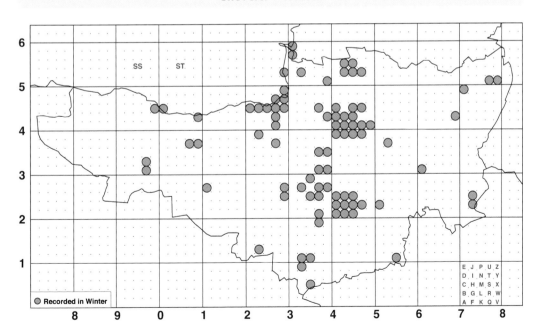

WIGEON *Anas penelope*

Wigeon were once considered to be largely a coastal species: the development of protected areas has brought large numbers inland, though they still prefer to feed at night if they are far from a safe haven (Trump and Ovenden 1999; Chown 2003). In the four winters from 2007 to 2011, the Levels were on average the second most internationally important site in Britain, with up to 28,000 birds in midwinter, and a record total of 51,000 in the freeze-up of January 2011. There have been WeBS counts of up to 41,000 on West Sedge Moor alone, and large numbers also on the nearby Tone and South Levels, and on the Avalon Marshes and King's Sedge Moor. Their distribution is dependent on flooding and frost levels, and in hard weather they make for the coast: during the big freeze in 2010/11, the regular flock of around 1,000 in the Parrett Estuary/Bridgwater Bay area swelled to 4,000. Small flocks winter along the western coast from Doniford to Minehead and at Wimbleball Lake, but there are now few seen on Porlock Marsh. Other sites regularly used by small numbers include Sutton Bingham Reservoir. The first arrivals may be from September, but most come in November and leave in early March.

Since 1998, breeding has been suspected on the Levels in several years. There has been no absolute proof and the occasional summering birds may have been sick or injured, but in 2011 there were six possible pairs present (Holling *et al.* 2013).

RED-CRESTED POCHARD *Netta rufina*

There have been annual records of wintering birds since the 1960s, usually at Cheddar Reservoir, but recently also in the Avalon Marshes. This pattern was maintained during the Atlas period, with scattered records from other sites, including Wimbleball Lake, Durleigh and Hawkridge Reservoirs, and Apex Park (Highbridge).

Most records have been of ones and twos, and have sometimes been suspected of being escapes, but the hard frosts of January and November and December 2010 brought flocks of up to 25 to Cheddar. It would be natural to suppose that the majority of birds originate from the Cotswold Water Park, in Gloucestershire and Wiltshire, where there has been a breeding population since 1973, and which now holds a wintering population of up to 300 (Kirk and Phillips 2013); these birds are thought to be largely sedentary, but do make hard-weather movements when their favoured pits freeze. On the other hand, at least some birds recorded in Somerset might have been immigrants from Central Europe, where breeding populations have increased.

Wigeon – Winter

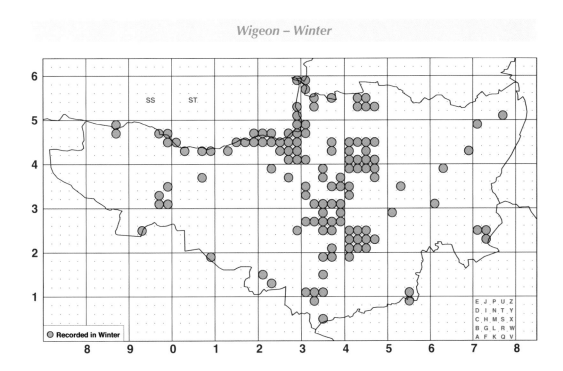

Red-crested Pochard – Winter

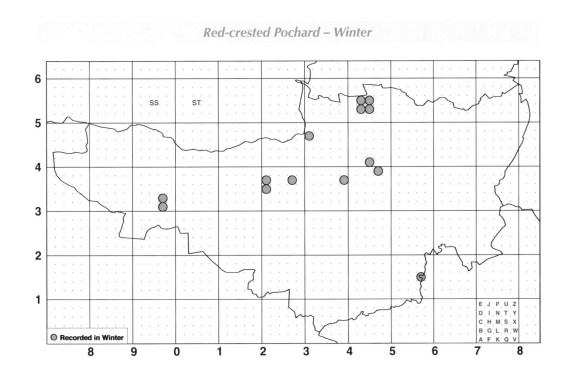

POCHARD *Aythya ferina*

The first Somerset breeding record for Pochard was in 1954 at Durleigh Reservoir. Though they have occasionally bred at a number of scattered sites since, the only known site since 1997 has been the Avalon Marshes, where they first bred on Ham Wall in 1994. Totals have always been hard to obtain, but in the spreading Ham Wall reedbeds the population built up rapidly from about 12 pairs in 2005 to 81 in 2010; there were 38 in 2011, and 65 in 2012, but breeding was seldom proved. The dense cover that they need spreads over much of the eastern part of the Marshes, where there are records of smaller numbers from at least five sites.

The species is unsurprisingly more widespread in winter, when birds arrive from their breeding grounds elsewhere in October and remain to late February or early March. Cheddar Reservoir is the most important site: Atlas counts have varied widely between 250 and an exceptional 1,800 in December 2010, a total probably due to very cold weather – Cheddar remains at least partially ice-free when other waters have frozen over. In the second half of the winter, the Avalon Marshes have proved attractive: they held about 300 in February 2010 and the protected habitat must have encouraged birds to remain for the breeding season. There are small and irregular numbers on many other waters, such as Torr Works Reservoir, Orchardleigh Lake, and Wimbleball Lake; coastal records such as those noted here from the Axe Estuary and Hinkley Point are rare, and almost entirely due to hard-weather movements.

FERRUGINOUS DUCK *Aythya nyroca*

Formerly a rare vagrant, during the Atlas period there were up to ten records from 2008 to 2011, of which two were in summer, but these records most likely refer to the wanderings of a very small number of birds. The most favoured sites have been Wimbleball Lake, Cheddar Reservoir, and the Avalon Marshes, though records in the Atlas period also came from Curry Moor and Ham Sewage Treatment Works in the south. All have been in the company of other diving ducks, particularly Pochards.

Nesting attempts probably occurred at Chew Valley Lake in 2003 and 2004, and a drake may have been successfully reared there in 2006 (Davis and Vinicombe 2011). With regular movements of diving ducks in particular to and fro over Mendip, these records are likely to be directly linked with those in Somerset. (No map.)

Pochard – Breeding

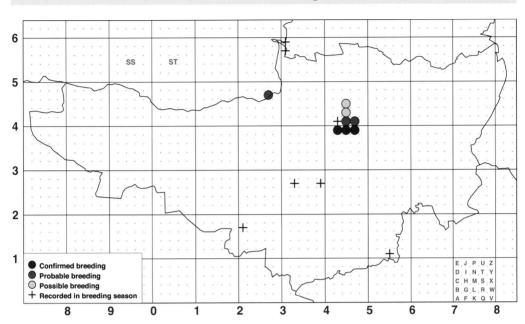

Pochard – Winter

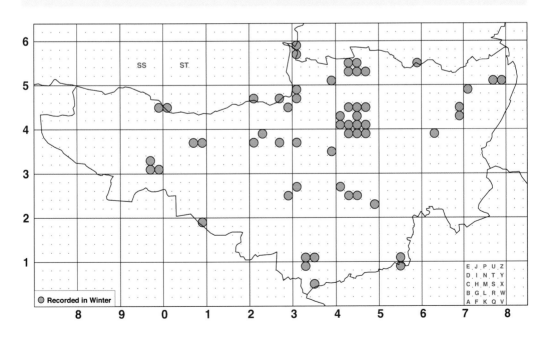

67

TUFTED DUCK *Aythya fuligula*

Though Tufted Ducks have long been occasional breeders in Somerset, it is only relatively recently (since about 1980) that they have become widespread. The Atlas map may represent the widest breeding range ever known in the county. Many summering birds do not nest, but the total Somerset population is at least 50 pairs, and perhaps twice that number. The highest concentration is in the Avalon Marshes, but they also occur in summer on most of the county's reservoirs and even on ponds on the Exmoor Plateau. Tufted Ducks will use quite small waters, and Atlas fieldwork uncovered several previously unknown breeding sites, often isolated pairs on recently created fishing or irrigation ponds, particularly where islands are provided. The proportion of 'probable breeding' records is quite high, but Tufted Ducks are relatively late breeders, and pairs noted earlier in the summer could have had broods which were missed in August.

From November to March there are many winter visitors, which are distributed over most suitable Somerset waters. Numbers are irregular, and counts outside of WeBS are complicated by flocks commuting over Mendip from Chew Valley and Blagdon Lakes to Cheddar Reservoir, and probably to other waters in the north-east. A single-day count in December 2010 produced a Somerset total of 610, the highest result since 1983, and that did not include minor waters; this is likely to have been affected by hard-weather movements. The most important sites are Cheddar, with from 50 to 315, and the Avalon Marshes, with up to 500. Other waters which sometimes hold 50 or more are the lakes at Orchardleigh, Mells Park, and Blakeway, and the reservoirs at Torr Works, Ashford, Hawkridge, and Wimbleball.

Tufted Duck – Breeding

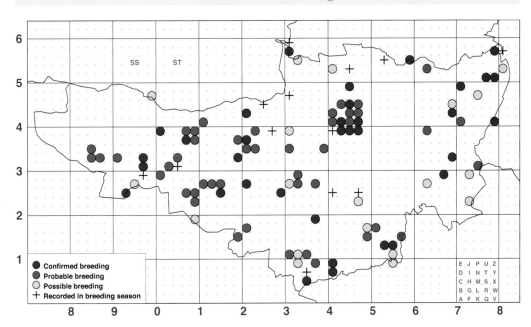

Legend:
- ● Confirmed breeding
- ● Probable breeding
- ○ Possible breeding
- + Recorded in breeding season

Tufted Duck – Winter

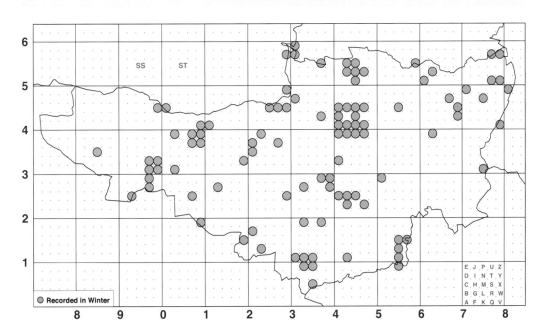

Legend:
- ○ Recorded in Winter

SCAUP *Aythya marila*

Scaup have always been scarce visitors to Somerset: during the first four winters of the Atlas period, the average annual total was only 14. As the map shows, the Parrett Estuary and Bridgwater Bay west to Hinkley Point are the favoured areas for the species, as they have been historically; a regular party off the Steart–Hinkley Point coast rose to a maximum of 11 in 2010/11. Inland, Cheddar Reservoir is by far the most regular site, with one to five present in most Atlas winters, often making extended stays. The map shows records from Ashford and Sutton Bingham Reservoirs, though they would have been equally unsurprising from a number of other reservoirs, and from various winter floods on the Levels, where singles or small parties may turn up on occasion either by themselves or in the company of other diving ducks.

RING-NECKED DUCK *Aythya collaris*

As might be expected for a westerly county with significant wildfowl populations, this North American species is one of Somerset's more regular vagrants. Since it was first reported in the county in 1972, there have been about 40 records, mostly drakes, though several birds have put in long stays and roamed between sites over several years, so there is an unknown, but probably quite large, amount of duplication. Ringing recoveries elsewhere have proved Atlantic crossings in both directions, so most at least of our birds are presumed to be genuine vagrants, though there is always the possibility of escapes. Records have been scattered throughout the year, though winter is the most regular season, and the birds are usually in the company of other diving ducks, particularly Tufted Ducks.

Five occurred during the Atlas period, of which three were in winter. The scatter of sites shown here is a relatively random snapshot; birds have appeared at several other sites both just before and after the Atlas period, including Wimbleball Lake and the Avalon Marshes.

Scaup – Winter

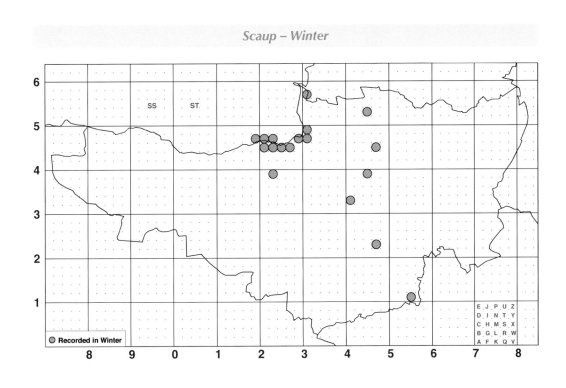

○ Recorded in Winter

Ring-necked Duck – Winter

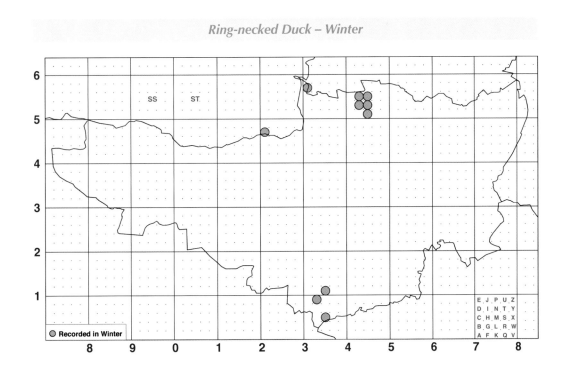

○ Recorded in Winter

LONG-TAILED DUCK *Clangula hyemalis*

Long-tailed Ducks were recorded in nine tetrads in the Atlas winter season, but this relates effectively to five records of single birds, three of which put in extended stays: Hurlstone Point, Wimbleball Lake, Hinkley Point, Durleigh Reservoir, and Shapwick Heath. This is a representative sample for what is an uncommon and irregular winter visitor to the county, apart from the omission of the most regular site, Cheddar Reservoir, where none were recorded during the Atlas period; one wintered there again in 2013/14.

There was one unusual summer record during the period: a summer-plumaged drake for just one day at Porlock Weir, 11 June 2008.

COMMON SCOTER *Melanitta nigra*

Common Scoters are most regularly encountered as passage migrants on seawatches, particularly off the western coast, perhaps related to the large flocks which gather in Carmarthen Bay, not far to the north-west. As the map shows, they may be seen anywhere along the coast in winter, but the only regular flock during the Atlas period was in Bridgwater Bay, most usually off Hinkley Point: numbers fluctuated, peaking at 45 birds in November 2011.

Small parties are frequently seen off the Somerset coast, especially west of Watchet, where commercial mussel-beds are currently being re-established. From 1995 to 2012 the peak months for sightings were April, July, and November.

Inland records are rare at any season, though such pattern as there is tends to agree with the peak months for coastal records. The handful of summer records not mapped here are mostly the result of dull, overcast weather which occasionally disorients and grounds birds migrating overland. They seldom stay more than a day; a similar pattern can be found on reservoirs in Southern and Midland England. Similar conditions were also responsible for a party of 27 which briefly visited Shapwick Heath on 23 November 2007. Other winter inland records came from Chard and Cheddar Reservoirs, though perhaps the most unusual record was a 'spring' one, a gale-blown adult drake which lingered on the Huntspill River from 27 March to 2 April 2009.

Offshore, the highest count in recent years was of 111 off Minehead on 8 November 2010.

VELVET SCOTER *Melanitta fusca*

Much rarer and unpredictable in its appearances than Common Scoter, Velvet Scoter is less than annual in occurrence, and has no likely source population nearby. During the Atlas period there were nine birds recorded between Berrow and Hurlstone Point, mostly in 2010 and 2011: all from November to early March. Most were seen as fly-bys on seawatches, with only the immature female in Bridgwater Bay in January–March 2010 putting in an extended stay. There are a very few previous inland records, but none in 2007–12.

Long-tailed Duck – Winter

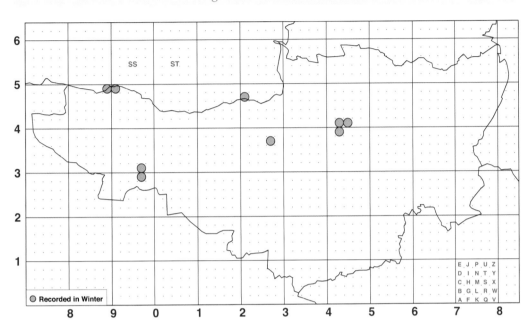

Common Scoter & Velvet Scoter – Winter

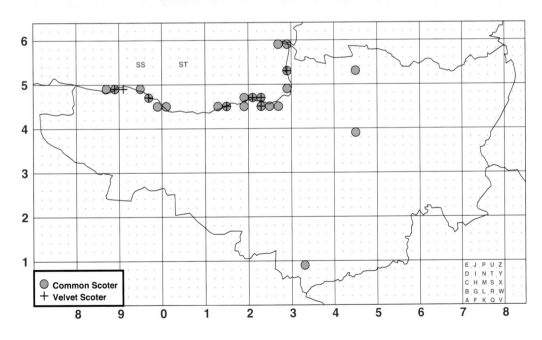

GOLDENEYE *Bucephala clangula*

Goldeneyes are widely but very thinly spread across the county in winter, from late November to March: the map could almost be one of the significant water bodies in the county, the notable omission being Durleigh Reservoir, where they have occurred in the past. Coastal records are restricted to the muddy and food-rich waters of the Axe Estuary and Bridgwater Bay, the rockier shores to the west presumably not being to the species' liking (the one 'coastal' record in the west was in fact on the freshwater Dunster Hawn).

In the 1980s Cheddar Reservoir was the prime site, with numbers regularly peaking at over 100, but they have declined markedly since, mirroring the national trend. During the Atlas years the peak count here was of 37 in December 2010, during a very cold spell. The Avalon Marshes is the other key area, Shapwick Heath, Westhay Moor, and Blakeway Lake being the most regular sites.

SMEW *Mergellus albellus*

This most attractive of ducks has never been more than an occasional visitor to Somerset, with anything more than occasional strays occurring in the hardest winters as refugees from further east. In the five winters of the Atlas period, about 27 birds were recorded, all but one in the three last years; Cheddar Reservoir and the Avalon Marshes reserves were the most favoured sites, with isolated records on the Axe Estuary, Ashford and Durleigh Reservoirs, and most

unexpectedly on floods at Muchelney. This is a representative scatter, though Smew have also been recorded before and after the Atlas period on other waters to the east and west of the distribution mapped here.

The Atlas records are also representative in that records of drakes ('white nuns') are very much outnumbered by females and immatures ('redheads').

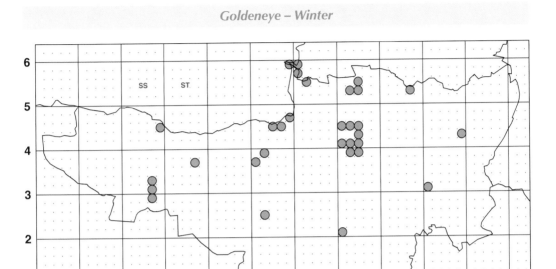

Goldeneye – Winter

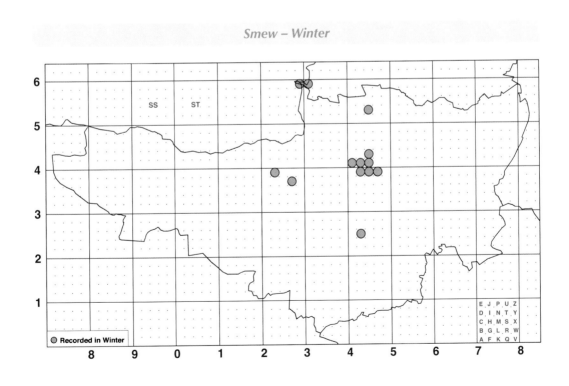

Smew – Winter

GOOSANDER *Mergus merganser*

Until the 1950s Goosanders were largely cold-weather visitors to the larger waters and rivers of Somerset. The southward expansion of the breeding range from Scotland reached Wales in 1970 and Dartmoor in 1980, but it was not until 1993 that a brood was first seen on the River Barle. There are perhaps now five or six pairs breeding regularly along the wooded sections of that river between Landacre Bridge and the Exe confluence. The Atlas period has seen a range extension, as the lower part of the Exe was colonised in 2009. There were thought to be no other suitable sites in the county, but a pair was recorded from Emborough Pond, Mendip, and more significantly a brood was seen on the River Frome in 2013, unfortunately after the end of the Atlas period.

In winter Goosander fish on rivers and smaller waters but prefer to roost on reservoirs, especially Cheddar and Wimbleball. At Cheddar the peak figures have exceeded 35, and an exceptional 63 were recorded during the hard weather of December 2010; these birds disperse in daytime to feed on the Avalon Marshes (especially SWT's Westhay Moor reserve) and on the Huntspill and Cripps Rivers. The Wimbleball roost attracts up to 90 birds from the Exmoor and Mid-Devon rivers, and these can be viewed as they arrive low over the dam at dusk. In the east, records from Orchardleigh Lake have been increasingly regular. The distribution as shown on the map has no doubt been influenced by periods of hard weather during the Atlas years, especially coastal records, but even with allowance being made for that, Goosanders are being recorded more regularly on reservoirs and the bigger rivers; the species is probably more widespread now than at any previous time.

Goosander sponsored by Roger Butcher

Goosander – Breeding

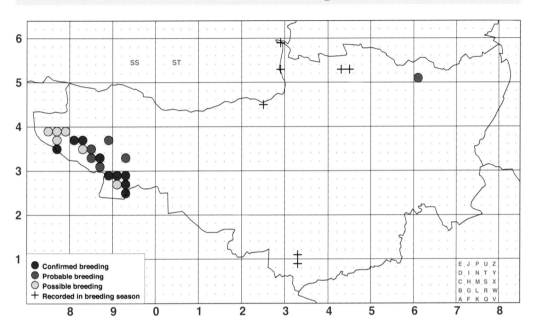

Legend:
- ● Confirmed breeding
- ● Probable breeding
- ○ Possible breeding
- + Recorded in breeding season

Goosander – Winter

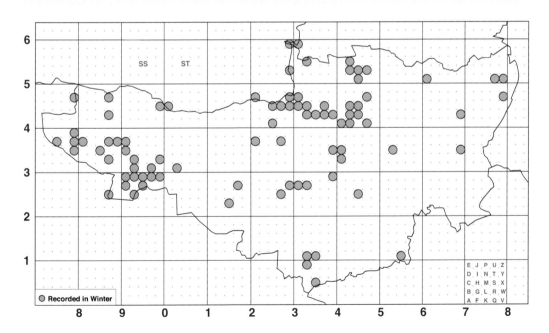

Legend:
- ● Recorded in Winter

RED-BREASTED MERGANSER *Mergus serrator*

There is no regular wintering area for Red-breasted Mergansers within Somerset waters, but they have become more frequently recorded over the last 20 years, perhaps in part because of the increase in autumn and early-winter seawatching. There were at most 19 in the Atlas winters, almost all in Bridgwater Bay or moving off Hurlstone Point, with perhaps some duplication involved. Freshwater records are relatively rare: in the Atlas period they came from Apex Park (Highbridge/Burnham), Wimbleball Lake, Durleigh Reservoir, and the most likely site for inland seaduck, Cheddar Reservoir. A further 35 were seen on the coast from August to October, outside the Atlas recording months but in the peak passage season.

RUDDY DUCK *Oxyura jamaicensis*

The history of this species in Britain has been well rehearsed elsewhere, as have been the concerted efforts made in recent years to eradicate them, and the reasons put forward for the cull. Breeding began in the Avalon Marshes in 1994, but was last confirmed in 2005. During the Atlas period there were only casual records, totalling about 50 birds, largely in December and January, and almost entirely confined to Cheddar Reservoir or the Avalon Marshes. Only the winter records are mapped here, but the few summer records do not change the picture significantly.

Influxes on to Cheddar Reservoir in particular seemed to coincide with periods of activity by the cullers on the other side of Mendip at Chew Valley and Blagdon Lakes, always the core of the population in the region. Ruddy Ducks on those lakes have now almost been eliminated, and there were only two records (of three birds) in Somerset in 2012, one after the end of the Atlas period. The map here may well record very nearly the last days of this species in the county.

Red-breasted Merganser – Winter

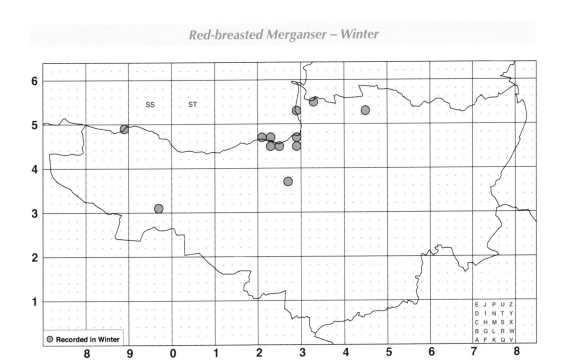

Ruddy Duck – Winter

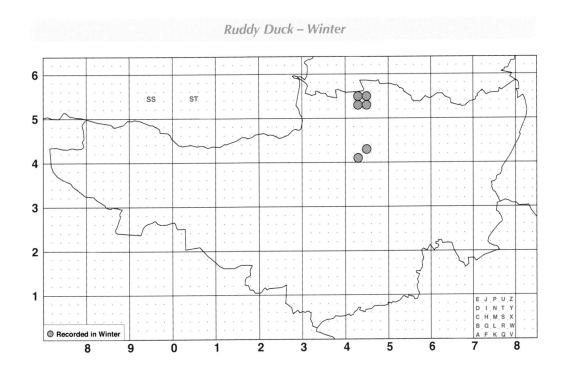

RED-LEGGED PARTRIDGE *Alectoris rufa*

The maps for the two seasons are remarkably consistent in showing the strongholds for this introduced species in the county. 'Red-legs' are well distributed on Exmoor and the Brendons, on the lower parts of the Mendip Plateau in the north-east, on the downland of the south-east, in the Chard and Ilminster areas, and on the edge of the Levels around Somerton and Street. They are seemingly nearly absent from many lowland areas, especially the flat and featureless Levels of improved grassland in the north-west, and from the high tops and steep slopes of the western Mendip ridge.

Though there are probably some areas where they are self-sustaining, the distribution shown here may do little more than reflect the distribution of shooting estates, which turn down very large numbers of this species annually. Following the decline of Grey Partridges, larger-scale introductions of Red-legs began in the 1950s and have continued on many sporting estates, where partridge shooting has the economic advantage of an earlier start to the season (compared to Pheasant). Very large numbers have been released, for example in North-east and Central Somerset, on the North Brendons, on North-east Exmoor and in the Exe Valley. Some are even kept in coops to be released only a day or two before a shoot. Although wanderers often find asylum in the surrounding country, few survive to breed in the wild. Many records were made after summer releases; by November, smaller introductions will have been entirely shot out, as may be deduced from the winter absences in some areas, most noticeably the Blackdowns.

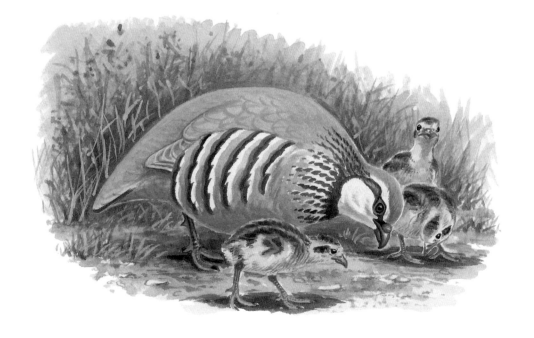

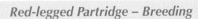

Red-legged Partridge – Breeding

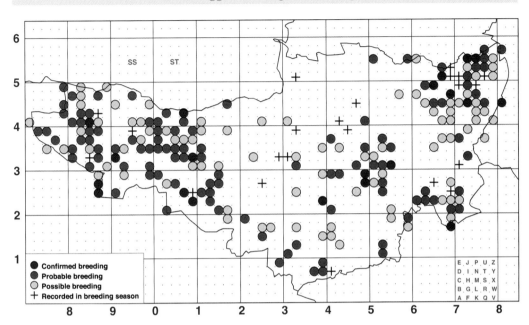

Red-legged Partridge – Winter

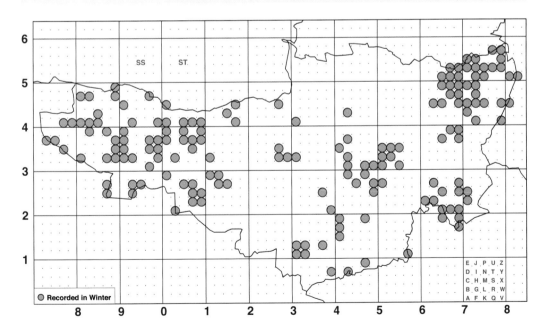

GREY PARTRIDGE *Perdix perdix*

This was a generally common species, except on the highest ground, until the 1950s. The earlier stages of its decline escaped notice, at least in published records. After the hard winter of 1962/63 the decline became apparent, and continued. By the time this Atlas started Grey Partridges appeared to be nearly extinct in the county, an impression not helped by their disappearance from a few well-known birding areas such as the Steart peninsula. The likely causes, as with other farmland species, are the use of pesticides which eliminate weeds and affect invertebrate populations, and the removal of headlands round fields, reducing the birds' food supply.

During the Atlas period, records averaged five or six a year, well scattered and mostly from the eastern half of the county and the Quantock coast; there were outliers from Thurloxton and Milverton. The picture improves when the winter and summer maps are combined, with records for as many as 40 tetrads: the Atlas engendered many trips to farmland areas rarely otherwise visited by birdwatchers. There were no records at all in the west, but there were some signs of concentration in coastal farmland west of the Parrett and in East Mendip, south of Radstock. Some evidently relate to small and unsuccessful local introductions, and doubt has been expressed as to whether there are any self-sustaining populations left in Somerset.

Grey Partridge sponsored by Roger Musgrove

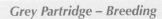

Grey Partridge – Breeding

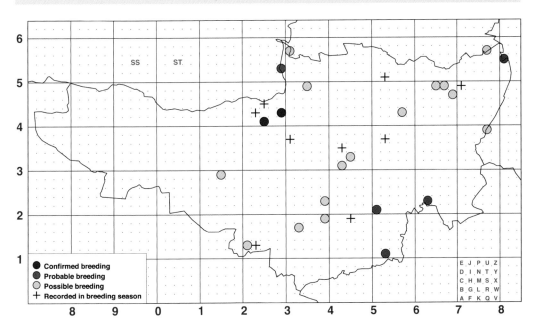

● Confirmed breeding
● Probable breeding
○ Possible breeding
+ Recorded in breeding season

Grey Partridge – Winter

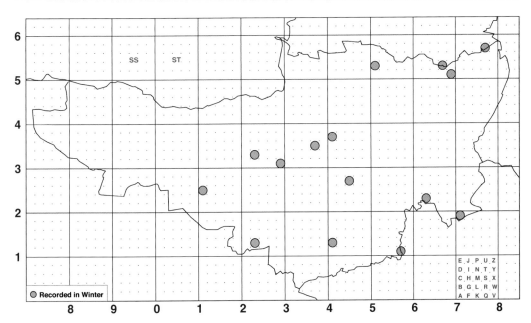

○ Recorded in Winter

PHEASANT *Phasianus colchicus*

Brown and Grice (2005) list Somerset among the ten English counties where Pheasants are most abundant: some estates put down tens of thousands of birds in the summer They are very widely distributed, though still scarce or absent in parts of the Levels and on the Mendip tops, as well as in urban areas. The most obvious gap is between Burnham and Cheddar; this is land with little shelter or organised shooting. Although there are no data on abundance, impressions from the field suggest that the species is most abundant in the west, where there are many shooting estates.

Given the size of the releases annually, it is difficult to assess the extent of wild breeding, which is in any case difficult to confirm without seeing broods of young chicks.

QUAIL *Coturnix coturnix*

Quail have always been highly irregular summer visitors, prone to years of abundance and others of scarcity. About 22 calling males were recorded in 2011, which nationally was the best year of modern times, although the year of greatest abundance in Somerset was 1989, another 'Quail year' nationally, when at least 70 were heard. The most favoured site has been West Sedge Moor, where they were heard in all but one of the five Atlas years. Records were submitted from other sites, mainly on the Levels and in arable farmland, but also on Mendip, and in tussock grassland on Exmoor. Breeding was last proved in 1998, on West Sedge Moor. It has presumably taken place in at least some years since then, but is very hard to confirm.

Quail – Breeding

Confirmed breeding
Probable breeding
Possible breeding
+ Recorded in breeding season

Pheasant – Breeding

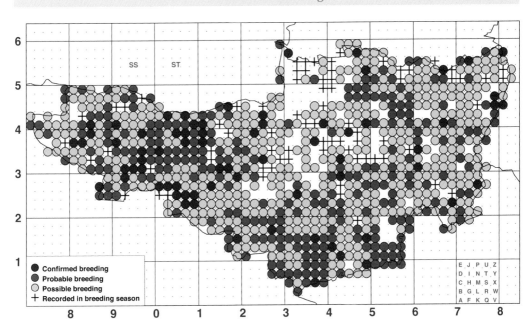

- ● Confirmed breeding
- ● Probable breeding
- ○ Possible breeding
- + Recorded in breeding season

Pheasant – Winter

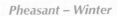

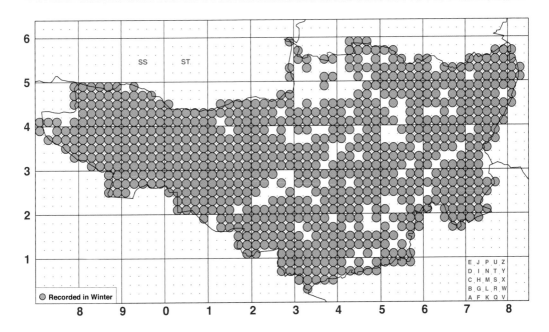

○ Recorded in Winter

RED-THROATED DIVER *Gavia stellata*

Since 1987, the great increase in seawatching has revealed Red-throated Divers to be regular in the Bristol Channel from November to March; they are sometimes numerous during westerlies in December and January. These birds are probably from the gatherings in Bideford Bay and off Hartland Point at that season, and are presumably connected with the movements of herring and mackerel shoals. Most observations of this species (and the other two regular divers) have been from watchpoints on the western coast, especially Hurlstone Point. There have been regular counts of up to 40 off Hurlstone and occasional ones of 70 or more, mostly flying by, though they sometimes linger for a few days. December numbers off Minehead have continued to increase since the end of the Atlas period.

They are rarer and usually wind-blown up-Channel beyond Minehead Bay: Atlas records off Stolford and Hinkley Point and Burnham-on-Sea are representative, but one on the Parrett Estuary near Combwich (ST24Q) was less so. Inland records are rare: the only one in the Atlas period was at Chard Reservoir in November 2009.

BLACK-THROATED DIVER *Gavia arctica*

The increase in seawatching from the western coast has also led to more records of this species. Black-throated Divers remain scarce, much scarcer than Red-throated, but are clearly more regular than was once thought. The highest day-count of Black-throated Divers during the Atlas period was just five, and sometimes fewer than that are recorded in a whole year. Unsurprisingly the map shows dots from the regular seawatching points either side of Porlock Bay (Porlock Weir and Hurlstone Point) and at Minehead. The only other coastal record during the Atlas period one was off Lilstock in November 2009.

Inland records are rare, though most of the larger reservoirs have played host to the species at some point. The only one in the Atlas period was at the most regular inland site, Cheddar Reservoir, in late December 2009; unfortunately it had to be taken into care and later died.

All Atlas records were in the winter, as is usual, though spring records are not unknown, including one in May 2007, just before Atlas recording began.

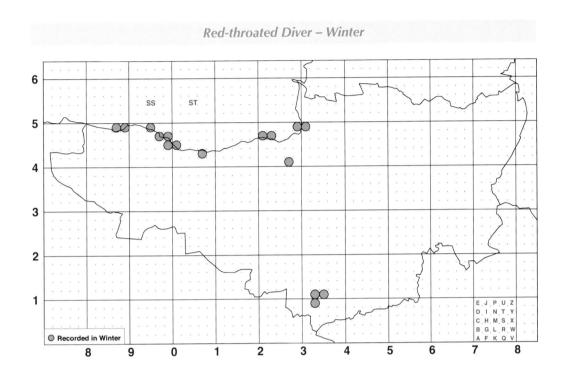

Red-throated Diver – Winter

○ Recorded in Winter

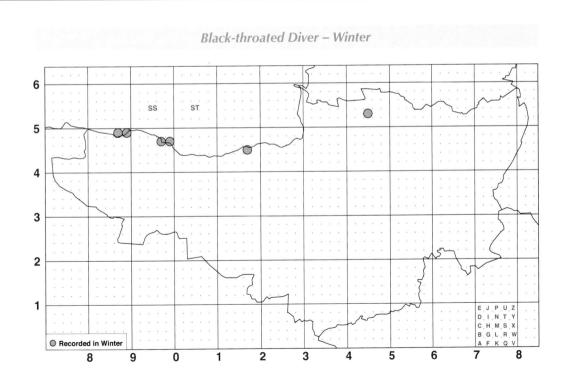

Black-throated Diver – Winter

○ Recorded in Winter

87

GREAT NORTHERN DIVER *Gavia immer*

Historically, Great Northern Divers have always been considered commoner than Black-throated, with about twice as many records, though still much scarcer than Red-throated. About 20 were recorded during the Atlas periods, and there were even counts of up to five in a single day. Great Northerns are usually seen singly, and over a broader winter period than the other species, starting in October; they are also more regularly seen around Bridgwater Bay, usually during gales.

Great Northerns are also commoner inland than either of the other two species, being recorded most regularly on Cheddar Reservoir, including in three of the five Atlas winters; there were two together there in early 2008 and three in the winter of 2006/07. The only other inland record during the period was at Shapwick Heath in December 2007, though this is splitting hairs, as the remarkable record of two over Torr Works Reservoir in late October 2007 missed out by just four days!

A distinctive Great Northern Diver in nearly full summer plumage was seen off Minehead and in Porlock Bay in November 2007. It had previously visited Grafham Water in Cambridgeshire, Coate Water in Wiltshire and Barrow Gurney Reservoirs in Avon.

FULMAR *Fulmarus glacialis*

The first suggestion of breeding in Somerset was in 1974, when a pair occupied a coastal ledge at Glenthorne Cliff, where breeding was confirmed in 1981. This tiny colony, just within the county boundary with Devon, has persisted ever since, but has never exceeded five pairs and has recently been down to two or three.

From March to August, many are now recorded off the western coasts, especially in westerlies. Counts of over 40 are unusual, though up to 500 have been seen during gales. Only small numbers penetrate up-Channel east of Watchet, and only wind-blown stragglers are recorded from October to February, even in the west. (No map.)

STORM PETREL *Hydrobates pelagicus*

Most records have been during strong westerlies in Bridgwater Bay or off the Exmoor coast. A total of 48 were recorded during the five Atlas summers; late May and June is the peak period, though a subsidiary peak in July is notable. In contrast, autumn records are scarce, particularly when compared with Leach's Petrel. Birds seen close inshore are often weakened, some falling victim to inshore Herring Gulls, or occasionally to a Peregrine. (No map.)

Fulmar sponsored by Rev. and Mrs L. Summers

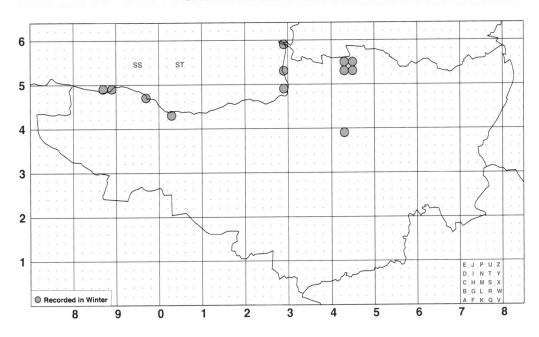

MANX SHEARWATER *Puffinus puffinus*

Considerable numbers may be in the Bristol Channel from May to August, especially off the western coast, where they are present even without the impetus of north-westerly winds and are frequently seen passing west after early-morning high tides. Counts of several hundred are normal, and in favourable conditions thousands may pass the Somerset coast; the record figure is of 7,000 in just under six hours on 11 June 1998.

It was long supposed that these birds were from the huge colonies on the Pembrokeshire islands, but it now appears that these feed mainly in the Irish Sea, so the Somerset birds are presumably non-breeders. However, the population of Skomer alone has recently been estimated as 316,000 pairs (Perrins *et al.* 2012) and it is hard to believe that none of these enter the Bristol Channel under stress of weather. In early autumn juveniles may be swept up-Channel, as is shown by some Gloucestershire ringing recoveries (Kirk and Phillips 2013). The eradication of rats on Lundy has led to an increase of breeding there, and about 3,000 pairs were present in 2012 and 2013. Recent experiments with tracking devices did not at first trace any of these birds east of Ilfracombe (Guilford, Freeman, and Morris 2009), but further work has found that a few are occasionally found in Somerset waters (Freeman *et al.* 2013). (No map.)

CORMORANT *Phalacrocorax carbo*

Prior to the Atlas period the only colony within the old county boundaries was that on Steep Holm (now part of Avon), which in 2009 held 109 nests; some of these birds feed in present-day Somerset. On the Avalon Marshes, a roost developed on Noah's Lake, which was flooded in 2000/01. Two pairs bred successfully there in 2007, and by 2011 there were 23 pairs, but the collapse of the long-dead and increasingly rotten nesting trees has led to a steady shift westward to a site on Canada Farm Lake; in 2012 there were eight nests at Noah's Lake and 12 at Canada Farm, and the Noah's Lake site was deserted in 2013. The wide spread of records of presence in the breeding season presumably refer to feeding birds, including immatures and non-breeders; the smaller number of 'possible' records probably also do so, but in at least some cases might represent undiscovered pairs or small colonies.

Outside the breeding season, there has been a great increase over the last 50 years, so that Cormorants are now widely distributed over the Levels and at all major reservoirs. Ringing recoveries prove that at least some of these have come from colonies as far away as West Wales, Ulster, the Solway, and the Isle of Man. An important factor has been their love of high daytime roosts on pylons, which have been regularly used on the Tone Levels and on King's Sedge Moor; there have been counts of up to 65 on Stawell Moor and 41 on Lang Moor, Westonzoyland. At night they prefer trees: up to 150 have been counted in the Avalon Marshes, mostly on Noah's Lake, and up to 60 near Muchelney. Coastal numbers are small, being mostly ones and twos, except in Bridgwater Bay (where they gather on Stert Island) and in migrating parties elsewhere in autumn.

The breeding birds at Shapwick Heath apparently belong to both the nominate *carbo* and the Continental *sinensis* subspecies (S. Parker *in litt.*). Most, but not all, tree-nesting British Cormorants are the latter, which tends to show whiter plumes in the breeding season, but can be separated reliably only by the shape of the gular patch. Seven Continental birds were identified in February 2009, in the Avalon Marshes and at West Coker, but they may have been part of a cold-weather influx from the enormously increased populations of Northern and Central Europe.

SHAG *Phalacrocorax aristotelis*

About 190 were recorded in the Atlas years, almost all off western coasts during the autumn migration from July to September, with a marked peak in August, which accounted for 105. Only 20 were in the winter period; there were no records for March, April, June, or October.

Most of the relatively few records away from the west were from the coast around Bridgwater Bay. Only four were seen inland, one only just so at Apex Park (Highbridge), one at Rooks Bridge, and two at Cheddar Reservoir, which (as with other seabirds) is the most regular inland site. (No map.)

GANNET *Morus bassanus*

Small numbers are regular in the Bristol Channel from May to August, and not only in strong westerlies; in most years the peak month is June or July. Single-day counts of more than 100 are unusual: during the five Atlas years the highest daily count was of 69 in June 2008. Most birds are seen down-Channel from Watchet, since they need the clearer water for effective fishing, though they are occasionally recorded in Bridgwater Bay during gales. There are few sightings from October to February.

The source of Somerset's records is still a matter of conjecture, but it is most likely the gannetry on Grassholm, 85 miles to the west, which had grown to 39,000 pairs by 2012 (Morgan 2012). (No map.)

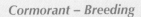

Cormorant – Breeding

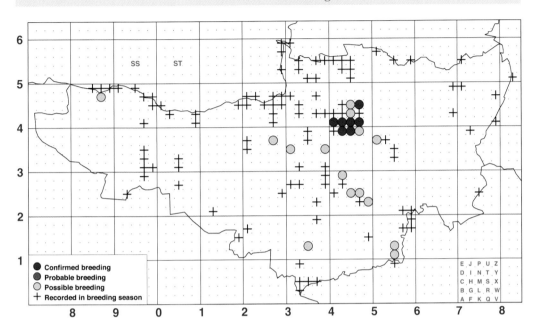

Legend:
- ● Confirmed breeding
- ● Probable breeding
- ○ Possible breeding
- + Recorded in breeding season

Cormorant – Winter

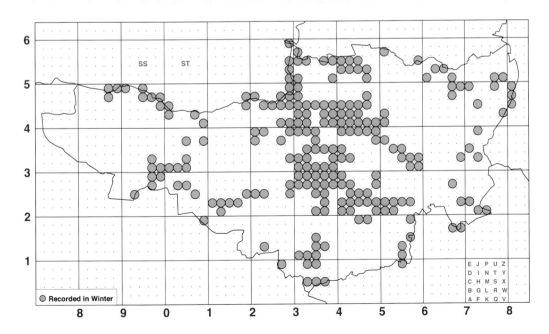

Legend:
- ○ Recorded in Winter

BITTERN *Botaurus stellaris*

It has sometimes been assumed, for instance by Holloway (1996), that Bitterns bred in Somerset before about 1850, but there is no documentary evidence that this was so. From 1952 to 1980 booming was occasionally heard on the South Levels and at clay-pits around Bridgwater, and successful breeding was proved in 1968 at Chilton Trinity and in 1969 near Huntworth, the only confirmed breeding records before the Atlas period.

Following the establishment of the Avalon Marshes reserves, booming was heard there from 1996, but it was not until 2008 that the long efforts of the RSPB at Ham Wall were successful. Two females raised young in that year. Bitterns have since prospered quite remarkably in several reserves on the Avalon Marshes: there were 14 nests in 2010 and 19 in 2011; in 2012, there were 29 booming birds, and the most recent early-spring count, in 2014, was of 42 'boomers'. These constitute nearly a quarter of all British breeders. Moreover, their reedbeds should not be at risk from inundation by rising sea-levels, as in parts of East Anglia.

Bittern is a Schedule 1 species, therefore the breeding-season records are plotted conventionally within 10-km squares. The main sites are well known and well publicised, but outlying pairs may still be vulnerable to disturbance.

The size of the winter population in the Avalon Marshes is not clear, but in 2012 Bitterns were seen in every month at Ham Wall. There have been occasional winter records elsewhere, usually in colder weather, from small reedbeds or along the coast. In the Atlas period, these included one photographed unconcernedly strolling across a road at Corton Denham on the Dorset border, far from any suitable habitat.

Bittern sponsored by Mendip Times

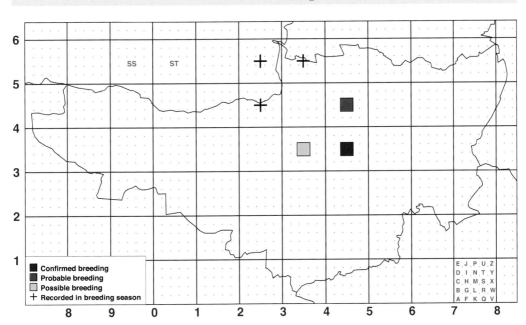

Bittern – Breeding

Confirmed breeding
Probable breeding
Possible breeding
+ Recorded in breeding season

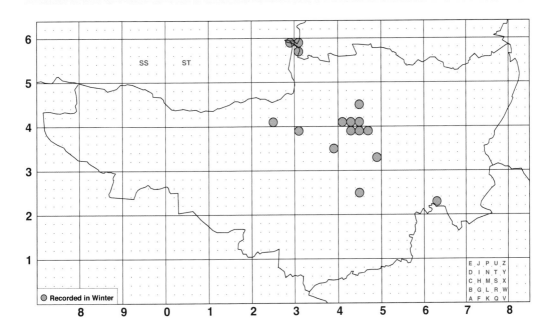

Bittern – Winter

Recorded in Winter

LITTLE BITTERN *Ixobrychus minutus*

Little Bittern was previously a rare vagrant to the county, as it is nationally, with only about 12 records prior to the Atlas period, the last in 1997. Then, in 2009, a 'barking' male frequented the reedbeds of Ham Wall RSPB reserve for much of the summer. In 2010, the same male returned, but suddenly fell silent after only a few weeks; later, the reason for this became apparent, when first an adult female was seen, and then, on 23 July, a juvenile in flight. This was only the second British breeding record, following that at Potteric Carr, Yorkshire, in 1984.

The birds returned and at least attempted to breed in all subsequent years: no young were seen in 2011, but at least two fledged in 2012. Beyond the Atlas period, in 2013, three males were present, and two pairs nested, though one failed – the female was thought to have been predated.

Little Bittern is a Schedule 1 breeding species, therefore the breeding records are plotted conventionally within 10-km squares, though in this case it may be unnecessary, as the breeding site has been widely publicised (and is well wardened).

CATTLE EGRET *Bubulcus ibis*

Prior to the Atlas period, this species was a very rare vagrant to the county, with only five records. From December 2007 to April 2008 there was a remarkable influx of Cattle Egrets throughout the South West, including parties of up to eight and a total of at least 15 birds in Somerset. In that summer, successful breeding was proved at two Somerset sites, the first breeding records for Britain. One pair was probably successful in 2009, when a juvenile appeared in August at Chew Valley Lake (*Avon Bird Report 2009*), but, though a pair was seen at one of the 2008 breeding sites in 2010, there has been no further evidence of breeding, and records have become scarce again following two severe winters. Both breeding sites were within existing heronries on private land, so are not mapped.

Only three birds were recorded in 2011, of which none was seen after September. In 2012, there were six records in the Avalon Marshes, none in Atlas months: one in March, and the remainder, believed to be of the same bird, from September to December.

Cattle Egret sponsored by Richard Pratt

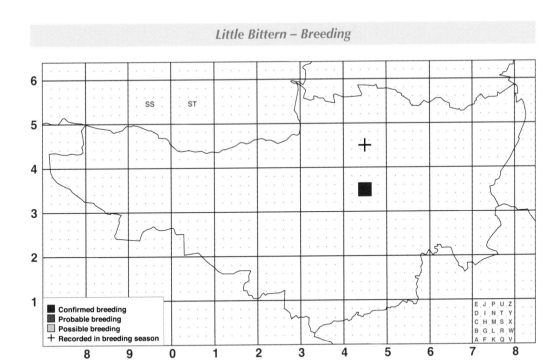

Little Bittern – Breeding

Legend:
- Confirmed breeding
- Probable breeding
- Possible breeding
- + Recorded in breeding season

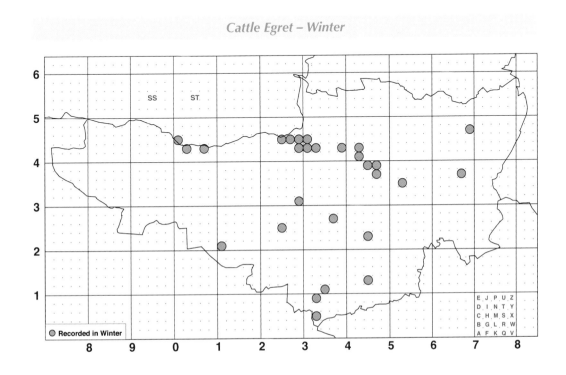

Cattle Egret – Winter

Legend:
- Recorded in Winter

LITTLE EGRET *Egretta garzetta*

This species first reached Somerset in 1965. Whilst it has been perhaps overshadowed by the more high-profile success of other heron species during the Atlas period, the recent history of Little Egret in Somerset is remarkable in itself. As elsewhere in Britain, Little Egret was a rare bird in Somerset up to 1988, after which records rapidly increased; by 2000 there were roost counts of up to 50 in late summer and autumn. Breeding began in 1998, and was confirmed at five sites during the Atlas period, all known heronries, and some of which fall within more than one tetrad. There are probably between 20 and 30 pairs, but counts have not always been possible.

The records of mere presence during the breeding season may refer to non-breeding birds or birds from known Little Egret colonies dispersing to feed. It is fair to say that some at least of the records of possible, and even probable, breeding are likely to be no more than the same, especially those in tetrads adjacent to known colonies. The range of this species is probably still expanding, however, and it is likely that further breeding sites will be recorded in the future. This is one of the more obvious cases where the Atlas has not only added to our knowledge, but raised questions concerning what further survey work may be required.

The winter distribution is, as one might expect, wider than the breeding-season range, with records from many tetrads on the Levels and along the coast, but few from higher ground, especially in the west.

There is no obvious pattern of movements, and in recent hard winters birds have survived by moving to the coast or to unfrozen waters. In Bridgwater Bay, numbers regularly increase from May to July, with counts of 30 or more. The highest WeBS count during the Atlas period was of 90 on the Levels in the winters of 2008/09 and 2009/10, but this can hardly be much more than a sample of those present; they can be conspicuous, but often feed out of sight in deep ditches. During the Atlas, there were the following maximum winter counts at favoured sites:

○	West Sedge Moor	51	March 2012
○	Parrett Estuary /		
	Huntspill River	46	August 2011
○	Avalon Marshes	40	August 2011
○	Chard Reservoir	22	February 2012
○	Queen's Sedge Moor	20	April 2012
○	Greylake RSPB reserve	20	March 2012
○	Aller Moor	11	January 2012

Immediately after the Atlas period, in the later stages of the 2012 flooding, there were counts of over 100 on West Sedge Moor and Wet Moor.

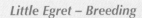

Little Egret – Breeding

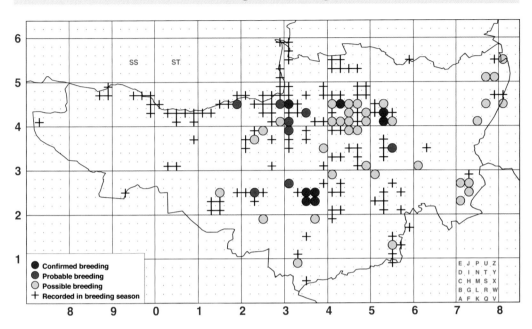

Little Egret – Winter

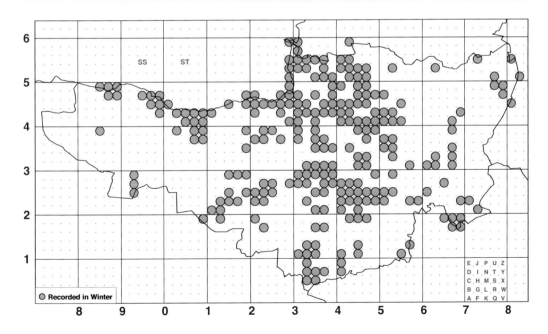

GREAT WHITE EGRET *Ardea alba*

It seems hard to believe now that the first Somerset record of Great White Egret was as recent as 1992. Since then, the number of records has exploded, both here and nationally, mirroring the spectacular European expansion after 1980, which included not only the re-establishment of long-extinct breeding colonies, but also, with climate change, an increasing habit of wintering (Lawicki 2014).

By the start of this Atlas period, birds were being recorded at least annually, and from 2010 they have been recorded year-round, with the Avalon Marshes proving particularly attractive, though, as the map shows, records in winter remain well scattered. An unprecedented six roosted at Ham Wall RSPB reserve in the winter of 2008/09, and numbers have since risen to a minimum of 12. They were affected to some extent by the cold winters of 2009/10 and 2010/11, but this species may be better equipped for wintering than the Little Egret. The cluster of records in ST45, near Cheddar Reservoir, refers to five birds which deserted the Avalon Marshes in favour of ice-free streams fed by Mendip springs.

A breeding attempt seemed inevitable, and it was indeed suspected at Shapwick Heath NNR in 2010, though no confirmation was obtained. In 2012, however, after the end of the national Atlas, but within the Somerset Atlas period, two pairs nested at Shapwick Heath, fledging four young: the first recorded breeding by the species in Britain (Holt 2013; Anderson, Clarke, and Lucken 2013). Two pairs nested again successfully in 2013, one each at Shapwick Heath and Ham Wall. Time will tell, but it is to be hoped that this is the first stage of a sustained and successful colonisation of the Avalon Marshes and perhaps beyond.

One of the first breeding pair was an individual which was colour-ringed as a nestling at Besne, near Saint Nazaire, in northern France in May 2009; it has been present in and around the Avalon Marshes almost continuously since early 2010. Remarkably, one of its siblings also visited Shapwick Heath in 2012.

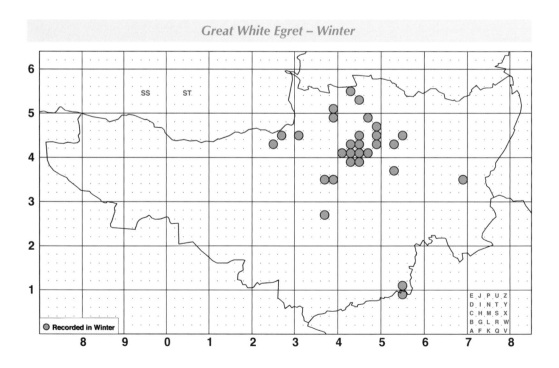

Great White Egret – Winter

● Recorded in Winter

Great White Egret sponsored by Tracey Ford

GREY HERON *Ardea cinerea*

It is probably true to say that no British species has been better documented than have Grey Herons; they have been the subject of annual counts for the BTO since 1927. During the Atlas period as a whole, 20 sites were known to be occupied, of which six held over ten pairs in at least one year. The map overleaf shows the known sites. In 2008, 18 sites were used, with at least 199 nests; in 2012, there were 17, with 161. Winter WeBS counts do not cover all heronries, but they confirm losses on the Levels: after the autumn of 2009, maximum totals fell from a peak of 161 in 2008 to 112 in 2010/11. Recovery seemed well under way by 2013, though full figures are not yet available for that year. The best indicator of the population is probably Swell Wood (the largest heronry, number 8 on the Heronries map), where the numbers were up to 90 in 2009. The figure of 73 pairs for 2012 represents a low point, following two hard winters; by 2013, numbers had risen again to 98 pairs.

The situation with heronries is not fixed: at least three of the numbered sites had been deserted by the end of the Atlas period, though one (number 14, Little Ranch) had moved only a short distance to bushes within Ham Wall RSPB reserve. This is an unusual site, but not alone: a pair has also nested in several recent years in a low bush on one of the islands in Noah's Lake, Shapwick Heath.

The confirmed breeding records entered in the Atlas database away from known heronries raise some interesting questions: these records can be identified by comparing the breeding-season map with that of known heronries. Most of these refer to fledged juveniles, and it is inevitable that some at least are birds which have moved some distance from their natal tetrad. On the other hand, some individuals may be from as yet undiscovered heronries, perhaps consisting of only one or two pairs. Further work is needed to ascertain the true significance of these records, and of others indicating some breeding evidence away from known colonies, which also perhaps need to be treated with an element of caution. However, in the east in particular there are a number of suitable woods that are private and difficult of access, where unrecorded heronries may exist.

South-westerly movement has often been seen along the coast, and ringing recoveries have proved that some birds arrive to winter, sometimes as early as July. Birds are widely distributed in winter, dispersing to find food sources as expected.

GREY HERON *Ardea cinerea,* continued

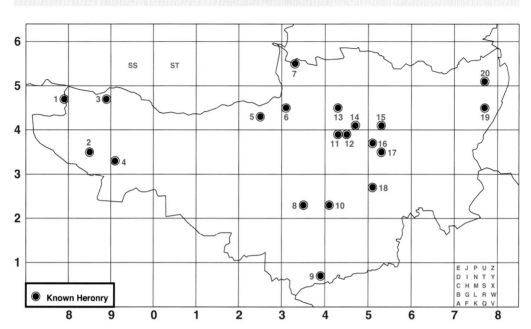

Somerset Heronries

Known Heronry

Pairs in Somerset Heronries, 2012

1	Oaremead, Oare*	3	11	Noah's Lake	1
2	Hayes Wood, Withypool	3	12	Walton Heath (new in 2012)	1
3	Bossington Lane, Porlock	1	13	The Bungalow, Tadham Moor	10 possibly
4	Week Wood, Coppleham Cross*	8	14	Little Ranch, Glastonbury Heath († 2012)	–
5	Home Covert, Otterhampton	1	15	Long Drove, Queen's Sedge Moor*	5
6	West Huntspill	5	16	Bere Wall, Edgarley Hall († 2012)	–
7	Lympsham Manor	3	17	Butleigh/Moorhouse, Baltonsborough	1
8	Swell Wood, Fivehead*	73	18	Somerton Erleigh	22
9	Wayford Rhododendon Woods*	1	19	Marston Wood († 2011)	–
10	Nine Acre Plantation, Midelney	11	20	Orchardleigh Lake*	12

*These overlap tetrads, or have moved a short distance locally during the Atlas period.
† = deserted

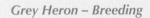

Grey Heron – Breeding

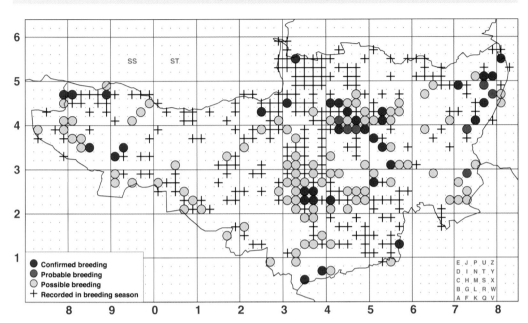

Grey Heron – Winter

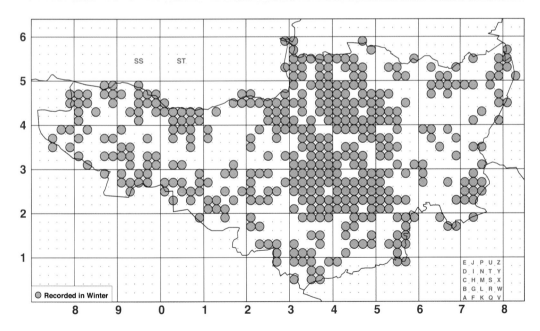

WHITE STORK *Ciconia ciconia*

At least ten appeared during the Atlas springs and summers, including four or five in 2012; they wandered far and wide over the county, and were recorded in at least ten tetrads. This is part of a longer period of increase in occurrences: previously very rare in Somerset, about 30 were recorded between 1971 and 2007. Storks have benefited from reintroduction programmes in a number of European countries, and many of the West European birds now winter in Spain instead of crossing to Africa, so more spring overshoots can be expected on the northward movement (Fraser 2013a).

GLOSSY IBIS *Plegadis falcinellus*

With only five records prior to 2007, Glossy Ibis was a very rare bird in Somerset. During the Atlas period, however, there were at least ten, and perhaps as many as 15, in various places on the Levels and in the Parrett Estuary, including ringed birds from France and Spain. They occurred in every year and in all months except July and August.

The much-increased number and frequency of recent British records are probably due to the recolonisation of Spain from 1996 and of the Camargue in southern France from 2006. These breeders may have been driven northward by periodic droughts in Iberia (Hudson *et al.* 2013).

SPOONBILL *Platalea leucorodia*

During the Atlas period there were about 17 Spoonbills, singly or up to four together, and largely from March to July. Most were in the Steart area or the Avalon Marshes, and others were at Greylake Reserve, Chard Reservoir, Dunster Beach and Porlock Marsh.

Spoonbills have bred at four British sites since 2008, and might well return to Somerset at some point in the future, though no breeding behaviour has yet been observed.

RED-NECKED GREBE *Podiceps grisegena*

The Red-necked has always been the rarest of the three scarcer grebes. Five single birds were recorded during the Atlas period: four at Cheddar Reservoir and one at Durleigh, all from October to April, and none in 2009, 2011 or 2012.

SLAVONIAN GREBE *Podiceps auritus*

Historically, Slavonian Grebe is nearly twice as common as Red-necked in the county (96 previous records compared to 50 Red-neckeds), but this was not the case during the Atlas period. Just three single birds were recorded for the Atlas: two at Cheddar and one at Durleigh, all from November to January, with none in 2007, 2008 or 2010.

BLACK-NECKED GREBE *Podiceps nigricollis*

Black-necked is the commonest of the scarcer grebes (about 145 records prior to the Atlas), and 20 individuals were recorded in the Atlas period, when they occurred in all months except May, June, July and September; 16 were at Cheddar, including from three to five in two winters, and the others at Orchardleigh, at Torr Works and in the Avalon Marshes. There were no records in 2012.

The species has bred in the past (a pair at Orchardleigh Lake in 1932), but no breeding has been even suspected in recent years.

LITTLE GREBE *Tachybaptus ruficollis*

Little Grebes are largely dependent on man-made waters, and will readily use quite small ponds if other conditions are right. The availability of grants has encouraged the creation in the last decade or so of many small ponds in farmland, for irrigation or recreation, and this appears to have been to the benefit of Little Grebes as well as a number of other waterbirds.

The breeding season map shows Little Grebes to be well scattered across Somerset, though generally avoiding higher ground where there are few suitable sites. The greatest concentration has been in the Avalon Marshes, which in 2002 held at least 160 pairs. However, survey results suggest that maximum breeding totals occur soon after restored areas are first flooded, but that they then fall rapidly. By 2012, Ham Wall was thought to hold only 30 pairs. Other noticeable clusters of tetrads are around the south side of Bridgwater Bay, in the Monksilver area to the west of the Quantocks (including the ponds at Combe Sydenham Country Park), and most notably in the Yeovil area. Most park lakes and irrigation and fishing ponds have Little Grebes, as have those reservoirs with suitable breeding sites. Many small sites may have passed unrecorded, particularly where they are on private land or are new and do not yet feature on OS maps.

In winter the distribution is slightly more extensive, as some birds move to less sheltered waters, such as Wimbleball Lake and Cheddar Reservoir, and to floods, drains and larger rhynes on the Levels. The coastal records in the west are from fresh or brackish water in the Porlock and Minehead areas – records of Little Grebes on the sea itself are very rare.

Little Grebe sponsored by Peter Kelly

Little Grebe – Breeding

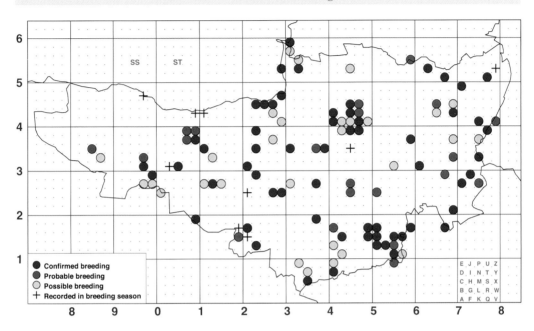

Little Grebe – Winter

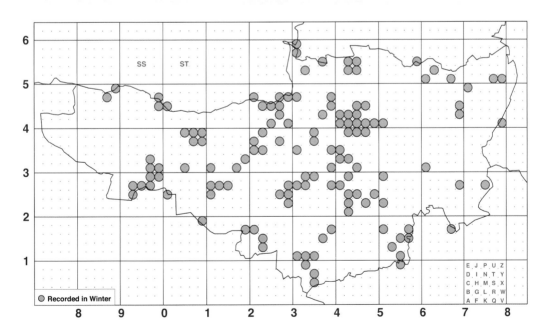

GREAT CRESTED GREBE *Podiceps cristatus*

This attractive species is found on most of the major reservoirs in the county, as well as being well distributed within the Avalon Marshes reserves. Displaying adults, nests, and young are all conspicuous, contributing to the high percentage of confirmed breeding records. In 2002 the Avalon Marshes held a breeding population of about 60 pairs, though more recent numbers have been lower, sinking, in 2011, to 22. Many nests fail through predation and through erratic water levels, despite every effort to manage the latter in reserves.

The maps from the two seasons are remarkably consistent, suggesting that many Great Crested Grebes remain faithful to a site year-round. Not all do, however. Cheddar Reservoir is unsuitable for breeding, but it is the most important wintering site, with regular counts of over 100 from December to February. Numbers are very variable, suggesting a considerable spring passage and presumably some interchange with the important site of Chew Valley Lake in Avon. Sutton Bingham, Durleigh, and Chard Reservoirs all regularly attract from 20 to 45 in winter. Smaller numbers are found on Hawkridge Reservoir and at Wimbleball Lake. Wintering on saltwater is a common habit elsewhere – Swansea Bay is an important wintering area – but very few are recorded on the Somerset coast.

Great Crested Grebe – Breeding

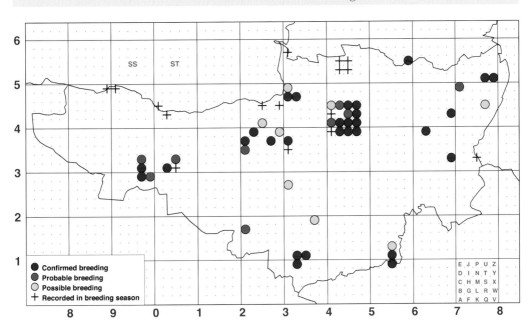

Great Crested Grebe – Winter

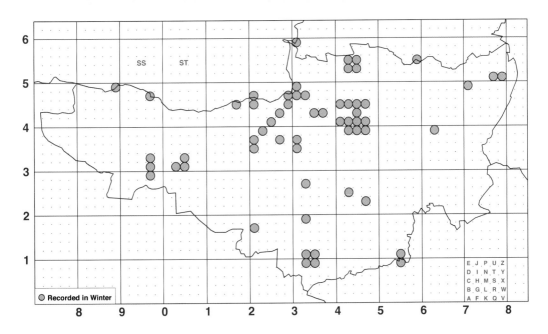

RED KITE *Milvus milvus*

Red Kites seem to have been regular breeders in Somerset up until 1880, when the last pair nested near Wells. For the next hundred years the relict population in Wales was probably responsible for the few Somerset records, which became more frequent as this population increased. Introductions into Eastern England and the Midlands have contributed greatly to another increase in records, as immature birds wander far afield, and in the last few years there have been at least 50 records annually in Somerset, distributed over the entire county. Most of these have been from March to June, with a peak in late May, and some were almost certainly of Continental origin. A breeding attempt was made near Dulverton in 2004, but the eggs were probably taken.

The one confirmed breeding record in the Atlas period was a pair which tried to nest in the Quantocks in 2010; an egg-shell was found, but the birds disappeared. One of the pair came from a Northamptonshire introduction. The small number of 'possible'

entries refer mostly to birds found in suitable habitat: though there have been other signs of breeding behaviour, often birds move on again quickly, and there is no evidence that other nesting attempts have yet taken place.

Red Kites now breed in a number of adjacent counties, however, and further attempts will surely be made in Somerset. The species is still subject to a certain level of persecution, at least in other areas, so all breeding-season records are mapped conventionally at 10-km square level.

The winter distribution as mapped is essentially a mixture of a few long-staying individuals and rather more seemingly random fly-overs, though the clusters around Exmoor and the Brendons suggest that these areas are favoured: given their general similarity to the upland sheep pastures within the species' Welsh range (assuming the birds come from this population), this is perhaps not surprising.

Red Kite sponsored by Martin Haselup

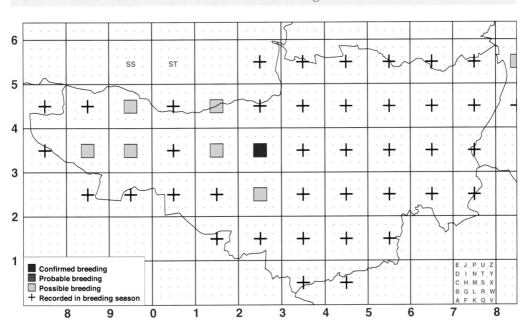

Red Kite – Breeding

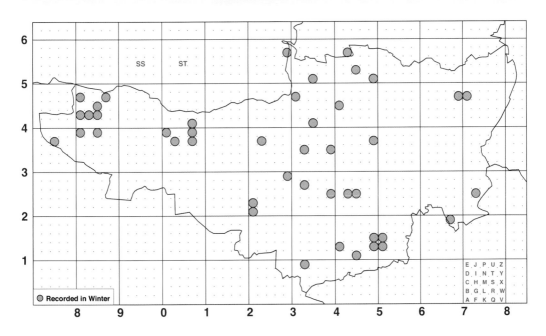

Red Kite – Winter

MARSH HARRIER *Circus aeruginosus*

This is one of the numerous success stories associated with the development of the Avalon Marshes. In the latter half of the 20th century Marsh Harriers went from being scarce passage migrants to regular annual breeders, with at least one active nest most years between 1986 and 1999, when the regular male disappeared.

The Atlas period saw not only the resumption of breeding with a single nest on the Avalon Marshes in 2009, but an increase and consolidation since. In 2010 and 2011, two nests succeeded, the male being bigamous. In 2012, he added a third female to his harem, but only one of three nests succeeded; two other males were also present. In 2013, after the Atlas period, four nests were known to have been

successful in the Avalon Marshes. Marsh Harriers are a common sight there now, and it is no secret that they breed in the area, but the population is still small and vulnerable, so the breeding-season records are mapped at 10-km square level. Away from this area there is little suitable habitat, and records are presumed to refer to wandering or passage birds.

Small numbers pass through in spring and autumn, mainly on the Levels, but there have been few records from December to February, except from the Avalon Marshes, where up to four birds were fairly regular during the Atlas period, and became more so towards its end. The winter population has been gradually increasing, though by the end of the Atlas period it was probably still in single figures.

Marsh Harrier sponsored by Roger Moses

Marsh Harrier – Breeding

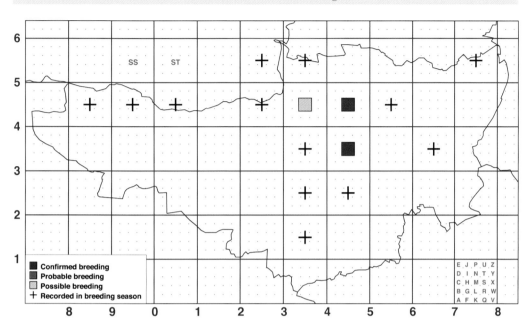

Marsh Harrier – Winter

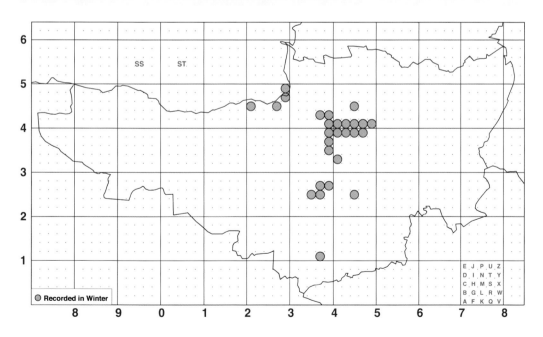

HEN HARRIER *Circus cyaneus*

Hen Harriers are mainly passage migrants in October–November and March–April, but a few regularly winter on the Levels, the coast of Bridgwater Bay and Exmoor, where small roosts have formed on Dunkery Hill in some winters. Numbers fluctuate, but a total of 10–20 individuals a year is quite normal. Four birds tagged as chicks in Scottish nests have been seen, and one from a nest in North Wales, where there are now 50 pairs or more (Brenchley *et al.* 2013). The paucity of records from upland areas away from Exmoor is puzzling, though it may be at least partly a reflection of low numbers of observers in those areas compared to the Levels.

Though wintering birds occasionally linger into April, especially on Exmoor, there was no evidence of breeding within the Atlas period: the last confirmed nest in the county is now over a century ago.

GOSHAWK *Accipiter gentilis*

This secretive species has probably been present in Somerset woods for over 40 years now, but the first absolute proof of breeding was not obtained until during the Atlas period, in 2009. A pair bred successfully at another site in 2011. In the last 30 years, birds have been present in summer or have been seen displaying in seven other areas, which have remained confidential, but have been regularly published in *SB* under a system of letter codes. They remain rare away from these areas, though passage birds are occasionally seen. Because of the risk of persecution and disturbance there is no map for this species in this Atlas.

SPARROWHAWK *Accipiter nisus*

Though the well-known effects of DDT and related pesticides in the 1950s and 1960s were not as serious in Somerset as in some parts of the country, apparent gaps in the breeding range were detected by *BA 1968–72* in the east and across the Quantocks; in *NBA 1988–91* these were more marked, especially over Exmoor and in parts of the Levels. The current Atlas shows some concentrations in heavily wooded areas, such as the north-east, the Upper Tone above Wellington and the Brendons. The high Buzzard population in some areas may lead to nest predation or to attacks upon Sparrowhawks carrying prey.

This is a notoriously difficult species for which to prove breeding, especially in areas where woodlands are mainly private, hence the high proportion of tetrads with only possible breeding recorded. During winter, numbers may be enhanced and the range is about 20% wider, especially over the Levels. Birds were scarce along coastal 10-km squares in *WA 1981–84*, but whether or not that was a true impression then, it seems not to be the case now. As with the breeding season, it is tempting to speculate whether the apparent gaps in the map truly reflect absences, or whether in some areas isolated pairs eluded discovery.

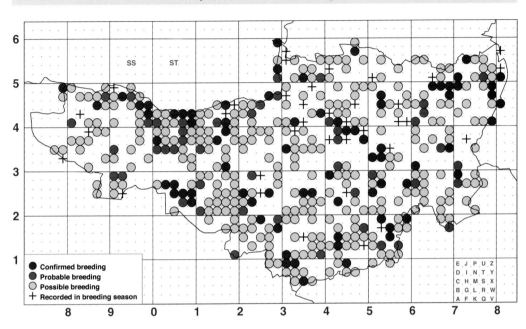

Sparrowhawk – Breeding

Confirmed breeding
Probable breeding
Possible breeding
+ Recorded in breeding season

Sparrowhawk – Winter

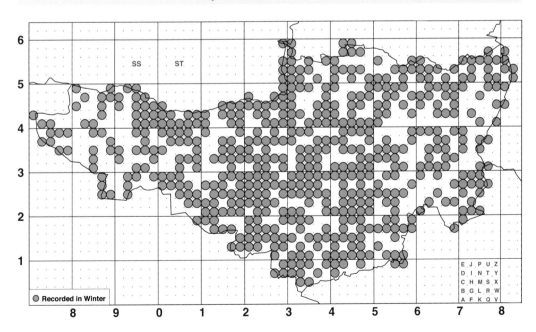

Recorded in Winter

BUZZARD *Buteo buteo*

In the mid 19th century, Buzzards were confined to steep and inaccessible woodland along the Exmoor coast, but as persecution pressure eased in the first half of the 20th century, their range expanded across the upland areas of the west. By the 1970s, Buzzards had spread over much farmland and woodland in East and South Somerset, but they were still absent around Bridgwater and on the western parts of the Levels. By 1990, *NBA 1988–91* showed Buzzards breeding in all 10-km squares except Bridgwater East (ST33), which also lacked them in *WA 1981–84*; this may at least partly be an artefact due to thin coverage. The current Atlas maps show that most gaps have now been filled, except in towns and treeless areas, and Buzzards are once again almost universally distributed at both seasons. The greatest concentrations are still in well-wooded parts, but hedgerow oaks have provided excellent nest sites in many places, such as the Vale of Taunton Deane. It is likely that most if not all of the probable and possible breeding records in reality refer to breeding pairs.

Buzzards have made formidable eastward advances in the last 30 years across many parts of Southern and Midland England. In Somerset it has been more a case of infilling. The population in Avon is thought to be of the order of one pair per square kilometre (*NAvA 2007–2011*) and a notable recent study by Prytherch (2013), in an area of 75 square kilometres between Bristol and Mendip, showed an increase from 13 pairs in 1982 to 105 in 2012, by which time almost all possible territories had been occupied. Similar growth may also have occurred in much of East and South Somerset.

Large gatherings of 40 birds or more occur in farmland after ploughing and silage cutting, and also feeding on the carrion produced by sporting estates.

Buzzard sponsored by David Hole

Buzzard – Breeding

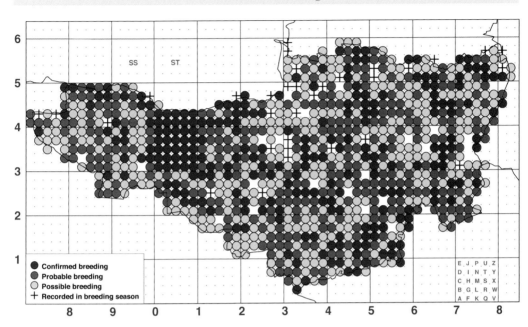

Confirmed breeding
Probable breeding
Possible breeding
+ Recorded in breeding season

Buzzard – Winter

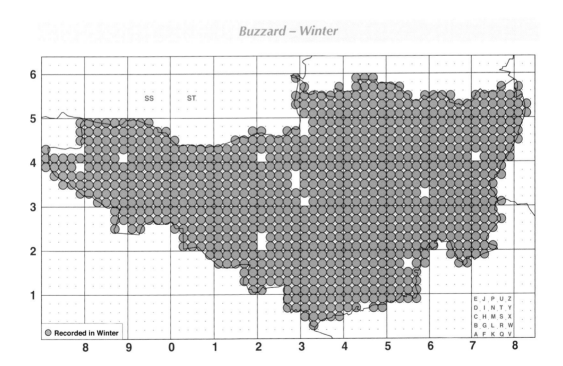

Recorded in Winter

KESTREL *Falco tinnunculus*

Kestrels need rough grassland and voles, and they are therefore fairly commonly recorded on the Levels, though records have declined on Exmoor. A decline in western parts of the British Isles was apparent in *BA 1968–72*, when they were already scarce in ten Somerset 10-km squares. The exact causes of this decline are unclear, but they are likely to involve the shortage of small mammals resulting from modern agricultural practices. Records of Kestrels are particularly scarce along the Wiltshire border, on the Blackdowns and the Brendons, and along the southern flanks of Exmoor. Although no 10-km square was entirely without them in summer, the greatest number of tetrads where breeding was proved or probable within a 10-km square was only

11, in ST34 (Huntspill), where transport lines cross grassland. They were particularly sparse in the Brendons, the Taunton area, and in parts of the East. On the abundance maps for both seasons in *BA 2007–11*, there is a well-marked frontier, roughly equivalent to the line of the Parrett, west of which numbers are far lower than they are to the east.

Breeders are known to disperse southwards, and there is passage in autumn across the Bristol Channel, so it is likely that there are winter visitors, at least on lower ground. The maps suggest that they are in general more widespread in winter than in summer, occurring in about 20% more tetrads, though in Avon there seems to be little seasonal difference (*NAvA 2007–11*).

Kestrel sponsored by A.J. Parsons

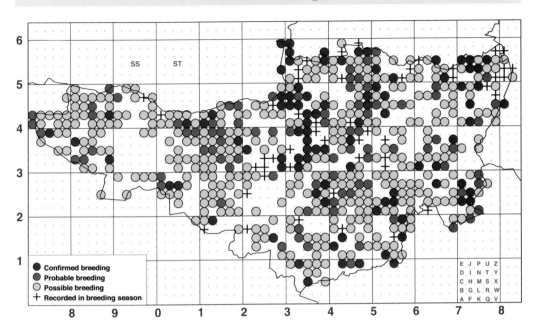

Kestrel – Breeding

Confirmed breeding
Probable breeding
Possible breeding
+ Recorded in breeding season

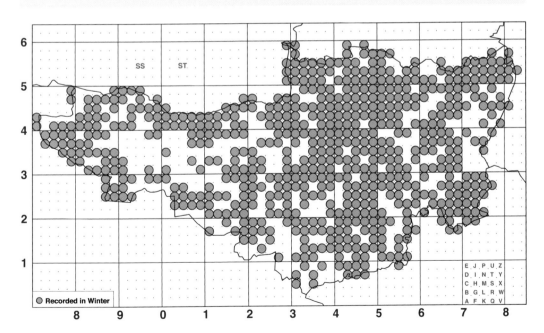

Kestrel – Winter

Recorded in Winter

MERLIN *Falco columbarius*

Between 1920 and the 1980s up to six pairs bred regularly on Exmoor, though some were on the Devon side. Their success was limited by egg-collectors, whose activities were made easier by the birds' use of tree-sites. Merlins have declined since then as a breeding species: since 2000 only two or three sites are known to have been used, and breeding has been successful at only one. No Somerset nests were found during the Atlas period; the last successful breeding was in 1999, and the last attempt in 2007. These were the southernmost breeding Merlins in the entire Western Palearctic, and it is likely that climate change has played a part in their decline.

While there is still hope for their return, it may be that the Atlas period has seen their last days as a breeding species. There is no breeding season map.

There are no such issues with the winter distribution which is much wider. Small numbers regularly visit the lowlands, including the Levels both north and south of the Poldens, the coast of Bridgwater Bay and around the Parrett Estuary. That there should be a cluster of dots on Exmoor, yet very few records from the other upland areas in winter is difficult to explain, as is the cluster of records from the Yeovil area.

HOBBY *Falco subbuteo*

Hobbies have probably bred annually during the last 50 years, but have been generally under-recorded, because of their crepuscular habits, their attachment to remote private woods, and the fledging of their young in August, which falls outside the Atlas recording period. Many observers will have been sensibly reluctant to search too closely for nesting pairs, for fear of disturbance or of attracting unwanted attention to a nest. Hobbies have markedly increased in the Brendons and on the fringes of Exmoor, and the Atlas found them to be widely distributed across the county. At least some of the possible breeding records may refer to undiscovered breeding pairs, or to hunting birds wandering from other nearby tetrads.

Hobby is a Schedule 1 breeding species, and vulnerable to disturbance, so all records are mapped conventionally at 10-km square level.

Hobbies now breed regularly around the Avalon Marshes, where they are best known for their spectacular spring gatherings to feed primarily on dragonflies and damselflies. First noticed in 1992, in the Atlas years there were regular assemblies of 35 or more, the highest count being of an exceptional 84, on 5 May 2010.

An unpublished study by J.D. Holmes found that a 10-km square of mixed farmland in Avon might hold seven to eight nesting pairs over a ten-year period. Nesting pairs were often close to villages with a good population of hirundines. There is much similar habitat in East and South Somerset, so breeding numbers may be much higher than existing records suggest.

The main arrival is from late April to early May; departure is mostly in August and September.

Merlin sponsored by Nick P. Williams
Hobby sponsored by Jeff Hazell

Merlin – Winter

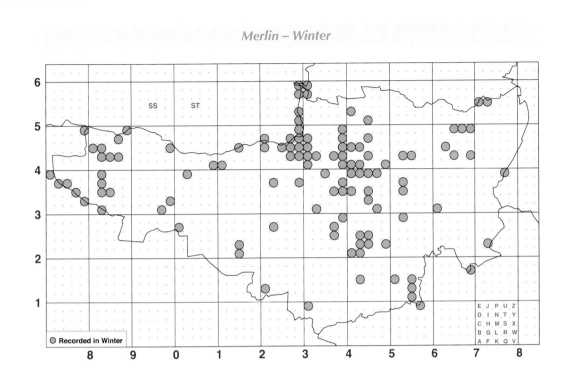

Hobby – Summer

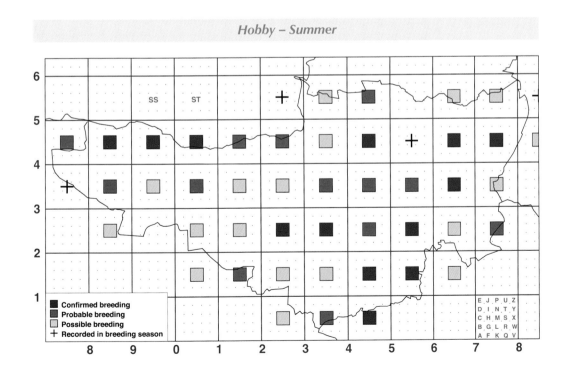

PEREGRINE *Falco peregrinus*

In 1940, all coastal Peregrine eyries were destroyed because of the very real threat to carrier pigeons, but three were quickly reoccupied after 1945. In the 1950s the successful breeding of Peregrines in Somerset was brought to extinction by the insecticide residues in their eggs. After aldrin and dieldrin were banned in the 1970s, eyries began to be occupied again, and by 1986 five were active. These increased to nine in 1991 and to 27 during the fuller coverage of a national survey in 2002 (Banks *et al.* 2003), of which nine were on the coast and 18 inland, where the huge Mendip quarries have provided many suitable cliffs. Breeding has now also been successful on at least one electricity pylon in the county.

Although some sites are well known, and others are inaccessible, locations are not published by either the BTO or SOS, since eggs and eyases are still taken illegally for falconry, and adults are sometimes shot by pigeon-fanciers. For the same reasons, breeding-season records are here mapped at the 10-km square level.

Some Peregrines no doubt stay all year round, but numbers are boosted in winter by migrants from further north. Peregrines are most regular along the coast and on the Levels, where large numbers of duck and waders are available as prey. Other areas are also used though; some even remain in the upland areas, though prey must be sparse there in winter.

Peregrine sponsored by Army Ornithological Society

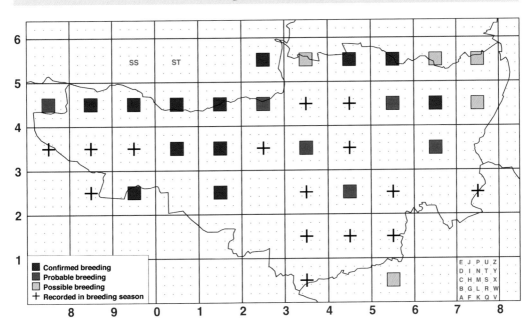

Peregrine – Breeding

Confirmed breeding
Probable breeding
Possible breeding
+ Recorded in breeding season

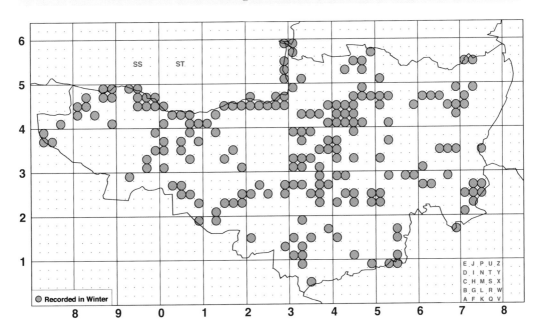

Peregrine – Winter

Recorded in Winter

WATER RAIL *Rallus aquaticus*

Breeding records are unsurprisingly restricted to wetland areas. A strong population has developed in the Avalon Marshes, where a survey in 2002 found 122 pairs and many single birds. Elsewhere, breeding was confirmed or suspected at Berrow Marsh, Greylake RSPB reserve, West Moor, Somerton Moor, Queen's Sedge Moor, and the recently created marsh at Cary Moor. For such a denizen of dense reedbeds and other marshland vegetation confirming breeding is naturally quite difficult and often dependent on chance encounters: it was not proved during the Atlas period for any of the four tetrads covering the Shapwick Heath and Ham Wall reserves, for instance, despite the evident year-round presence of many Water Rails.

In winter, odd birds may be encountered almost anywhere, especially in cold weather, when they are often most conspicuous: no doubt at least some of the records mapped relate to birds forced out of the Levels during the two big freeze-ups in Atlas winters, and may not be regular sites. The Levels are the prime British site, with maximum annual totals of between 38 and 62 being recorded in the Atlas years, though it is strongly suspected that such figures are only a sample of the numbers actually present. Outside the Avalon Marshes, the Blackmoor Vale has held up to ten birds, and areas such as the coastal marshes of the Steart peninsula and the River Tone from Taunton downstream also appear to be regular sites. By 2011, populations were evidently at a low level after two hard winters, though anecdotal evidence suggests at least a partial recovery since then.

Water Rail sponsored by John McGeoch

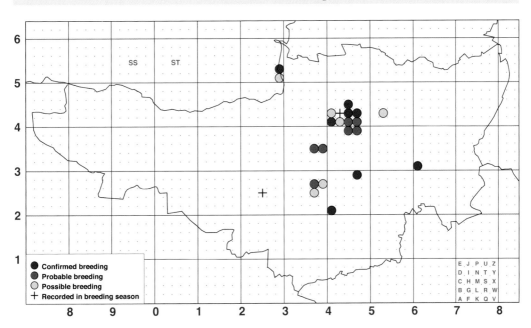

Water Rail – Breeding

- ● Confirmed breeding
- ● Probable breeding
- ○ Possible breeding
- + Recorded in breeding season

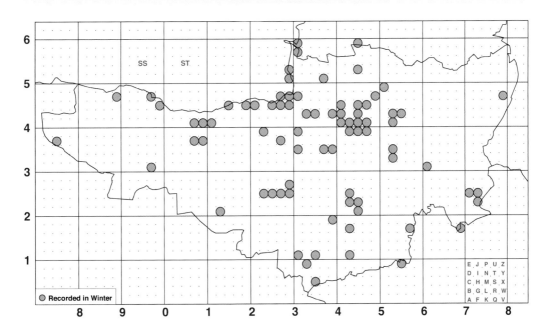

Water Rail – Winter

- ● Recorded in Winter

MOORHEN *Gallinula chloropus*

Moorhens are commonest on low ground with still or slow-moving waters and thick cover along banks. The maps for both seasons show them to be remarkably widespread for a species essentially tied to water, but this may be largely explained by their habitual use of smaller waters than many other species can tolerate. Atlas fieldwork uncovered a proliferation of new small ponds, for fishing, irrigation, and ornamental uses; most of these are capable of holding a pair or two of Moorhens. It is impossible to guess how many of these, very often on private land, were either not found by Atlas observers, or offered only limited opportunities for confirming breeding. The distribution as mapped is probably therefore incomplete to an unknown extent and might even be considered to be a minimum.

In a largely sedentary species, the winter map may be the more accurate, for Moorhens are often easier to see at that season, but allowance has to be made for some vertical movement, as can be seen in parts of the western hills, where birds are likely to move from small ponds which freeze over to unfrozen larger waters. Outside the Levels, few 10-km squares had Moorhens in more than half their tetrads. There is little suitable habitat on Mendip, on the Blackdowns and Quantocks, or on the western hills. Although Moorhens have now been found in some areas of the last where complete blanks appeared in *BA 1968–72* and *NBA 1988–91*, they are entirely absent from Exmoor Forest, where the few waters that are present are oligotrophic and unsuitable.

Most Moorhens are probably resident. As noted above, some desert smaller waters and higher ground in winter. The WeBS counts for the Levels since 2005 have shown them to be up to the fourth site in importance in Britain, with a mean of 278; the highest counts have been in October, just outside the Atlas period. As with other species tied to fresh water, two cold winters in the Atlas period took their toll, but with each pair capable of raising two or even three broods in a summer, losses can be made up fairly rapidly.

SPOTTED CRAKE *Porzana porzana*

A century and more ago Spotted Crakes may have been relatively common in the lush, soggy landscape of the Levels, and nests could be found up until the 1930s. Now it seems that, possibly after a long absence, they are back, albeit in small numbers. During the Atlas period there were eight records of calling birds, mostly from the Levels south of the Poldens, and at least some of which may refer to breeding attempts rather than briefly calling transients. Given the fragile and vulnerable nature of both this tiny potential breeding population and the favoured habitat, the decision has been taken not to map records of this species.

Moorhen – Breeding

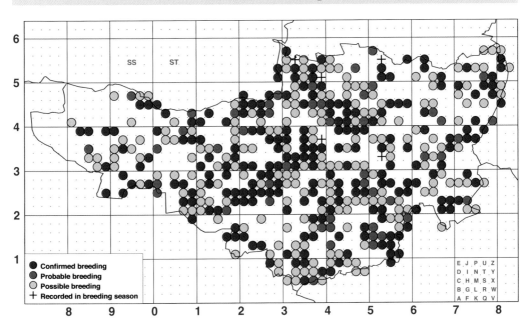

Confirmed breeding
Probable breeding
Possible breeding
+ Recorded in breeding season

Moorhen – Winter

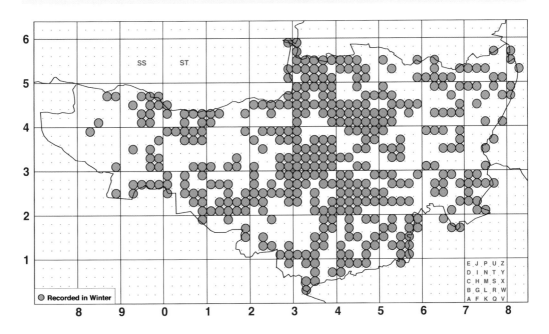

Recorded in Winter

COOT *Fulica atra*

Coots favour bigger waters than Moorhens, and even a cursory comparison of the breeding map with the map of waterbodies and waterways on page 11 will show the correlation. They will take to some of the larger of the newly man-made ponds (see under Moorhen), though, and their breeding distribution across the county may now be wider than it has ever been previously. Until the construction of large reservoirs and the flooding of many brick-pits in the last century, the Somerset distribution of Coots was limited to a few park lakes, though they probably bred on flooded Levels in wet summers. Even now they are largely absent from higher ground. The most important breeding concentration is on the Avalon Marshes, which held 277 pairs in 2002, though they have declined since and breeding success appears to have been low, perhaps because of predation. In the summer floods of 2012, Coot successfully reared young on Curry Moor and Wet Moor.

Cheddar Reservoir is by far the most important wintering site for Coots, and it has recently figured as sixth in importance among British sites, with counts usually exceeding 3,000 in December; in 2010 there were a record 4,300, but that was an exceptionally cold month when other waters were solidly frozen over and even Cheddar itself was partly frozen. Other important sites are the Avalon Marshes and Wimbleball Lake. The most obvious difference between the two maps is the small wintering population around Minehead and Dunster. Floods on the Levels are less dependable, and are mostly a late-winter resource.

CRANE *Grus grus*

Before the current reintroduction programme began, Cranes were rare migrants in spring and autumn, not annually recorded. In 2010, 21 juveniles from North German stock were introduced by the RSPB and these were reinforced by a further 16 in 2011 and by others in 2012. About 60 survive at the time of writing, and are in general to be found on Aller Moor and West Sedge Moor, though occasionally they wander north of the Poldens and elsewhere on the Levels. The intention is to establish a population of at least 20 pairs by 2030.

During the Atlas period, about 14 wild birds were also identified on passage, of which some joined the released birds, including one that spent the whole winter with them in 2011/12. (No map.)

Coot sponsored by Roger Halsey

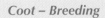

Coot – Breeding

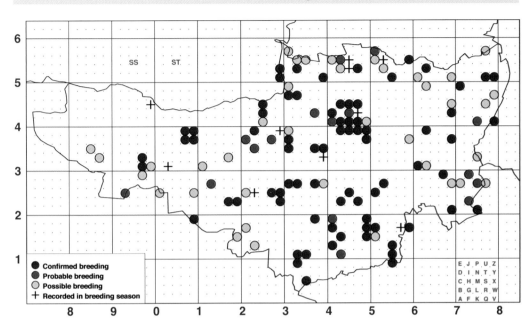

Legend:
- ● Confirmed breeding
- ● Probable breeding
- ○ Possible breeding
- + Recorded in breeding season

Coot – Winter

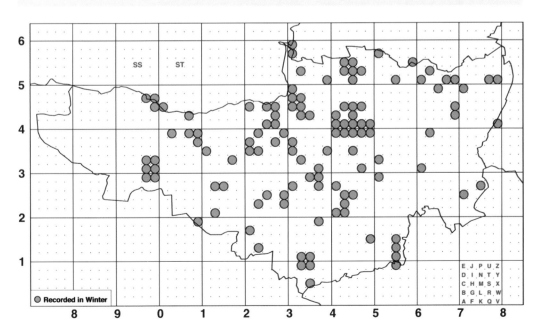

Legend:
- ● Recorded in Winter

OYSTERCATCHER *Haematopus ostralegus*

The history of breeding on the coast around Bridgwater Bay goes back to 1830. In recent years there have been up to 12 pairs from Burnham to Hinkley Point, and along the tidal stretch of the Parrett as far inland as Bridgwater. Suitable areas of shingle in the Axe Estuary and at Porlock Marsh were also successfully used by Oystercatchers during the Atlas period. In 2009, breeding was attempted inland at Stockland Bristol, though the pair recorded displaying at Durleigh Reservoir that year probably did not breed there. In 2011 a pair tried to nest on a factory roof at Bridgwater. This habit, long established in the Aberdeen area, and generally confined to flat roofs covered in gravel, has been recently noted in Northern England and on the Avon side of the Axe at Weston Sewage Treatment Works (White *et al.* 2008; *Avon Bird Report* 2011); it is the Oystercatcher's habit of bringing food to its chicks rather than them foraging for themselves that makes this breeding strategy possible, and reasonably successful.

On passage and in winter small numbers may be found all along the coast, but the main winter concentrations are in the Axe Estuary, around Bridgwater Bay and on Dunster Beach. The last two are the only sites that regularly hold over 100, though autumn counts can be as high as 500 around Steart. There are no sizeable cockle-beds to sustain a large population, unlike on the Welsh side of the Bristol Channel, where the Burry Inlet and Carmarthen Bay may hold 25,000 between them.

BLACK-WINGED STILT *Himantopus himantopus*

This species is a genuine rarity, with only six previous county records. During this Atlas period, there were three records of six birds in total: two on King's Sedge Moor in May 2008 were assumed to be a pair, but they lingered only a few hours.

In 2012 a national influx of Black-winged Stilts occurred, driven by a prolonged drought in southern Europe, Spain in particular. That same drought drove many Baillon's Crakes (*Porzana pusilla*) north too, though unfortunately not to Somerset. One Stilt appeared briefly at Ham Wall on 29 May, but then a male and two females were discovered in early June on Curry Moor. Two of these were a pair, and by the time of their discovery they were incubating four eggs, but unfortunately they abandoned shortly afterwards during a period of particularly poor weather (Thomas 2012).

This was the eighth British breeding attempt, and the first in Somerset, but only two of these have been successful. Two or three successful attempts were made elsewhere in the country in 2014. (No map.)

Oystercatcher sponsored by Maureen Horne

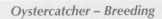

Oystercatcher – Breeding

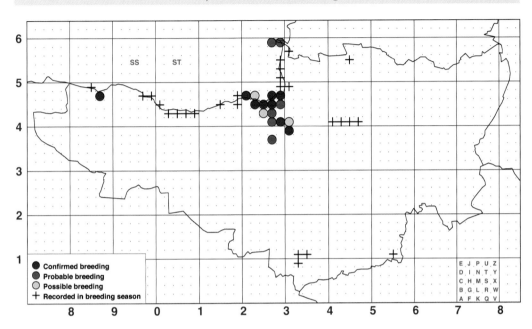

Legend:
- ● Confirmed breeding
- ● Probable breeding
- ○ Possible breeding
- + Recorded in breeding season

Oystercatcher – Winter

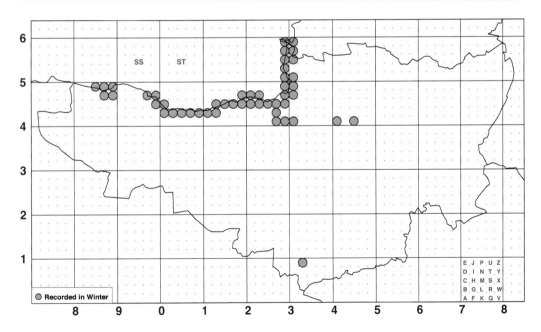

Legend:
- ○ Recorded in Winter

GOLDEN PLOVER *Pluvialis apricaria*

Large numbers of Golden Plovers arrive and pass through in October and November; on Exmoor they are often more conspicuous then than in mid-winter. The Levels have become a wintering area of international importance, with a highest count of 18,000 in 2008/09; these were all on West Sedge Moor, the most important site, but good numbers are often seen elsewhere on the southern Levels, particularly King's Sedge Moor. Numbers are usually smaller on the north side of the Poldens, but there are still regular flocks around Tealham Moor and the moors either side of the River Axe. High numbers around Bridgwater Bay are generally recorded only in hard weather. Not many appear to visit Mendip in winter, and there are large swathes of lowland farm-land, for instance in the Vale of Taunton Deane, where none were recorded during the Atlas period. By contrast, the farmland of the east, south, and south-east seems to be well used by Golden Plovers, though submissions to *SB* suggest that numbers are small and thinly spread.

West Sedge Moor has provided a safe daytime roost, from which birds may disperse to feed at night over a wide area of arable and pasture, so the distri-bution may be wider than is suggested here; on the other hand the map also includes records from two cold winters, when birds were displaced from their usual haunts as the Levels froze. On Exmoor, the winter population, usually numbered only in hun-dreds, is often concentrated in a few traditional cen-tres, for example near Lucott Cross; these birds feed on upland pastures and recently also on areas where moor grass (*Molinia*) has been baled in the summer. Flocks are very mobile in winter, adjusting their feed-ing and roosting patterns so as to find soft ground.

There is a strong spring passage from late Febru-ary to late April, or even into May, when the hand-some 'Northern' males can be conspicuous. Breeding has not been confirmed on Exmoor for a century now, and may have been rare then; climate change makes it less and less likely that it will happen again in the foreseeable future.

GREY PLOVER *Pluvialis squatarola*

This is a relatively scarce species everywhere in the South West. The most important site is the south side of Bridgwater Bay, where numbers in the five Atlas winters from 2007/08 to 2011/12 ranged from 100 to 224. Not long before the Atlas period there was an exceptional count of 518 in January 2006. Dunster Beach usually holds fewer than five, and occasional birds may be found on other parts of the coast.

In recent years there have been very few inland birds, mostly on passage; the only inland Atlas record in winter was one on Cheddar Reservoir in January 2011, the dots apparently inland south of Bridgwater Bay being in fact along the tidal stretch of the Parrett near Combwich.

Wintering birds are present from late August to April, but mainly from November to February, and there is some passage at both seasons. One or two often remain for the summer on the coast from Stert Point to Stolford.

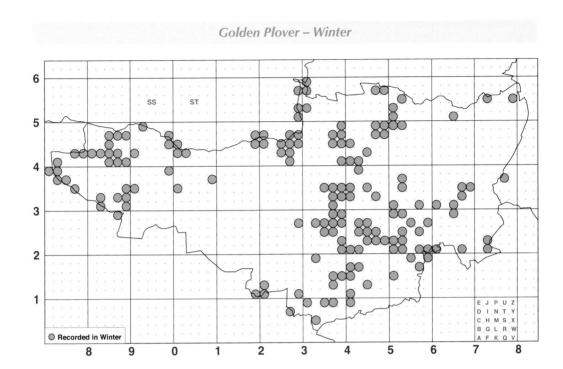

Golden Plover – Winter

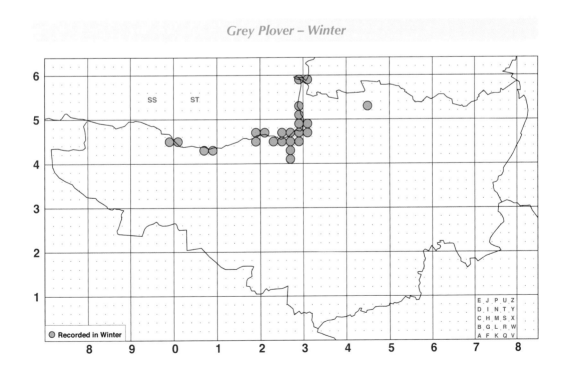

Grey Plover – Winter

LAPWING *Vanellus vanellus*

As breeding birds, Lapwing have always been at the mercy of changing natural conditions and human practices: a field chosen in March may soon be too wet or too dry, too lush or too bare; cattle may trample eggs or a single treatment by heavy machinery ruin all nesting attempts; foxes may take what man has missed. Of all the possible hazards, only egg-collecting for food has vanished.

In *BA 1968–72*, there were breeding attempts in every 10-km square except ST23 (Bridgwater West), but the range was already contracting and by the time of *NBA 1988–91*, breeding Lapwing had vanished from almost all Somerset west of the Parrett, and from the extreme south.

In the 1990s a national survey concluded that about half the English and Welsh population had gone, the worst results being in the South West, where the loss was of 64% (Wilson, Vickery, and Brown 2001). The main factors behind this decline in farmland nesting are the growth in autumn-sown cereals, the loss of mixed farming, and the use of machinery on crops in the spring; on the Levels the decline can be attributed to drainage and intensified grassland management, as well as to predation. The Somerset Lapwing Project in 2007 found a maximum of 190 territories in the county as a whole, of which all but about 15 were on the Levels.

During the period of the present Atlas, 131 breeding pairs were found in 2009 (again, with all but 15 on the Levels), but there were only 93 in 2010 and 86 in 2011. In the wet summer of 2012 there were 107, but this total was probably enhanced by an RSPB survey. The main sites have been the Cheddar Moors, Tealham and Tadham Moors, King's Sedge Moor, West Sedge Moor, and the South Levels around Muchelney and Long Load. Fox-proof fencing has been helpful at Greylake RSPB reserve.

Breeding was at least attempted at a number of other sites by a few pairs during the Atlas period, including: the Blackmoor Vale; the South Brewham area; Selwood, Mells Down, and Faulkland; Martock and Tintinhull; Pawlett Hams; and Kilve. For a further analysis of Lapwing problems in recent years, see Archer (2013).

The winter picture is a startling contrast, with birds widespread across the lowlands and also present in some upland areas. The Levels are usually the leading British site of international importance, with a mean total of 41,000 for 2007/08 to 2010/11; in January 2011 there were 72,000, of which half were on West Sedge Moor. Much the lowest figure was the 19,000 in 2009/10, when many left the frozen reserves, and wandering parties spread widely over West Somerset, appearing in many places where they had not been seen for years. In the last Atlas winter of 2011/12, the maximum was 31,000, in December, of which two-thirds were on West Sedge Moor. During short freeze-ups, flocks from the Levels may feed on the southern slopes of adjacent ridges and hills. On the Bridgwater Bay coast, they have often favoured the Pawlett Hams (Burton *et al.* 2003).

Lapwing sponsored by Eve Tigwell

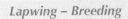

Lapwing – Breeding

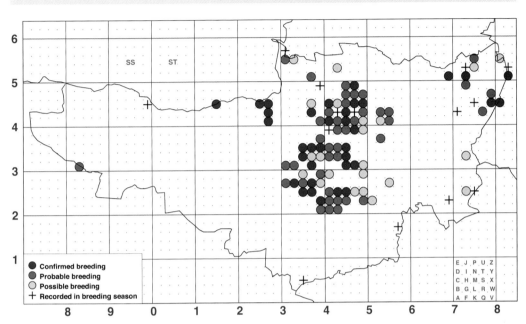

- ● Confirmed breeding
- ● Probable breeding
- ○ Possible breeding
- + Recorded in breeding season

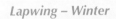

Lapwing – Winter

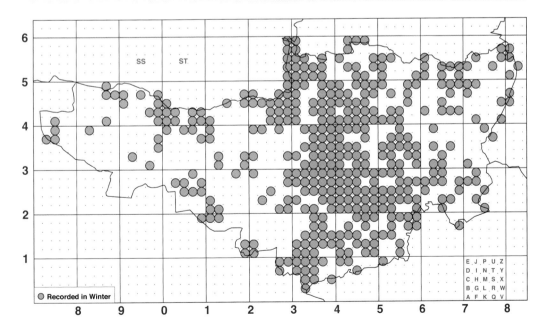

- ○ Recorded in Winter

AVOCET *Recurvirostra avosetta*

Avocets started appearing in small parties, on passage or in winter, during the last quarter of the 20th century, usually in Bridgwater Bay or the Parrett Estuary. In the winters from 2002/03 to 2009/10 these became more regular, up to 75 being found along mudbanks downstream from Combwich. Much larger numbers arrived in the autumn of 2010, when there were 223 in November; there were 204 in the last Atlas winter, 2011/12. The Parrett Estuary now seems firmly established as a regular wintering site for this attractive and successful species.

In the final Atlas year, 2012, a pair bred successfully at Steart, raising a single chick (Best 2013). This was the first recorded breeding by Avocets in Somerset, though unfortunately it was not repeated in 2013. The source was probably the relatively recently established but flourishing breeding colony on the Gwent Levels.

In the past there have been occasional reports elsewhere on the coast and inland, but during the Atlas period there were only two winter records from the Axe Estuary.

LITTLE RINGED PLOVER *Charadrius dubius*

Little Ringed Plovers have been annual on passage since the mid 1960s, and can turn up in any suitable wader habitat. In recent years the scrape at Meare Heath, wet fields on Tealham Moor, and the Steart peninsula have all been favoured areas, while in the autumn low water levels in the reservoirs also make them attractive to waders, including this species.

The first county breeding record was not until 1995, when a pair took advantage of temporarily suitable habitat on Glastonbury Heath. Since then they have bred annually somewhere in the county, though there is only one regular site, at Torr Works Reservoir in the east of the county, where up to five pairs attempted to nest during the Atlas period. Birds were also recorded in suitable habitat in three other 10-km squares. Little Ringed Plover is a Schedule 1 species and prone to disturbance, so while the main breeding site is openly acknowledged (and has been published previously in *SB*), records are mapped at 10-km square level.

Avocet sponsored by Dick Best

Avocet – Winter

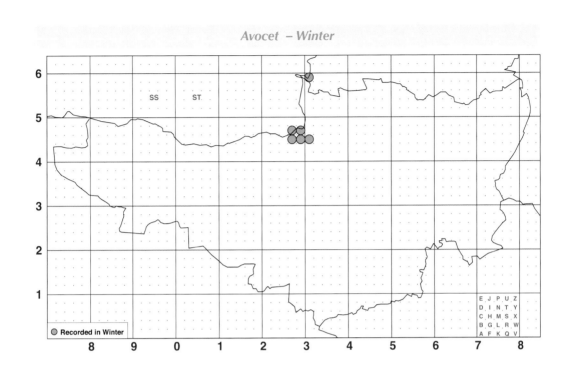

○ Recorded in Winter

Little Ringed Plover – Breeding

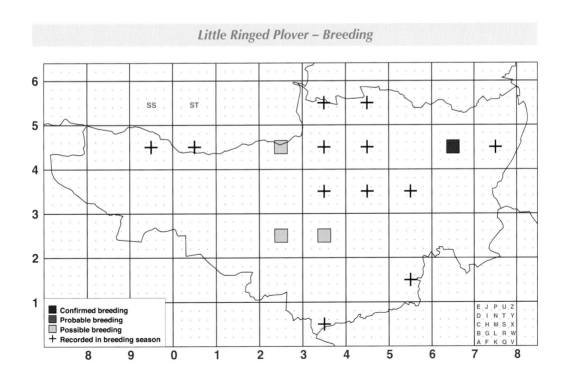

■ Confirmed breeding
■ Probable breeding
□ Possible breeding
+ Recorded in breeding season

RINGED PLOVER *Charadrius hiaticula*

During the Atlas period of 2007–2012 from three to ten pairs attempted to nest in three regular areas: Stert Island, Wall Common, and Dunster Beach. A couple of nesting attempts were made at Berrow in years immediately preceding the Atlas, but a former site, Porlock Marsh, is no longer used.

Inland breeding records are very unusual in Somerset: of the two mapped here, one is not 'inland' in the strict sense, as it was along a tidal stretch of the Parrett on the outskirts of Bridgwater: it will be interesting to see if further attempts are made here in future years. The other is of a pair seen displaying at a site on the Avalon Marshes; in this case it is likely that an actual breeding attempt was not made.

About 150 regularly winter from November to February, of which two-thirds are between Berrow and Hinkley Point, and most of the remainder in the Axe Estuary or on Dunster Beach. Passage numbers are much higher in May and from August to October; these are mainly at the same sites, though in recent years a few birds have also favoured the wader scrape on Meare Heath. Most other inland records have been at reservoirs when water levels are low.

Ringed Plover – Breeding

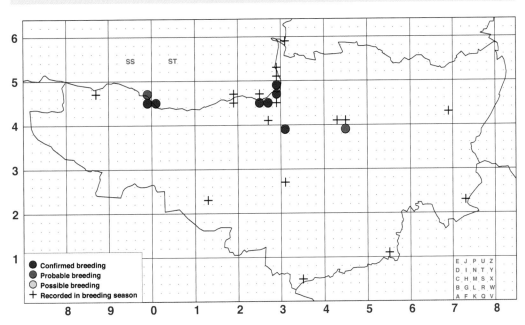

- ● Confirmed breeding
- ● Probable breeding
- ○ Possible breeding
- + Recorded in breeding season

Ringed Plover – Winter

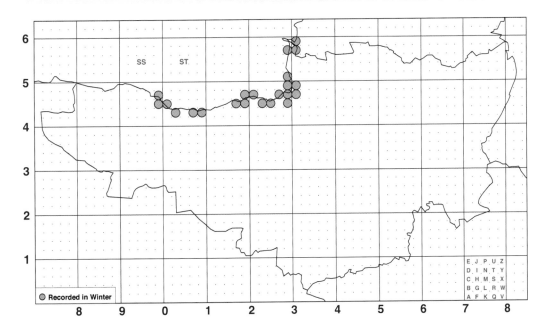

- ○ Recorded in Winter

CURLEW *Numenius arquata*

Historically Curlew was generally considered as an Exmoor breeding species, with only a few pairs on the Levels and on Mendip. By 1950 they had spread more to the Levels and so occupied their widest range in historic times. A gradual decline, for reasons which are not fully understood, means that the current Atlas may have chronicled their last days as a breeding species on the Somerset side of Exmoor: no breeding pairs could be found in 2012. There has been a parallel decline on Dartmoor (Smaldon 2005). An isolated pair or two may cling on in the Blackdowns, though breeding was not confirmed during the Atlas, but it was not even suspected on Mendip or the Quantocks (where it has never been regular).

On the Levels, where they have typically used hay meadows, they have been more successful. They may return as early as February. There have been up to 46 pairs, of which at least half have been on West Sedge

Moor, and others on Tealham Moor, King's Sedge Moor and the South Levels. An excellent summary of fluctuations and problems in the last 40 years with the breeding of waders on the Levels can be found in a recent paper by Archer (2013).

The main wintering site is the south coast of Bridgwater Bay, where numbers in November and December during the first four Atlas years varied from 1,050 to 1,600, though in severe weather they sometimes halved in the New Year. However, in the last winter, of 2011/12, the highest count was only 650. Passage numbers can be slightly higher in autumn and up to 100 non-breeders can be found in summer. There are regular wintering flocks of up to 150 on Minehead Marshes and up to 80 on Porlock Marsh, though numbers at both sites have shrunk.

Odd birds and small parties may appear almost anywhere on passage and in winter, especially on the Levels and along other parts of the coast.

Curlew sponsored by Eve Tigwell

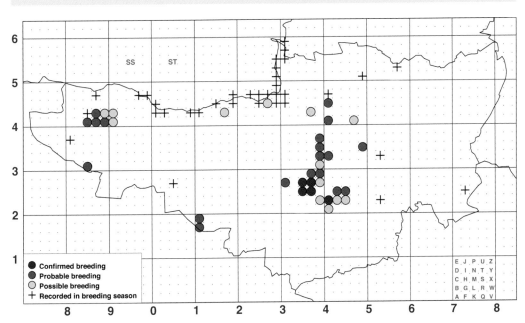

Curlew – Breeding

SS ST

- **Confirmed breeding**
- **Probable breeding**
- **Possible breeding**
- **+ Recorded in breeding season**

E J P U Z
D I N T Y
C H M S X
B G L R W
A F K Q V

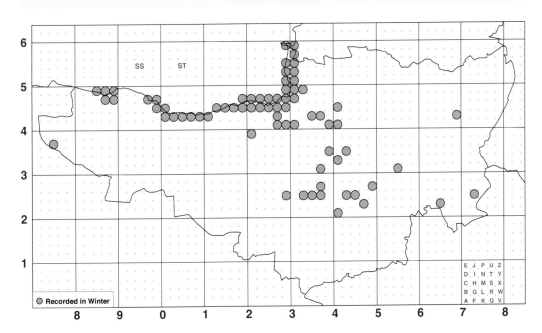

Curlew – Winter

SS ST

- **Recorded in Winter**

E J P U Z
D I N T Y
C H M S X
B G L R W
A F K Q V

BLACK-TAILED GODWIT *Limosa limosa*

Black-tailed Godwits bred on Wet Moor in 1963 and from 1969 to 1985 there was a small colony on West Sedge Moor, with a maximum of seven pairs, but this died out, and none has bred successfully since. Breeding was not suspected during the Atlas period, despite the presence since 2008 of a regular summering flock of up to 117 on Meare Heath.

Winter numbers have usually been between 100 and 150 in recent years, split between the south coast of Bridgwater Bay and the Levels, where they are more widespread across the South Levels than in the Avalon Marshes. Small numbers occasionally visit other sites, including the Axe Estuary.

BAR-TAILED GODWIT *Limosa lapponica*

Bar-tailed Godwits are largely passage migrants in Somerset. For a short time in the 1960s a winter flock of up to 200 developed on the south coast of Bridgwater Bay, but the highest winter count during the Atlas period was 62, in December 2009. Higher numbers occur here on passage, mostly in April and May: in 2007 there were 500, and an exceptional 800 were recorded in 2011. Berrow is the other site which regularly attracts more than a handful of Bar-tailed Godwits, though there is much interchange of birds with Steart, so some duplication is almost inevitable. The Axe Estuary and Dunster Beach both hold a few birds for a while in most winters.

They are rare birds inland, even during passage periods when birds are occasionally recorded on or over the Avalon Marshes; none were recorded inland in winter during the Atlas period.

TURNSTONE *Arenaria interpres*

This is a species of shingle, rocks, and mud. There are two main wintering areas. The first is from the Brue Estuary west to Stolford, where late-autumn and winter counts during the Atlas period were generally in the 100–200 range. The second is the coast from Quantoxhead to Minehead, where there were 117 in December 2005, but a maximum of only 50 during the Atlas period, in November 2009, although these figures may not be complete: the ribbed platforms of rocks exposed at low tide around Watchet in particular are attractive to the species, but the area is underwatched. The recent decline in the winter population of West Somerset may be in part due to the constant and ever-increasing disturbance from free-ranging dogs (J.R.White *in litt.*). Smaller numbers occur elsewhere on the coast, including the Axe Estuary in the north of the county, but Turnstones have never been regular west of Hurlstone Point.

Nationally, there have been losses in Southern England in recent years, perhaps because of warmer conditions further north. Most British wintering birds probably come from Greenland and Canada.

Larger numbers are normal at passage seasons, when the Brue Estuary is a favoured roosting site, and birds are sometimes found at reservoirs. These are mainly from Scandinavia and Siberia, on their way to and from West Africa.

Bar-tailed Godwit sponsored by David Reid

Black-tailed Godwit & Bar-tailed Godwit – Winter

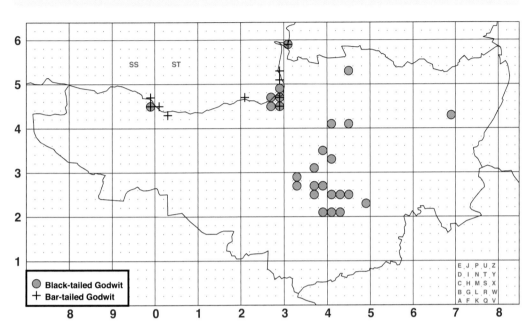

Turnstone – Winter

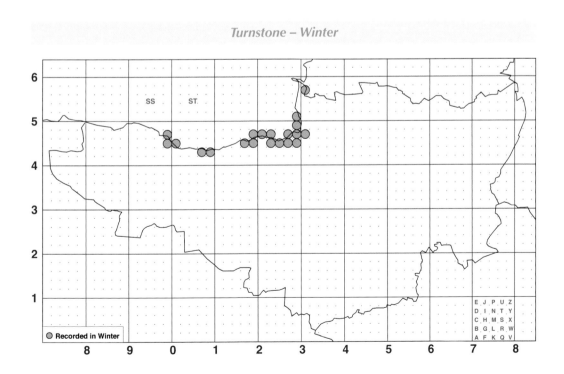

KNOT *Calidris canutus*

Knot are largely visitors from November to March to the coasts of Bridgwater Bay, attracted like other waders to the extensive and food-rich mud-flats that stretch between Berrow and Stolford at low tide. Numbers in recent years have averaged about 1,600, though an exceptional 5,000 were counted in February 2009. As might be expected, the other coastal records during the period were from another regular site, the Axe Estuary, and from the Dunster Beach area. The coast in between the latter and Stolford is rocky and less attractive to most waders.

Inland records are not unusual, especially on passage when parties of up to 92 have been recorded on the Meare Heath scrape in autumn during Atlas years. Inland winter records usually involve much smaller numbers, singles or small parties, which may perhaps only be present for a few days. Those recorded during the Atlas winters and mapped here (at Catcott Lows, Southlake Moor, Curry Moor, and Sutton Bingham Reservoir) are representative of the scatter of records, though many other sites have been used in other years, especially on flooded Levels.

RUFF *Calidris pugnax*

As the map shows, the main area where Ruff winter in Somerset is the Levels south of the Poldens, King's Sedge Moor (including Greylake RSPB reserve), West Sedge Moor, and Aller Moor being particularly favoured. The winter population on the Levels may be up to 100, greatest in years of extensive flooding and perhaps inflated after New Year by fugitives from a frozen Continent. Coastal records are scarcer, but the Brue and Axe Estuaries are regular haunts; the isolated record at Dunster Beach is a fair indication of the species' rarity further west.

Ruff are regular passage migrants at both seasons in small numbers, but while the species may have bred historically on the Levels, they have not done so for a very long time. Both the breeding range and the migration flyway have moved eastward (*BA 2007–11*). This shift makes any possible re-establishment of breeding on the Levels less likely.

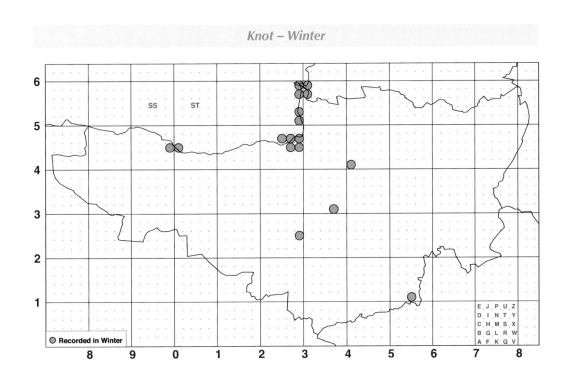

Knot – Winter

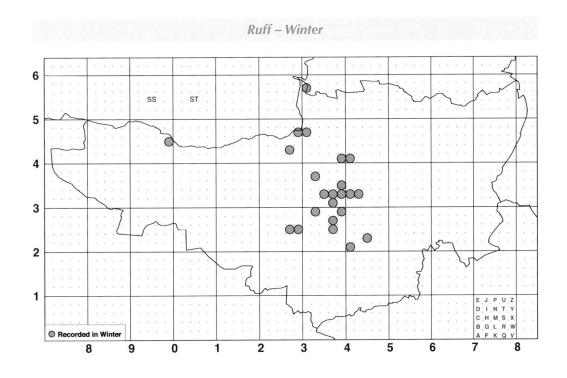

Ruff – Winter

SANDERLING *Calidris alba*

This is a very local species, confined to sandy shores. The main site is the long stretch of sandy beach between Berrow and Brean Down, where the winter flock averages about 200. Unlike other small waders, it is much less common on the mudflats on the south side of Bridgwater Bay, though small numbers do occur. Sanderling were largely absent during the years of *WA*, from 1981 to 1984, but in the Low-tide Survey of 2002/03 the only occupied sector of the entire Severn Estuary was the northern part of Berrow Flats (Burton *et al.* 2003). Increased numbers have been regular in recent years, after a period in which birds were much more numerous on passage in May and late summer, when moving between Greenland and West Africa. The only other regular wintering sites are Dunster Beach, which holds up to 20, and the Axe Estuary, where the few birds seen are presumably offshoots from the Berrow and Brean flocks.

The few inland passage records have been largely from Cheddar Reservoir; none were recorded inland in winter during the Atlas.

DUNLIN *Calidris alpina*

The chief wintering site is Bridgwater Bay. Apart from the main flock around the Steart peninsula, there can be separate but much smaller groups in the Axe Estuary and at Stolford. They are present from late October to early March, and are of the North-west European race *C. a. alpina*. Passage birds, numerous in May and from July to September, are largely of the North European race *C. a. schinzii*. In the Atlas winters from 2007/08 to 2011/12, the highest totals varied between 15,000 and 22,000.

Small numbers also frequent Dunster Beach, where over 100 are unusual, though few use Porlock Marsh, which is much less attractive to waders than it once was. Shallow flooding can attract up to several hundred on the Levels, particularly south of the Poldens, the most regular site being West Sedge Moor. In exceptionally good conditions, numbers can rise to over 1,000; there is no other inland population of this size south of the Derwent Valley in Yorkshire. King's Sedge Moor, Greylake RSPB reserve and the South Levels also regularly attract small parties.

Breeding has not even been suspected since the last confirmed record, on Lype Hill in the Brendons a century ago. Restoration of a number of mires on Exmoor Forest gives hope, however, that more suitable habitat might attract Dunlins to remoter parts of the moor to nest: the nearest breeders are not far away on Dartmoor.

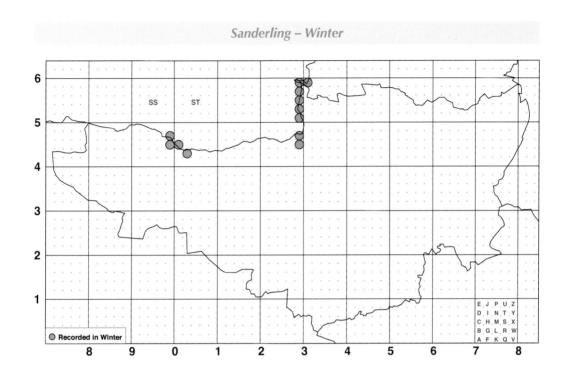

Sanderling – Winter

SS ST.

Recorded in Winter

E J P U Z
D I N T Y
C H M S X
B G L R W
A F K Q V

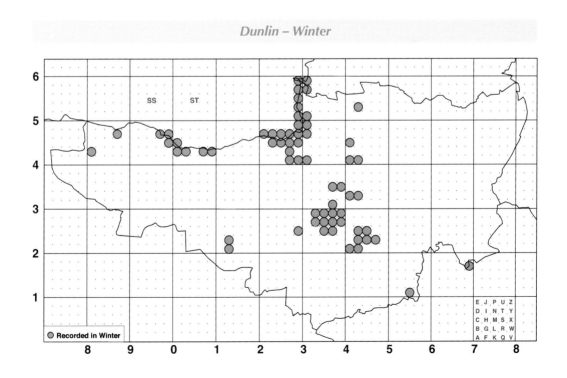

Dunlin – Winter

SS ST.

Recorded in Winter

E J P U Z
D I N T Y
C H M S X
B G L R W
A F K Q V

PURPLE SANDPIPER *Calidris maritima*

Somerset has relatively little of the rocky coastline that is the preferred habitat of Purple Sandpipers. In the years immediately preceding the Atlas the only birds that had wintered with any regularity had been one or two in the rocky bays east of Watchet and from Stolford to Knighton Beach, until in 2007 a roost of up to 13 was found in this latter area, on the intake structure at Hinkley Point power station. This was used annually throughout the Atlas period, and numbers rose to 22 in January 2010, though records from the Watchet site have been less regular. Most of the coast between Hinkley Point and Watchet is suitable for Purple Sandpipers, but attracts few other waders and the area is very much underwatched. By contrast there are Atlas records from Dunster Beach, Steart, and the Axe Estuary, where the habitat is less suitable, but there are more pairs of eyes looking. Inland records are exceedingly rare, and there were none in the Atlas period.

Wintering birds are usually present from November to January or early February, but there have been records up to May, which suggest that these could be High-Arctic birds.

COMMON SANDPIPER *Actitis hypoleucos*

Common Sandpipers are most familiar in Somerset as passage migrants, with Cheddar and Sutton Bingham Reservoirs particularly favoured in spring, and a wider spread in autumn when reservoir water levels are usually low. Wintering is a relatively recent phenomenon, dating back only to 1950, but has become increasingly regular, though in very small numbers, perhaps no more than six in any one winter. The Parrett Estuary is the most regular area, with Combwich Reach particularly favoured, but during the Atlas period wintering birds were well scattered across the county, from Porlock Marsh, Dunster Hawn, and Wimbleball Lake in the west, to the River Brue at Castle Cary and Torr Works Reservoir in the east.

Common Sandpipers probably bred regularly on the Barle and the Exe until the middle of the 20th century, but the last nest was found in 1970 near Pickedstones Bridge. Odd birds have been seen along the Barle in midsummer, including one during the Atlas period in 2008. Some likely areas are even now very little disturbed, and a pair could easily breed undetected, though as yet there is little evidence to suggest this.

Purple Sandpiper – Winter

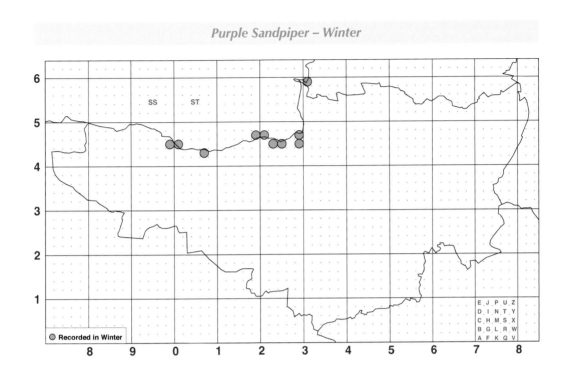

Common Sandpiper – Winter

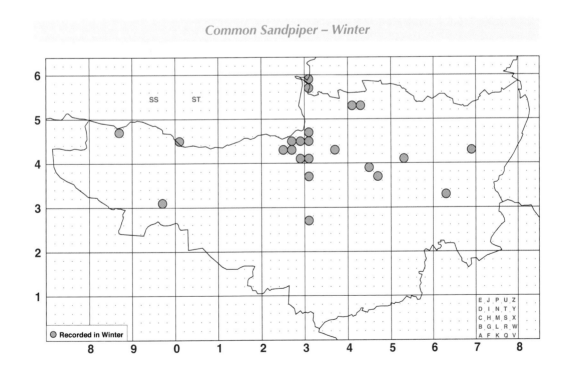

GREEN SANDPIPER *Tringa ochropus*

This is largely a passage migrant, whose movements show a marked and surprisingly early peak in late summer, so it has sometimes figured as a non-breeding visitor among breeding-season entries for the Atlas. It is a familiar sight on the wader scrape at Meare Heath and along the shores of reservoirs from late July to early October.

It is also a winter visitor, however, widespread but in small numbers across the lowlands, when it may make unexpected appearances at silage pits and along rhynes. Since 2000, the total recorded annually

in *SB* has usually been between 15 and 30, but both on the Levels and on coastal grazing marshes this species is easily overlooked pottering along the side of a deep rhyne unless inadvertently flushed, and the number recorded may be only a small part of the winter population.

SPOTTED REDSHANK *Tringa erythropus*
GREENSHANK *Tringa nebularia*

These two 'shanks' are mapped together, as both are scarce and their winter distributions are very similar.

Greenshank is by far the commoner and more widespread as a passage migrant, inland and on the coast, especially in autumn, but is noticeably rarer and more irregular as a winter visitor. During the Atlas period, one or two tended to winter in the Parrett Estuary, usually in the Combwich area, but they were generally absent in the coldest weather.

Spotted Redshank is the reverse, much scarcer as a passage migrant, especially inland, but with a small but regular wintering presence in the Parrett Estuary. They usually occur further downstream than the occasional Greenshanks, with Huntspill Sluice and the Brue Estuary being particularly favoured areas. During the Atlas period the most recorded in a single winter was eight, down from the peak of 19 at the beginning of this century. Spotted Redshanks also occur regularly on the Axe Estuary in winter, usually singly.

Green Sandpiper – Winter

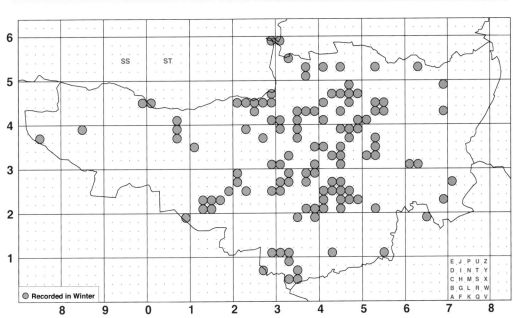

SS ST

○ Recorded in Winter

E J P U Z
D I N T Y
C H M S X
B G L R W
A F K Q V

Spotted Redshank & Greenshank – Winter

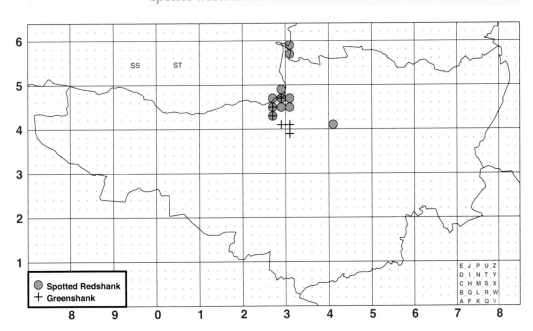

SS ST

● Spotted Redshank
+ Greenshank

E J P U Z
D I N T Y
C H M S X
B G L R W
A F K Q V

REDSHANK *Tringa totanus*

Redshanks colonised the Somerset Levels in the early part of the 20th century: the Levels Survey of 1976/77 found a total of 52 pairs, to which should be added a few around the Parrett Estuary and on Porlock Marsh (Round, 1978). From then to 2002 numbers varied between 50 and 80. In 2004 they fell as low as 20, but during the Atlas from 2008 to 2012 there were between 38 and 43 pairs recorded. The major site is West Sedge Moor, but there are others on Tealham Moor, in the Avalon Marshes, on King's Sedge Moor (mainly within Greylake RSPB reserve) and, less frequently, on the South Levels. For a useful summary of nesting success and the habitats required for it, see the recent paper by Archer (2013). One or two pairs have continued to attempt to breed on Porlock Marsh and have occasionally succeeded in spite of the spring tides which inundate the marsh.

The main wintering sites are the Axe Estuary and the coast of Bridgwater Bay. The former holds an average of 200, the latter between 650 and 1,600, which are generally concentrated around the inlets of fresh water; most roost in the Brue Estuary. In Britain and Ireland as a whole, numbers declined by about 40% from 1995 to 2010, but current Somerset figures are an improvement on those of the 1990s, though breeders are almost entirely confined to reserves and areas where there is some measure of water control. Inland records away from the Levels are usually at passage seasons; the few winter records at reservoirs mapped here are unusual, though not unprecedented, and short stays are the norm.

Redshank – Breeding

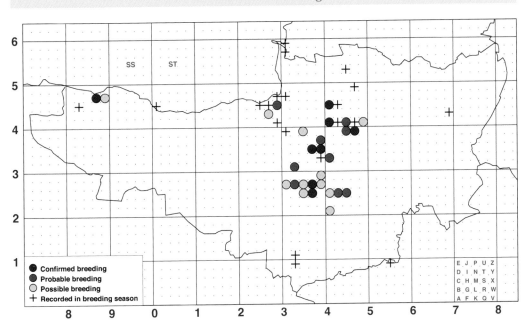

Redshank – Winter

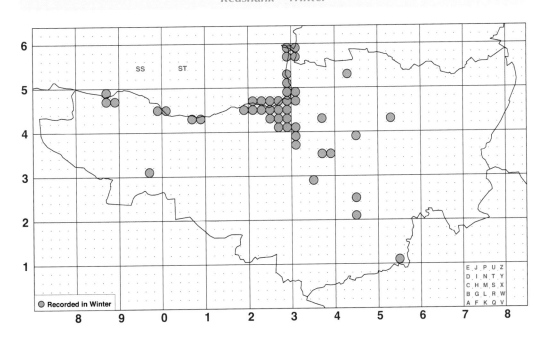

JACK SNIPE *Lymnocryptes minimus*

Wintering birds are present from October or November to March or April. In the jargon of the *Wetland Bird Survey*, 'the species has very low detectability', as any would-be finder of Jack Snipe will attest; their habit of sitting tight until virtually trodden on makes them hard to find even at known sites. The distribution and numbers of Jack Snipe were almost certainly understated in *WA 1981–84*, which found them over the three winters in only eight 10-km squares, and nowhere west of the Parrett. Contrast this with the current map, with records from

28 10-km squares, spread across the county. The salt-marshes of the Axe, Brue, and Parrett Estuaries, and along the Steart peninsula are regular and well-known sites for Jack Snipe. These have provided the biggest counts during the period (up to 14 in the Brue Estuary), but this is at least partly because they are the most visited by observers seeking the species. The map shows how well distributed they are also across the Levels, north and south of the Poldens. Other small concentrations are around Minehead Marshes, Templecombe in the south-east, and the recently created wetland at Cary Moor, where particular recording and ringing efforts are ongoing. Jack Snipe are rare on high ground, especially in the west, though a few were found on Mendip.

The distribution as mapped may in fact be wider than that of a single normal winter, as the two big freeze-ups in 2009/10 and 2010/11 not only pushed more birds towards traditional sites at the coast, but also led to them being found in unusual places along rhynes and ice-free streams.

WOODCOCK *Scolopax rusticola*

Few species are less prone to discovery by normal survey protocols than this nocturnal woodland wader. *WA 1981–84* recorded Woodcocks in 20 10-km squares, of which 12, including three on the Quantocks, had only a single contact. Many woods that may be regular sites are on private land, and anecdotal evidence suggests that they may be common in places from which they have never been formally reported. Unfortunately, however, most attempts to obtain information on the distribution of this species from the shooting community (and evidence of numbers from 'bags') came to nothing, though up to 100 were recorded at one Exmoor site. The map is therefore incomplete to an unknown extent.

Countering that, the hard weather during the two Atlas winters of 2009/10 and 2010/11 was nationally responsible for unusually high numbers, and many were flushed during snowy walks by Atlas observers during those times. So, equally, the wide distribution in those winters may overstate the case in a normal winter, again to an unknown extent.

Woodcock are usually present from late October to February. March records may well be of potential breeders, but males often display in early spring without finding a mate. Summer records came from only four sites in the south and east of the county, and in only one, near Aller, were birds recorded on more than one date. Nationally, the breeding population is thought to have at least halved since the 1960s, and the results of a national BTO survey are eagerly awaited. Somerset, however, has always been on the margin of its breeding range.

Woodcock sponsored by Nigel Palfrey and Andrew Parker

Jack Snipe – Winter

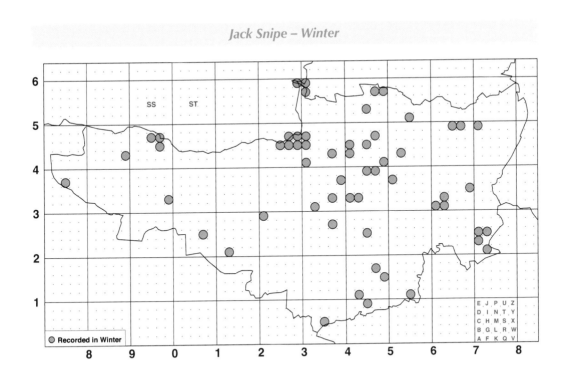

Woodcock – Winter

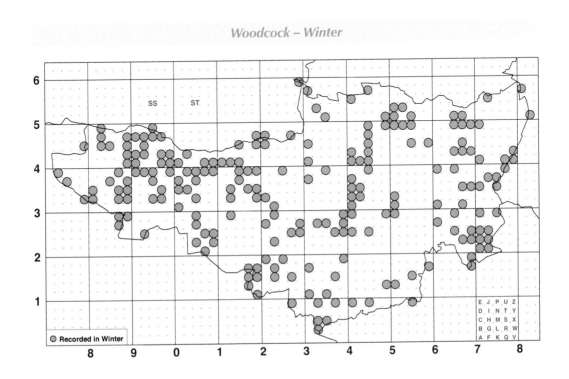

SNIPE *Gallinago gallinago*

Snipe were formerly so common as breeders on the Levels that few details were ever published. Drainage brought about a decline, but the full Levels Survey of 1976/77 still revealed 231 drumming males, of which 40% were on West Sedge Moor and the South Levels (Round 1978). Then numbers fell rapidly, so that in 1997 there were only 32 (Chown 1997). An even lower point of 18 was reached in 2001, when breeding reports were confined to Catcott Lows and West Sedge Moor. This decline was part of a wider picture across Southern and Midland England, following drainage and agricultural improvements.

In Somerset at least, some recovery followed, assisted by good management on the reserves and the creation of Raised Water Level Areas, so that by the start of the current Atlas in 2008 there were 120 drumming males on the Levels. Two-thirds of them were on West Sedge Moor and others at eight sites. Only one of these was on the South Levels, which have usually been too dry, though there were ten displaying on Wet Moor in 2008 (D.J. Chown *in litt.*). In 2011, there were about 72 pairs, 64 on West Sedge Moor and eight on King's Sedge Moor (including Greylake RSPB reserve). In the wet summer of 2012, a more extensive, though incomplete, survey by the RSPB found 119 possible breeding pairs on the Levels: the main concentrations were of eight on Tealham and Tadham Moors, ten on King's Sedge Moor and 90 on West Sedge Moor. For an account of the recent position on the Levels, see the paper by Archer (2013).

Small numbers have always bred on Exmoor. The 2008 RSPB survey was the first to concentrate on this species, of which 14 displaying males were found in Somerset, three being associated with the newly created mires (Stanbury *et al.* 2008). A special survey of these in 2011/12 suggested that even the most suitable sites may not be occupied every year, the one exception being the deep bogs on the south side of Winsford Hill, which may hold up to three pairs (Boyce 2012).

Wintering numbers have always been high on the Levels, though they may have declined through drainage, which has tended to concentrate them in reserves. In most recent years those recorded by the WeBS counts have exceeded 1,000 and the Levels have been first or second among British sites. Such figures must represent only a small fraction of the numbers present in the area, due to the difficulties in detecting this species, which might be in the region of 10,000. Smaller numbers can be found throughout Somerset, in rough, damp fields (for example Cary Moor), on coastal marshes, and even on the highest ground of Exmoor, but they may be concentrated in coastal areas during hard weather.

Snipe sponsored by John McGeoch

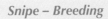

Snipe – Breeding

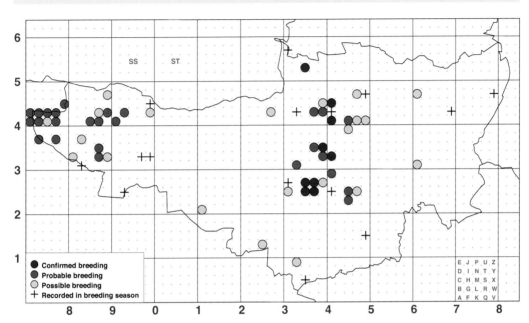

Snipe – Winter

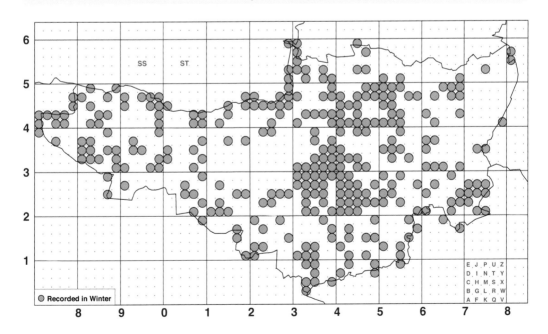

POMARINE SKUA *Stercorarius pomarinus*

ARCTIC SKUA *Stercorarius parasiticus*

LONG-TAILED SKUA *Stercorarius longicaudus*

GREAT SKUA *Stercorarius skua*

The greater effort put into seawatching in recent years means that records of skuas off the Somerset coast are much more frequent than 20 years ago, though Long-tailed remain scarce and barely annual. Most records are during passage periods and usually involve birds blown in from the west by gales, but many autumn skuas are westbound after an overland crossing from the North Sea.

Total sightings during the five years of this Atlas give some idea of the relative frequency of the species: the figures in brackets are for those seen in the Atlas months. There were 84 Pomarines (22), 172 Arctics (59), seven Long-taileds (one) and 158 Greats (57).

No skuas in the Atlas months came further inland than the tide-line, and most were well offshore. The majority of these records fall in the spring and summer period, but are of obvious migrants, so are not mapped here. A few Great Skuas are regularly present even in winter in the Western Approaches, where they can kleptoparasitise Gannets and gulls. During the Atlas period there were no January or February records, though there were 28 in November or December. Great Skuas have in the past been seen in every month off the coast of Somerset. (No maps.)

GUILLEMOT *Uria aalge*

Small numbers are regularly seen offshore westward of Minehead Bay from April to July. However, the only possible breeding record ever, from Brean Down in 1912, was not confirmed, and breeding has not been suspected since, despite up to 1,200 pairs breeding between Lynton and Heddon's Mouth, a mere seven miles beyond Glenthorne and the Devon border.

A second annual peak of records occurs in the west when birds appear off Hurlstone Point and Minehead from October to December, especially in westerlies. Up-Channel, occasional birds straggle or are blown by gales, when they often appear weak and may be attacked by gulls or found later as beach corpses. Some non-Atlas observations suggest that birds are regularly present in the Channel during the winter, though normally well offshore. The winter map is representative of records in both seasons.

RAZORBILL *Alca torda*

Perhaps unsurprisingly, the pattern of records is similar to that of Guillemot, though the North Devon breeding numbers are at most two-thirds of that species. Birds also reappear in late autumn. As with Guillemot, winter records only are mapped, but they are representative of records at both seasons. It is interesting to note that this species appears slightly more widespread along the Somerset coast than are Guillemots, which may be a result of its propensity to migrate and disperse further from the breeding colonies in winter (*BWP*), but, given the small number of records of both species involved, this may be no more than a random effect.

PUFFIN *Fratercula arctica*

Large numbers breed on the Pembrokeshire islands, and there has been a revival of the small Lundy colony, yet Puffins remain rare up-Channel. The surge in interest in seawatching has increased the number of records, so that they are now seen just about annually in Somerset waters, but in very small numbers. Seven were found off western coasts during the Atlas period, none of which were in winter; spring seems to be the favoured season. (No map.)

LITTLE AUK *Alle alle*

Over 80 have been recorded since 1942, usually after autumn or winter gales in the Channel. During the Atlas period there were six, all but one in November, and evenly split between watchpoints in the west and around Bridgwater Bay. (No map.)

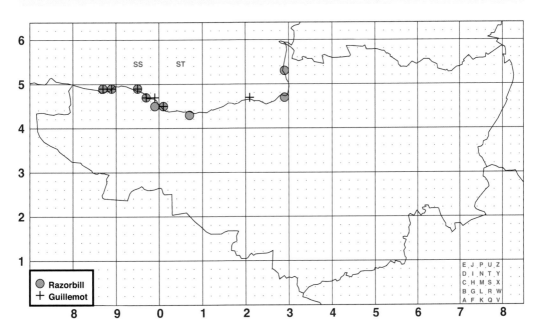

Guillemot & Razorbill – Winter

Razorbill
+ Guillemot

COMMON TERN *Sterna hirundo*

In the Avalon Marshes, breeding was attempted by one pair in 2005 and 2006 and was successful in 2007 and 2008, but not again within the Atlas period; subsequently a single pair attempted to nest there in 2014. These were the first Somerset breeding records. Other birds have occasionally summered, but they are normally only passage migrants, appearing much more frequently inland at reservoirs and wetlands than any other tern species.

KITTIWAKE *Rissa tridactyla*

The nearest breeding colonies are in North Devon, but they now hold no more than 200 pairs. The few summer Kittiwakes off Somerset's western coasts may be from these colonies or from the Gower peninsula, but May to September account for only about five per cent of recent records, the peak months being November and December. All the highest counts, and many lower ones, were made during strong westerlies and were of birds returning westward when the wind has abated. However, small numbers have been seen feeding off Hurlstone Point in various months and they are probably more regular further offshore.

From 2007 to 2012, numbers in Somerset reflected the poor state of many British colonies. Even in the most favourable conditions there was only one count of over 1,000, in November 2007, and there have been very few inland records of storm-blown vagrants. The British population fell by 44% between 1986 and 2011 (JNCC 2012), and this no doubt accounts for the lower passage and winter figures, which are also apparent in the Cornish coastal records published in *BA 2007–11*.

Common Tern sponsored by Sterna Word Services

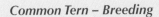

Common Tern – Breeding

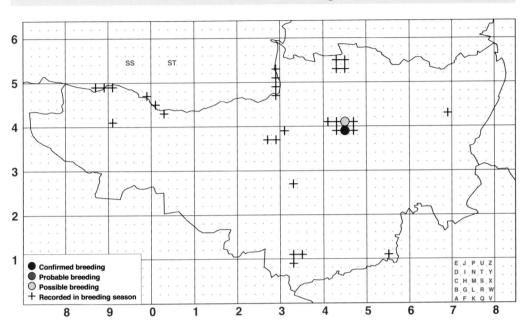

SS ST.

● Confirmed breeding
● Probable breeding
○ Possible breeding
+ Recorded in breeding season

E J P U Z
D I N T Y
C H M S X
B G L R W
A F K Q V

8 9 0 1 2 3 4 5 6 7 8

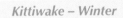

Kittiwake – Winter

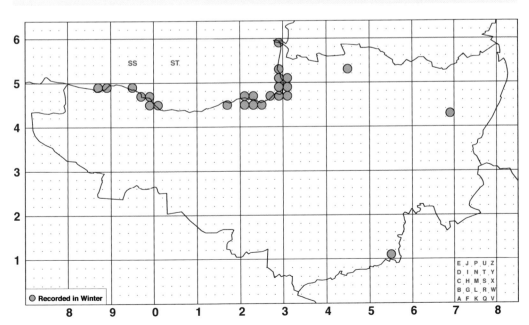

SS ST.

○ Recorded in Winter

E J P U Z
D I N T Y
C H M S X
B G L R W
A F K Q V

8 9 0 1 2 3 4 5 6 7 8

BLACK-HEADED GULL *Chroicocephalus ridibundus*

This is not a regular breeding species anywhere in the South West away from Poole Harbour, and there have only ever been sporadic breeding attempts in Somerset in the past. One or two pairs almost certainly nested on the Avalon Marshes in 2005 and during the Atlas period in 2009; though the exact site was not found, young were seen which must have been fledged in the area. In the summer floods of 2012, a pair was seen carrying nesting material at Hay Moor in May, but the waters swiftly receded, and nothing came of their efforts. Other records of possible or probable breeding may refer to briefly-staying birds in suitable habitat or even displaying, but most breeding-season records probably refer to over-summering non-breeders.

Large numbers pass through Somerset from March to May and again from July to October. Many thousands regularly winter, feeding widely inland, though they seldom frequent the Exmoor Plateau, where they are actually rare west of Wheddon Cross. The breeding-season map shows that they also avoid high ground on the Blackdowns and Quantocks; on the high Mendip pastures they are far outnumbered by Common Gulls. They roost in Bridgwater Bay, on the Dunster and Minehead shore, and on the reservoirs, including Cheddar. A small roost of a few hundred is now regular at Sutton Bingham Reservoir. Large numbers have always been attracted to flooding on the Levels, where they feed on waterlogged ground. In recent years up to 10,000 have roosted on Wet Moor when it has been widely flooded.

Black-headed Gull – Breeding

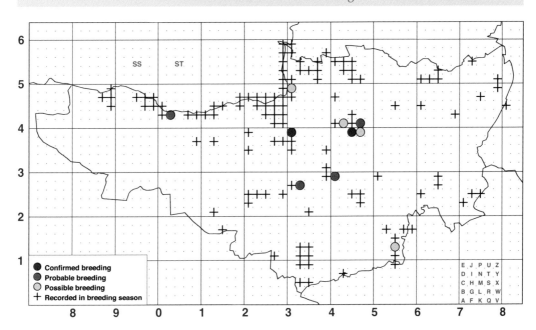

- ● Confirmed breeding
- ● Probable breeding
- ○ Possible breeding
- + Recorded in breeding season

Black-headed Gull – Winter

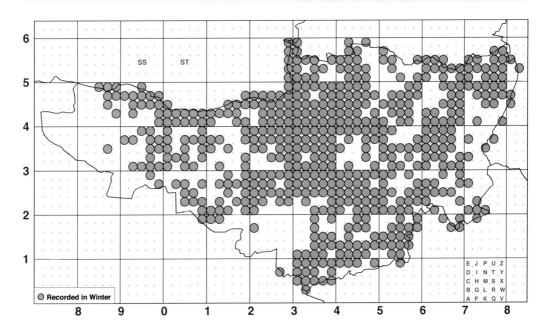

- ○ Recorded in Winter

LITTLE GULL *Hydrocoloeus minutus*

A westward extension of the Baltic breeding range in the 1960s made Little Gulls, previously rare in Somerset, more familiar as passage migrants, though still scarce. Records in the Atlas period fit the general pattern established during the last decade or so of passage migrants mostly in March and April, and September and October, with a few midsummer immatures and equally few birds (adults and immatures) overwintering.

Only the winter records are mapped here – a maximum of 26 individuals are involved, giving an average of only five birds per winter. The scatter shown on the map is typical – there have been regular January records in recent years around Hinkley Point, where they are attracted to the power station cooling-water outlet, with other records mostly shared between the coast, various lowland reservoirs, and the Avalon Marshes.

At other seasons the pattern is roughly similar, with a slightly wider spread of sites; Cheddar Reservoir is the most regular site, accounting for about 40% of all records, though in summer the Avalon Marshes also seem particularly attractive to the species. Most summer records are of second calendar-year birds, however, and there has never been any suspicion of breeding.

MEDITERRANEAN GULL *Larus melanocephalus*

The first county record was as recent as 1956, but records have been annual since 1978, and continue to increase. Most birds have been recorded in Bridgwater Bay or along the western coast, among flocks of Black-headed Gulls; in recent years there has been an increase in records from reservoirs and the Avalon Marshes. In the last decade, the annual totals have risen slowly, from 70 to about 100, of which 60% have been adults and fewer than 30% appear to be true winter visitors. The rest are transients, mainly from August to October, though there are now earlier arrivals: the July flooding in 2012 in the Blackmoor Vale attracted a remarkable gathering of 25. These sites are not far from the established sites in Poole Harbour in Dorset and at Langstone Harbour in Hampshire, where two major colonies held about 500 pairs in 2011, about half the British population (Holling *et al.* 2013).

Interesting work has been done on the origins and movements of colour-ringed birds wintering between Watchet and Dunster Beach (Gladman 2004). These were from nests in Hungary, the Netherlands, Belgium, and Germany.

Little Gull – Winter

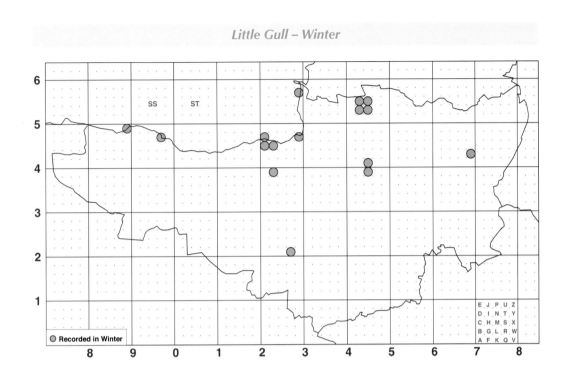

Mediterranean Gull – Winter

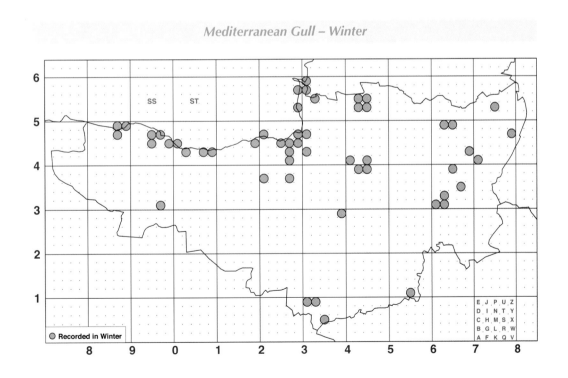

COMMON GULL *Larus canus*

In general, wintering Common Gulls prefer hill pastures in Somerset for feeding, but they usually roost at lower levels, either on the coast or on large reservoirs. In *WA 1981–84* they were shown as commonest along the Wiltshire border, on Mendip, and on the Brendons and the adjacent coast, but as almost entirely absent on the Levels and in the south (except at Cheddar and Sutton Bingham Reservoirs), in the Vale of Taunton Deane, and on the Blackdowns. The statement in *BA 2007–11* that they avoid 'uplands' evidently refers to higher ground than Somerset's modest hills.

For this Atlas the basic pattern shows little change: in much of lowland Somerset and on Exmoor there were hardly any records, the emptiest area being the Vale of Taunton Deane, where the three squares of ST22, 12, and 02 had only eight tetrads with Common Gulls between them. Most of the larger gatherings were in the east and on Mendip, where Torr Works Reservoir attracts up to 2,000 birds; there were over 1,000 at Wyke Champflower and Dimmer Tip, and on the Mendip Plateau around Charterhouse, where they have always been especially fond of the limestone grassland. In the five Mendip 10-km squares, they were present in 52 of the 87 tetrads. Many birds cross the Avon border at dusk to roost on Chew Valley Lake, which may hold up to 18,000. At Sutton Bingham Reservoir, where counts of up to 1,000 or more were once regular, there are now seldom as many as 100. Further west, up to 2,000 have roosted in Bridgwater Bay and 350 at either Wimbleball Lake or Dunster Beach. Erratic flocks may be found in many places where unusual feeding opportunities occur, for example on fields spread with slurry.

YELLOW-LEGGED GULL *Larus michahellis*

Until 2005, this expanding species was considered a race of the Herring Gull. There have been records since 1979 and annually since 1982. Of about 280 birds identified from 2005 to 2012, 70% were on autumn passage from July to October and 18% in the four winter months. Most have been found by careful inspection of gull flocks, particularly at Torr Works Reservoir. The summer floods of 2012 attracted up to six to the Blackmoor Vale.

CASPIAN GULL *Larus cachinnans*

The first Somerset record of this species, also recently split from the Herring Gull complex, was of a first-winter bird at Torr Works Reservoir in January 2007. A further three single birds, all in their first or second winter, were recorded during the Atlas period, also at Torr Works, but two of these were autumn migrants in September or October. A further record from Chard Reservoir remains under review.

Common Gull – Winter

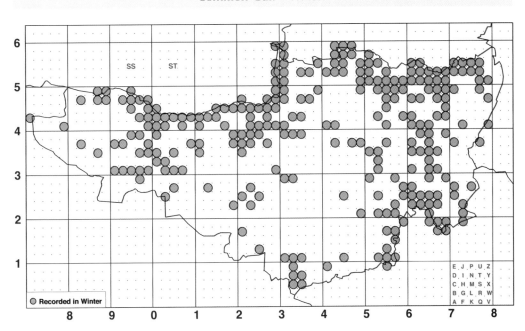

Yellow-legged Gull & Caspian Gull – Winter

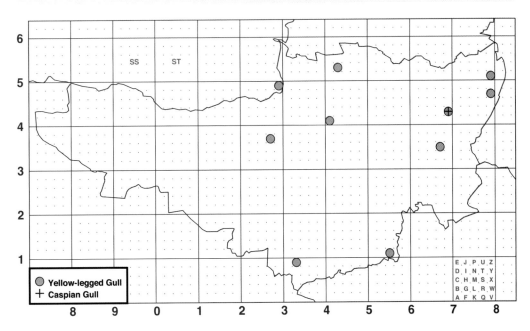

LESSER BLACK-BACKED GULL *Larus fuscus*

A breeding colony on Stert Island died out in 1979, but by that time the widespread use by the larger gulls of rubbish tips on the mainland had led them to attempt breeding on the roofs of nearby industrial buildings. Lesser Black-backs now breed at a number of sites, including Taunton, Bridgwater, Yeovil, Highbridge, Glastonbury, Hinkley Point, Chard Reservoir, Watchet, Williton, and Butlin's at Minehead. Some towns have successfully controlled the spread, so few sites hold more than ten pairs. The exceptions are Bridgwater, which has at least 75, despite the efforts of professional falconers, and Hinkley Point, with about 40. This species appears to prefer flatter sites than those chosen by Herring Gulls. In Avon, Bristol and Bath, Steep Holm and Weston-super-Mare now hold over 3,100 pairs between them (*NAvA*); there are also around 4,000 pairs on Flat Holm, East Glamorgan (Ross-Smith *et al.* 2013). In recent years, small numbers have sum-

mered on the Avalon Marshes, where two pairs bred on Shapwick Heath in 2005, but none were proved to do so during the Atlas period. Foraging birds can now be seen almost anywhere in Somerset, even on the Exmoor Plateau, but usually in smaller numbers than the Herring Gulls which they accompany.

Lesser Black-backs were once entirely migratory, arriving in Britain in February or March and leaving for South-west Europe and West Africa in September. In Somerset, the wintering habit developed in the 1950s and is strongly associated with the use of reservoirs as overnight roosts. Many do still migrate, but whereas *WA 1981–84* found birds in only 18 Somerset tetrads they are now widespread in winter, though scarce or absent in the western and southern hills. They are especially numerous at afternoon gathering grounds on their way to roost. Torr Works Reservoir has recently attracted up to 8,000 in winter, although the highest counts are in late autumn.

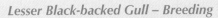

Lesser Black-backed Gull – Breeding

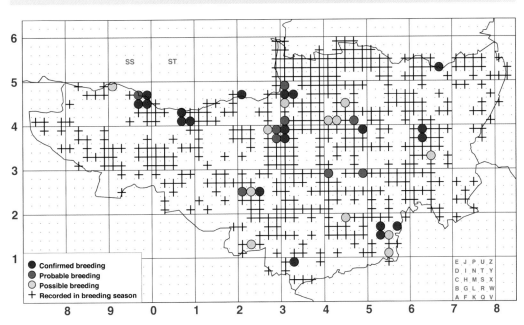

- ● Confirmed breeding
- ● Probable breeding
- ○ Possible breeding
- + Recorded in breeding season

Lesser Black-backed Gull – Winter

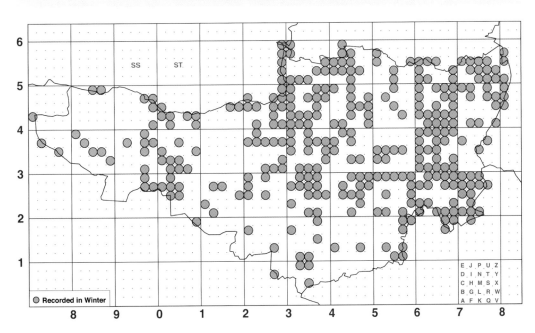

- ○ Recorded in Winter

HERRING GULL *Larus argentatus*

The history of breeding Herring Gulls is closely parallel to that of the Lesser Black-backed Gull, including a spread to urban sites from 1980. Avon, including Bath, Bristol and Steep Holm, now has some 3,000 pairs (*NAvA*), of which about half are urban. However, small numbers of Herring Gulls also bred regularly on cliffs from Minehead to Glenthorne and usually around Quantoxhead. Except at Hinkley Point, where they nest on the buildings, the Somerset coastal population has never recovered from a disastrous decline in the 1980s, and the only regular cliff-nesters are now the one or two pairs at Glenthorne, though a similar number have occasionally bred at Hurlstone Point and perhaps on the Ivy Stone below Culbone.

Much trouble has been taken to control urban breeders. The Taunton population, which had risen to over 100 pairs by 2005, has now been reduced to about 40, but Bridgwater, where suitable buildings continue to be erected near the M5, still holds at least 120. The largest colonies counted recently are at Hinkley Point Power Station, with up to 400 pairs, and at Butlin's, Minehead, where they have stabilised at about 120 pairs, concentrated on the restaurant roof. There are small numbers at Burnham, Highbridge, Street, Yeovil, Ilminster, Crewkerne, Chard, Wellington, Williton and Watchet; about 15 pairs breed in residential and industrial areas of Minehead.

Feeding flocks are widespread, but Herring Gulls are not particularly common on the Levels except when flooding is extensive, and the wintering map shows them as irregular or absent along the Wiltshire border. There are occasional counts of up to 1,500, the highest being of birds on their way to Chew Valley Lake on winter evenings. Many on the Exmoor coast move west to roost in Devon.

Herring Gull – Breeding

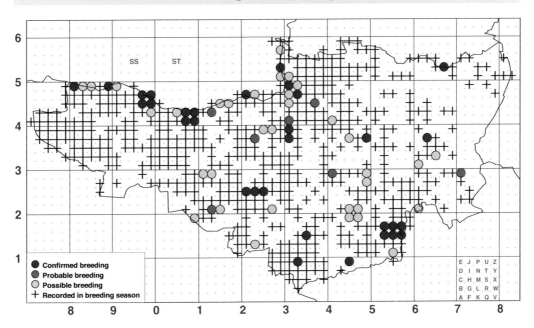

Legend:
- ● Confirmed breeding
- ● Probable breeding
- ○ Possible breeding
- + Recorded in breeding season

Herring Gull – Winter

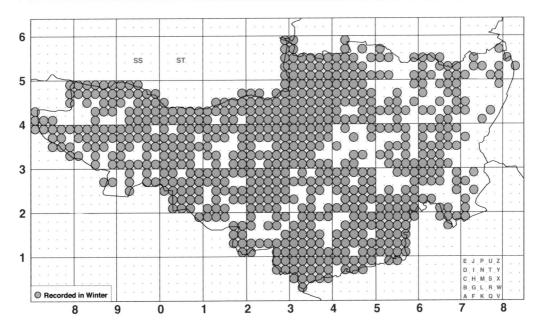

Legend:
- ○ Recorded in Winter

GREAT BLACK-BACKED GULL *Larus marinus*

As with the other commoner large gulls, there has long been a breeding colony on Steep Holm, which has yielded ringing recoveries in Somerset. Though there was a small colony on Stert Island from 1956 to 1981, and occasional pairs elsewhere along the coast west of Steart, there were no confirmed breeding records during the Atlas period. Three 'probable' or 'possible' records are shown on the map, including one for Hinkley Point, but it is not thought that breeding actually took place.

A few are always present along the coast, especially west of the Parrett. Their numbers do not vary much during the year; there can be up to 50 in Bridgwater Bay in early autumn and there are occasional double-figure counts from Dunster Beach. A few wander inland, where they can be met with almost anywhere, though they have been generally recorded at reservoirs or on flooded Levels; there is no apparent pattern to such forays.

ICELAND GULL

Larus glaucoides

During the Atlas period there were about 25: 18 at various inland sites and seven on the coast, though there may have been some duplication of records. There were single birds in November and December; all the rest were from January to May.

Four records, in three tetrads, fell within Somerset's Atlas period but not the national one, so are not in *BA 2007–11*.

GLAUCOUS GULL

Larus hyperboreus

Historically the numbers of records of Glaucous and Iceland Gulls are similar, but recently this species has been the scarcer. During the Atlas period there were six: four inland and two on the coast, and all from December to April.

Three records, in three tetrads, fell within Somerset's Atlas period but not the national one, so are not in *BA 2007–11*.

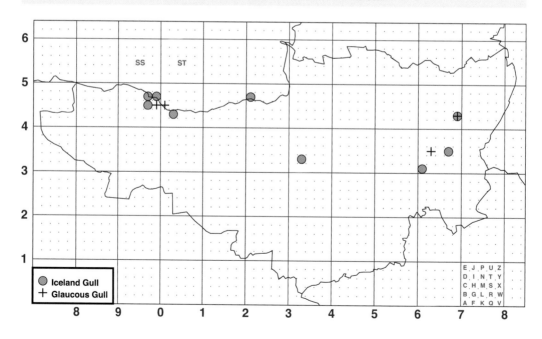

Iceland Gull & Glaucous Gull – Winter

172

Great Black-backed Gull – Breeding

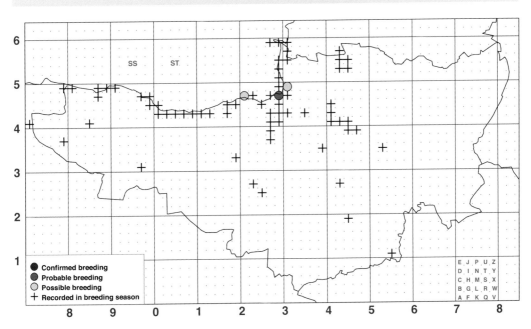

Legend:
- ● Confirmed breeding
- ● Probable breeding
- ● Possible breeding
- + Recorded in breeding season

Great Black-backed Gull – Winter

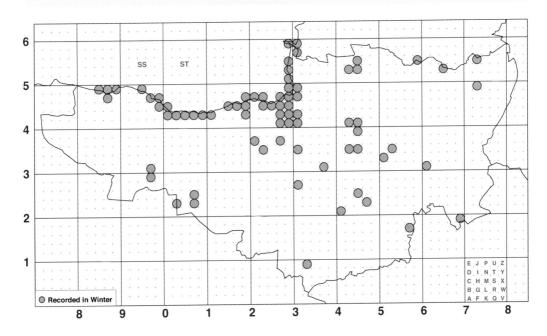

Legend:
- ● Recorded in Winter

FERAL PIGEON *Columba livia*

Most observers have little interest in this species, which is present in variable numbers in most towns and some rural areas. Records in the SOS database suggest that the highest concentrations are in Taunton; around Bridgwater they may have suffered from competition with urban gulls. The low figures for confirmed, or even probable, breeding may in part be due to their capability of year-round nesting, which is even more marked than in the Collared Dove. Feral Pigeons are probably commoner in lowland farmland than is generally recognised, and could have benefited from the increase in oilseed rape. The breeding map shows the general distribution fairly accurately, but it must be recognised that it is likely to be incomplete or inaccurate to an unknown extent. Records have very likely been distorted in both directions: some observers may have ignored Feral Pigeons altogether, while a few submitted records probably refer to ornamental birds from garden dovecotes.

There are no Feral Pigeon population figures for Somerset towns. However, those of Bristol were studied 20 years ago, when the late John Tully (1993) found about 11,000 birds within the City limits in the winter of 1991/92.

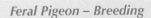

Feral Pigeon – Breeding

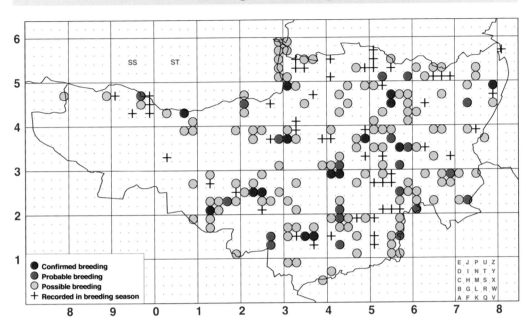

Legend:
- ● Confirmed breeding
- ● Probable breeding
- ○ Possible breeding
- + Recorded in breeding season

Feral Pigeon – Winter

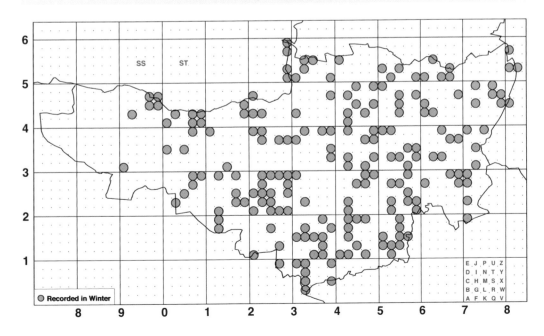

Legend:
- ○ Recorded in Winter

STOCK DOVE *Columba oenas*

There has been a long history of advances and retreats (Ballance 2006). In the 1950s and 1960s Stock Doves seem to have suddenly increased, with winter flocks of up to 300 and increased nesting in farm buildings: the use of pesticides and the felling of elms worked against them nationally, but apparently not in Somerset.

Within the Atlas period, during the breeding season birds were present in 56% of tetrads, though records were scarcer on higher ground, in areas with little arable, and in towns: for example, on Mendip, around Shepton Mallet, Taunton and Bridgwater, on King's Sedge Moor, along much of the Wiltshire border, and on the seaward Levels traversed by the M5. The abundance map in *BA 2007–11* suggests that Stock Doves are commonest in arable country south and east of the Poldens, extending towards the Dorset border. In farmland, mature hedgerow trees, copses, and outbuildings are used for nesting. The species breeds widely in Mendip quarries, and many of the

larger farms in the western hills have breeding pairs in isolated barns, especially on the Brendons with their higher acreage of arable, though the birds are seldom conspicuous and need to be searched out. The peak season for breeding is in late summer, after the end of the Atlas survey period; up to five broods can be reared in a year.

In *WA 1981–84*, there were no records in four 10-km squares; in 12, fewer than 15 birds were reported. The winter map here shows an apparent contraction of the summer range by about 12%, though scattered pairs are less conspicuous outside the period of the far-carrying song and may have been missed. There may also have been a lack of immigrants: whereas in the 1980s and early 1990s flocks of up to 500 were sometimes found, and there was even a record of 1,100 at Witcombe Bottom in 1983, there have recently been only a few counts of over 50. In Avon, too, the numbers in winter flocks have fallen steeply.

Stock Dove – Breeding

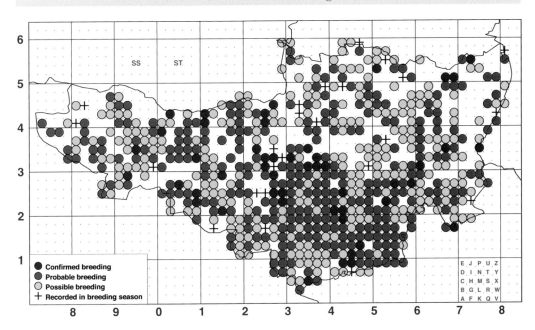

- ● Confirmed breeding
- ● Probable breeding
- ○ Possible breeding
- + Recorded in breeding season

Stock Dove – Winter

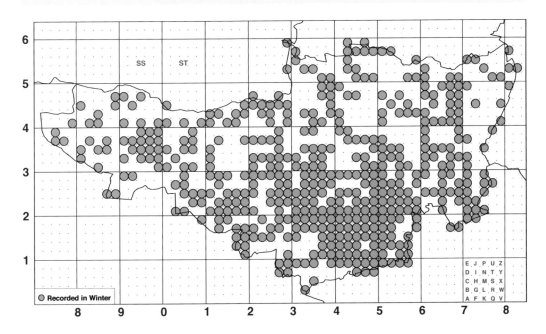

- ○ Recorded in Winter

WOODPIGEON *Columba palumbus*

It has always been a very common bird, though numbers have perhaps been slightly smaller than in counties with a higher proportion of arable. Wood-pigeons benefited from the extension of conifer plantations in the last century; more recently, oilseed rape and game crops have provided some compensation for lack of winter stubbles. The species has steadily and almost imperceptibly become a common bird of suburban housing, perching on television aerials and foraging along roads in early mornings. Distribution was probably almost universal by 1970, with breeding in all tetrads apart from a few on Exmoor.

Large flocks, chiefly of immigrants, have always been noted, but seem to have increased in recent years. They arrive rather suddenly in late October, when many cross the Bristol Channel from Wales at first light and rapidly disperse inland. Most flocks are of fewer than 500. The 9,000 put up by one gunshot from above West Sedge Moor on 6 December 2008 was by far the largest single flock ever reported; they had evidently been attracted by the acorn crop.

Woodpigeon – Breeding

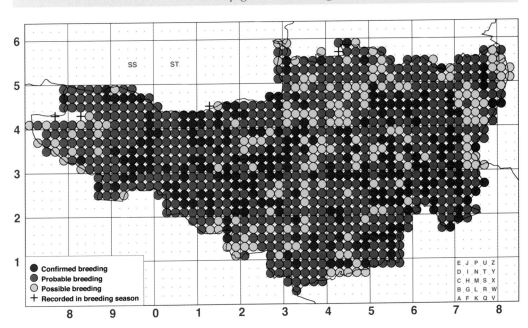

- ● Confirmed breeding
- ● Probable breeding
- ○ Possible breeding
- + Recorded in breeding season

Woodpigeon – Winter

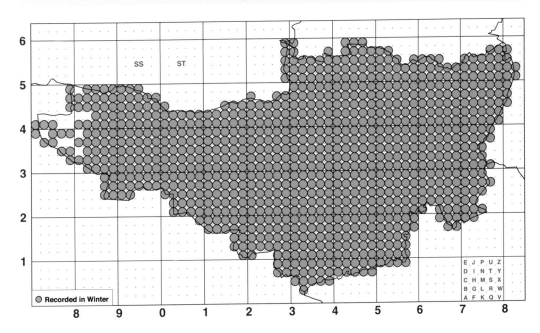

- ● Recorded in Winter

COLLARED DOVE *Streptopelia decaocto*

Collared Doves first reached Somerset in 1963, and spread rapidly, first along the coast and then inland. In *BA 1968–72*, they were found breeding in all but about six 10-km squares and by 1991 they were absent only from the north-west corner of Exmoor. They are hardly ever out of sight of human settlements.

The rapid expansion up to 1975 was followed by some contraction, as granaries controlled or excluded flocks, which had sometimes reached several hundred. Some surprising gaps appeared in *WA 1981–84*. There has been some thinning out over the last five years, where hard winters may have taken their toll and Woodpigeons have assumed control in suburbs. It is noteworthy that some villages in an area may have many Collared Doves, whereas others, apparently similar in habitat, have none. In more rural tetrads not all farms hold pairs. Confirmation of nesting can be affected by the long breeding season, from February to October. Taking the county as a whole, Collared Doves are present in all 10-km squares, but not in all tetrads, varying between 50% to 100% of tetrads in any 10-km square. They are least recorded in parts of the Levels, along the Wiltshire border, and on Exmoor.

Most Collared Doves are probably sedentary, though occasional explorers are met with in unlikely places. If both seasons are taken into account, about three-quarters of all tetrads are occupied, and most of the slight discrepancy between winter and summer records may be accounted for by the greater ease with which calling and displaying birds can be picked up in the breeding season. In the wintry uplands, birds often feed inside open-ended barns, and many are drawn to garden bird feeders.

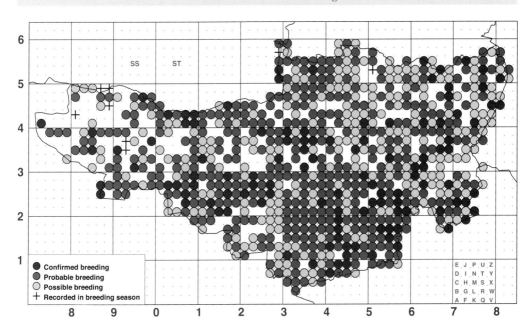

Collared Dove – Breeding

Legend:
- Confirmed breeding
- Probable breeding
- Possible breeding
- + Recorded in breeding season

Collared Dove – Winter

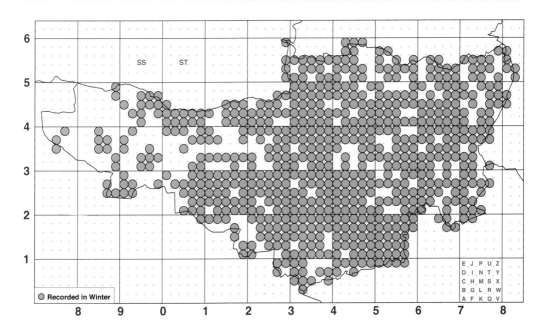

Legend:
- Recorded in Winter

TURTLE DOVE *Streptopelia turtur*

At the extreme north-western end of their summer range, Turtle Doves were always local in Somerset, where they generally shunned high ground without arable and the barer sections of the lowlands. A marked decline, which began about 1965, accelerated from the late 1980s, even in favoured areas such as the south-east end of the Poldens. In *BA 1968–72* they were absent from only five 10-km squares, mostly in the west. However, *NBA 1988–91* could confirm breeding in only seven and presence in 13 out of the Somerset total of 34 10-km squares.

As elsewhere, the decline has continued, and there has been no proof of breeding in Somerset since the early 1990s, though it probably continued until about 1998. Song was heard at a site in the Brendons in 2008 and two birds were seen in the same area in August 2010 (not mapped). Somerset is now well beyond the boundary of the breeding range shown in *BA 2007–11*, and most of the few records in recent years have been of obvious migrants; in 2011 no records were submitted to SOS, for the first time ever.

CUCKOO *Cuculus canorus*

It is likely that few current Somerset children have ever heard a Cuckoo. This harbinger of spring was widespread until the late 1960s, but during the next decade losses began to be reported in lowland farmland, especially in the south. By the time of *BA 1968–72*, birds were still present in every 10-km square, but more thinly spread. By 2002 SOS records showed 16 10-km squares in the east, the south, and the Brendons with only one contact or none. However, the position was probably not quite as bad as this appears, since coverage outside the Atlas period has often been thin except in popular areas.

Most Atlas records were from Exmoor, where Cuckoos still flourish among the Meadow Pipits in heather and grass moorland, and where 2011 and 2012 were particularly good years. They are also widespread on Quantock moorland. On Mendip, the only regular site was Rowberrow Warren. Birds are still found widely on the Levels, but the only area in which Cuckoos are frequently recorded is the Avalon Marshes, where Reed Warblers are their primary victims. The years from 2010 to 2012 apparently saw a slight improvement on farmland in many parts,

though this may be mainly a product of increased coverage because of Atlas searches. The map may overstate the breeding distribution, since some of the 'possible' entries may be of late-spring migrants.

Away from the wetlands, the main lowland host has always been the Dunnock, which has suffered only local declines in range. It is reasonable to suggest that the losses of breeding Cuckoos have been mainly due to a shortage of food, especially the larger caterpillars, which remain common on moorland; it appears that Dartmoor has also suffered no notable decline. The abundance map in *BA 2007–11* emphasises the importance of this habitat, for in Cornwall Bodmin Moor and the Penwith and Lizard Moors are still key sites; further afield Central and Northern Scotland and the West of Ireland have retained large, and in some areas increasing, populations. Recent satellite tracking of birds by the BTO suggests that losses on migration may be high, and it is also possible that Cuckoos have been affected by the earlier breeding of Dunnocks.

Most breeders arrive from the last ten days of April and are gone by early July.

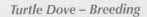

Turtle Dove – Breeding

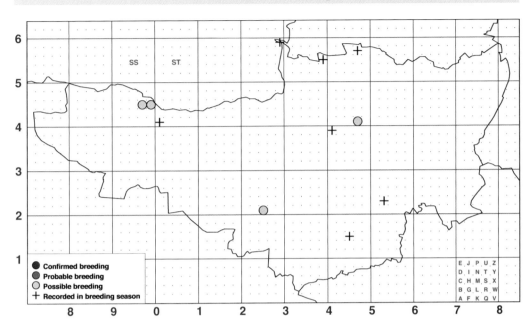

SS   ST

- ● Confirmed breeding
- ● Probable breeding
- ○ Possible breeding
- + Recorded in breeding season

E J P U Z
D I N T Y
C H M S X
B G L R W
A F K Q V

8   9   0   1   2   3   4   5   6   7   8

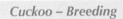

Cuckoo – Breeding

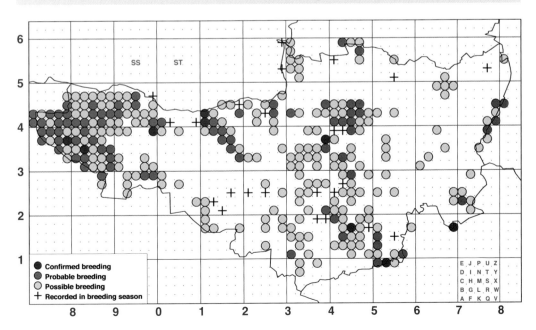

SS   ST

- ● Confirmed breeding
- ● Probable breeding
- ○ Possible breeding
- + Recorded in breeding season

E J P U Z
D I N T Y
C H M S X
B G L R W
A F K Q V

8   9   0   1   2   3   4   5   6   7   8

BARN OWL *Tyto alba*

A national RSPB survey in 1932 estimated 360 pairs within the old Somerset boundaries (Blaker 1934). Barn Owls were badly affected by cold winters in 1947 and from 1961 to 1963; the first of these almost eliminated them from Exmoor. There were ups and downs over the next 30 years. There was much disagreement on numbers: one national survey estimated a maximum of 156 pairs, but a more realistic local search suggested only 100 individuals (Shawyer 1987; Williams 1989). *BA 1968–72* found them present in all but three 10-km squares, of which two were on Exmoor. Ten years later, *WA 1981–84* recorded presence in 15 10-km squares, of which only two had more than a single bird; and *NBA 1988–91* showed a fragmented distribution, with a strong concentration on the Levels and, again, none on Exmoor, where coverage for nocturnal species was bound to be thin.

In the last 20 years much effort has gone into providing nest-boxes and there was some increase, at least in areas with ample rough grassland, as on the Levels. It was farmyard rodents that had supported a large population elsewhere. There have been many road casualties, perhaps more so as pastures have been 'improved' and the small-mammal populations surviving in the rough grass verges of busy main roads are likely to attract Barn Owls.

Normal Atlas visits to tetrads were naturally not very productive for nightbirds, and this species, as with other owls, was always likely to be under-recorded, though it was also difficult to find even in known haunts following prolonged harsh weather in two Atlas winters. An unknown but no doubt significant proportion of records came from contacts with local residents, often chance conversations, though some enterprising observers sought out farmers and landowners to ask them. There were regular sightings in many places in the east and on Mendip, and enough to suggest a number of breeding pairs on the Levels, in the south and on the Exmoor Plateau. Birds were recorded in 30% more tetrads in winter than in summer, perhaps because of the wider dispersal of the population and the greater likelihood of contacts by observers searching, or just travelling, in the earlier dusk.

We have no population estimates for the county, but in the 10-km squares allocated to Avon, which include 90 Somerset tetrads, the population had shrunk by 1992 to a mere ten pairs. By 2011, however, there were thought to be at least 50. Much good work has been done in recent years with installing nest-boxes; the Hawk and Owl Trust (HOT), the Somerset Wildlife Trust (SWT) and the Cam Valley Wildlife Group have all been active. Indeed the apparent concentration of breeding Barn Owls in the north-east of the county is largely due to the efforts of the last group in locating isolated pairs, whilst the Community Barn Owl Project, run jointly between HOT and SWT, has provided further useful records.

This species' fortunes since the end of the Atlas period have been mixed. Two cold winters had already had an effect in some areas, but in the disastrous summer of 2012, after a very warm spring, there was a widespread collapse both in the adult population and among nestlings (Sperring 2013). There were further losses in the cold periods of the following winter. By autumn 2013, it was thought that more than 80% of Somerset Barn Owls had been lost. However, there are some preliminary signs of a possible recovery in 2014, with three breeding pairs on Ham Wall RSPB reserve alone.

Barn Owl sponsored by Somerset Wildlife Trust

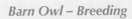

Barn Owl – Breeding

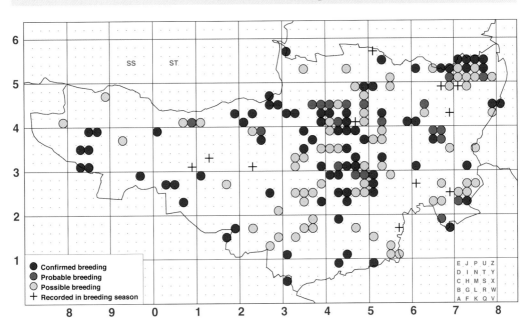

Barn Owl – Winter

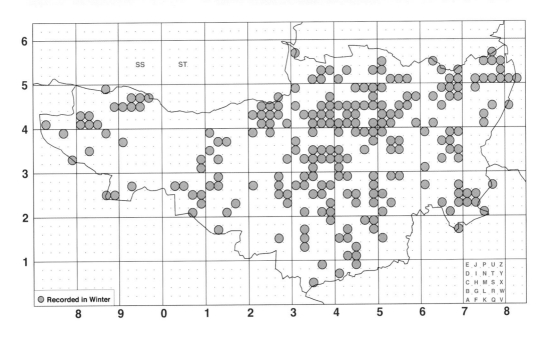

LITTLE OWL *Athene noctua*

Little Owls have now been present in Somerset for over a century, and by the 1920s they had spread to most lowland farmland, where they remained generally common until about 1990. They seldom reached the Exmoor Plateau, and have always been most numerous on the Levels, in old orchards, and in areas where stone walling is practised and there is a wide choice of nesting sites. This distribution is clearly shown in *BA 1968–72*, though coverage seems to have been reduced in *WA 1981–84* a decade later, when records in *SB* did not support the decline that it suggested in much of the county south of Mendip.

By 1990, a retreat had set in throughout the South West. In Somerset, they had been lost from seven 10-km squares in the east and south-west. From then to 2005, local surveys suggested that the Somerset population may have halved; the Breeding Bird Survey (BTO, JNCC, RSPB) found a 40% decline in distribution between 1995 and 2010 (Risley *et al.* 2012). This seems now to have stabilised, though there have been further local extinctions. If the seasonal maps are taken together, they suggest that Little Owls may be present in at least 20% of all tetrads. They remain most widely distributed on the Levels and along the coast west to the Williton area; there are scattered records in the east, on Mendip (where they are perhaps under-recorded in inaccessible quarries), in Central Somerset and in the south, but they thin out towards the south-west and are absent from the highest parts of the Blackdowns, and from the Brendons and Exmoor.

Many potential nesting sites have been lost in recent decades through the conversion or demolition of old farm buildings. The grubbing out of old orchards may also be a factor in local declines.

Little Owl sponsored by Steve Pilkington

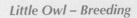

Little Owl – Breeding

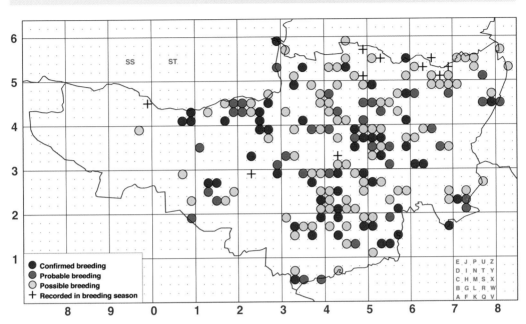

Little Owl – Winter

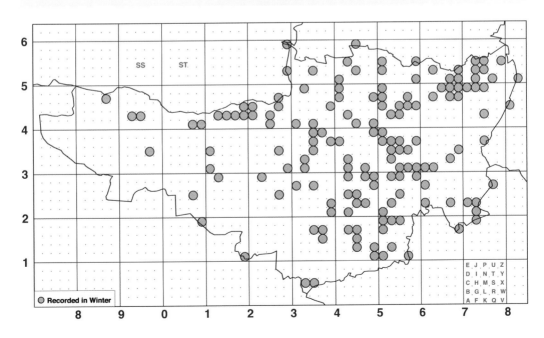

TAWNY OWL *Strix aluco*

It has always been generally distributed except in a few areas with little woodland. If the seasonal maps are taken together, Tawny Owls were present in 47% of all tetrads. They are certainly absent from large areas of the barer lowlands, such as the coastal Levels and King's Sedge Moor, and from the edges of Bridgwater Bay, as well as from the treeless uplands. Owls are always likely to be under-recorded, to an unknown extent, and it is likely to be no different here. Some observers made considerable efforts to locate Tawny Owls, either by their own visits or through contacts with local landowners and residents, and appeals to SOS members produced more records, but circumstances did not permit the organisation of large-scale targeted searches. Nonetheless we have achieved better coverage than for previous Atlases: *WA 1981–84* shows large blanks, including two Exmoor 10-km squares with much ancient woodland.

Nationally, the Tawny Owl is thought to have undergone a 'shallow decline'. In Somerset the position is unclear: it seems hard to believe that it is really absent from quite so many tetrads in some areas, such as the east side of the Brendons, where there is much suitable habitat, but equally, repeated visits to some suitable sites in ST52 and ST74, for example, continued to draw a blank.

Tawny Owl sponsored by Jayne Webber

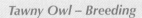

Tawny Owl – Breeding

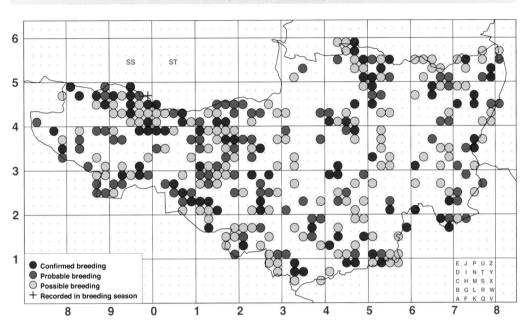

- ● Confirmed breeding
- ● Probable breeding
- ○ Possible breeding
- + Recorded in breeding season

Tawny Owl – Winter

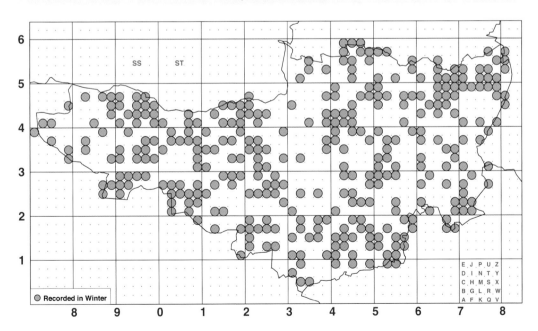

○ Recorded in Winter

LONG-EARED OWL *Asio otus*

Historically, published breeding records in the county have come from a wide variety of sites: in the east, on Mendip, on the Levels, on the Blackdowns, and on the Brendons or Exmoor. During the Atlas period breeding was confirmed (not necessarily every year) at two or three Mendip sites, and at others on the coast of Bridgwater Bay, and on the Quantocks and Brendons. Given that this species is rare and at the edge of its range in Somerset, a certain level of secrecy has to be maintained; SOS does not publish the exact location of known sites, and they are mapped here conventionally within 10-km squares. While a few sites have been occupied regularly for several years (over 20 years for one Mendip site), and the general feeling among local observers is that Long-eared Owls are probably commoner in the county than we know, it is still not clear whether we can claim that a permanent population has ever been truly established.

A number of small and irregular winter roosts have also been found over the years, though none could be said to be in use during the Atlas period, when most of the dozen or so winter records were of single birds, often seen on only one occasion. These are not mapped.

SHORT-EARED OWL *Asio flammeus*

Numbers of wintering and passage birds have always been highly irregular: annual totals prior to the Atlas ranged from 64 (in 1982/83) down to only six. There has been some general decline in recent years, but this was offset by a very large influx of migrants in 2011/12, Somerset's last Atlas winter, but beyond the limits of *BA 2007–11*. Wintering birds generally arrive in October or November and remain to March, though they occasionally linger into April or even later. They are most frequently recorded on the Levels and around the Parrett Estuary; hardly any observers visit Exmoor in winter, and it is likely that Short-eared Owls are more frequent on the grass moorland than the records show.

The striking influx in 2011 began with one at Berrow on 23 September. Most arrived in October/November and about 70 had been seen by the end of the year. Many of these remained for the winter, and there was some passage in early spring. Most were on the Levels and along the coast, but there were small numbers on Mendip and Exmoor, especially on the Forest. Groups of up to five were frequent, and there were even nine on Aller Moor.

A few, probably first-year birds, lingered throughout the summer of 2012; however, there was no evidence of any nesting attempt. Breeding has previously been confirmed on a handful of occasions, but the last was on Exmoor in 1977, though it was suspected on the Levels in 1979.

Short-eared Owl sponsored in memory of Malcolm Eric White

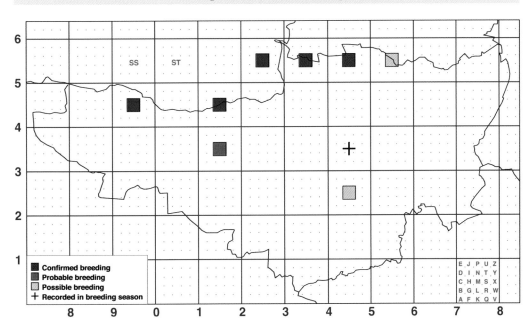

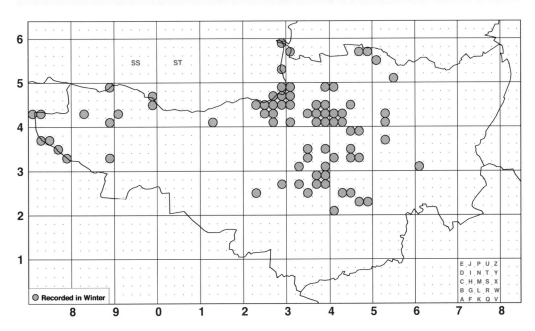

NIGHTJAR *Caprimulgus europaeus*

Our knowledge of the Nightjar's recent distribution depends largely on work done for national surveys in 1981 (Gribble 1983), 1992 (Morris *et al.* 1994) and 2004 (Conway *et al.* 2007), and on organised annual searches of recognised sites, which have been widely practised over the last decade on the Quantocks, the Brendons, and Exmoor (Ballance 2006). The national surveys recorded 50 churring males in Somerset in 1981, rising to 147 in 2004; there was some real increase over this period, but most was almost certainly due to better coverage. In 2004, about 80 were found on the Brendons and Exmoor: the main areas were conifer plantations and heaths between Croydon Hill and Selworthy Beacon, and on Dunkery Hill, with outliers on Willett Hill and Haddon Hill. Numbers had been remarkably steady from year to year, but in the last Atlas summer of 2012 some losses were noticed, and there was little or no improvement in 2013. A decline in the acreage of clear-fell has now been reversed by widespread removal of larches in 2011/12. Nightjars have suffered recently from cold late-summer weather, which has frustrated the production of second broods.

Birds usually arrive in the second or third week of May and depart in August. At the end of the season they are under-recorded, since churring falls off after July.

SWIFT *Apus apus*

Swifts are with us for less than four months. All towns and most larger villages have a few pairs, but, as Perrins commented in *NBA 1988–91*, no-one has been able to make an estimate of their numbers 'in any reliable, quantitative way'. Even the authors of *NAvA 2007–11*, otherwise eager to present accurate figures, declined a population estimate, as it would be 'pure guesswork'. Local colonies are best viewed in the evening, and an observer in late morning could be unaware of their existence. The highest concentration is probably in Taunton, where a colony at Musgrove Park was studied by Holdsworth (2004), and an extensive survey by Leech (2013) identified 17 'clusters' during the Atlas period, amounting to about 150 occupied nests. Most were found in Victorian and 1930s housing, and none in church towers, popular sites elsewhere.

Swifts may feed miles away from their nests; they are, for instance, a common sight over Exmoor grassland in midsummer. Due caution was applied by many Atlas observers in recording Swifts, though it is likely that some of the 'possible breeding' records in more rural tetrads also refer to feeding flocks from colonies elsewhere. Young birds arrive after breeders and they may appear in flocks or visit buildings where they are not actually breeding. Numbers in the national Breeding Bird Survey have fallen by about 30% since 1995 and this accords with a general impression that Swifts have declined in Somerset too, perhaps through losses of suitable sites, perhaps because of recent cool summers. Nevertheless, the map shows this species to be widespread throughout most suitable areas of habitat in Somerset.

Nightjar sponsored by Nigel Banks and Terry Gifford
Swift sponsored by John Matthews and Peter Bright

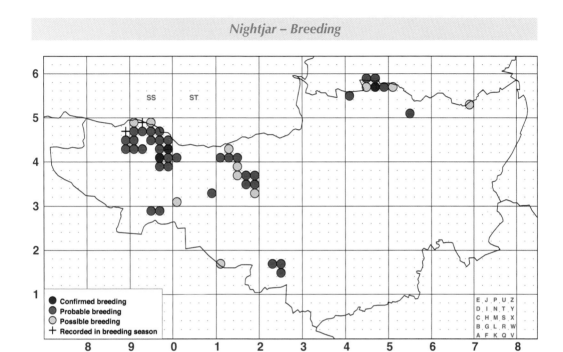

Nightjar – Breeding

- ● Confirmed breeding
- ● Probable breeding
- ○ Possible breeding
- + Recorded in breeding season

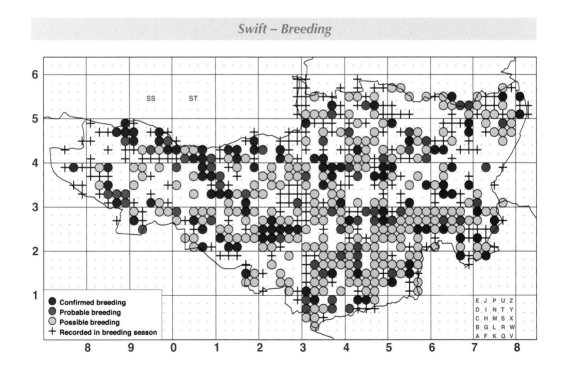

Swift – Breeding

- ● Confirmed breeding
- ● Probable breeding
- ○ Possible breeding
- + Recorded in breeding season

KINGFISHER *Alcedo atthis*

The distribution of such a brilliant and noisy species should be easy to establish, but Kingfishers are easily missed, since the banks of suitable rivers and pits may not be readily accessible. Breeding was confirmed in only about ten 10-km squares for *NBA 1988–91*, where the greatest concentration was in the south and south-west rather than on the Levels. In the present Atlas period, it was confirmed in 23 10-km squares, including most of those on the Levels. Most Kingfishers are found along the lower reaches of rivers and on ponds, disused pits and reservoirs. On Exmoor, distribution is restricted to the Exe and the Barle; even where the fishing is good, there are few suitable banks beyond these rivers.

After breeding, there can be rapid dispersal, so it cannot be assumed that birds in June and July are from nests in the tetrad where they are seen. Kingfishers were recorded in 239 tetrads in winter and in 221 in summer, but overall in a total of 326: this points to high mobility among the residents and to some passage or immigration, which was more likely in the two coldest of the five winters of the Atlas. The effects of the early-winter freeze-up in 2010 were particularly severe, as evidenced by records submitted to SOS falling 23% in 2011 compared to the previous year. In both cold Atlas winters there were many coastal reports, as can be seen in the pattern of records around Bridgwater Bay; the streams of the moors west and south of Cheddar, fed by Mendip springs, also proved to be attractive ice-free refuges.

In winter, the Levels as a whole have usually been among the three most important Wetland Bird Survey (WeBS) sites in England. The other two sites elsewhere are small groups of gravel pits and may represent far greater concentrations than occur in Somerset. Counts from the Levels of up to 22 birds cannot be more than a sample of the birds present in most years.

Kingfisher sponsored by DJEnvironmental (Tim Davis and Tim Jones)

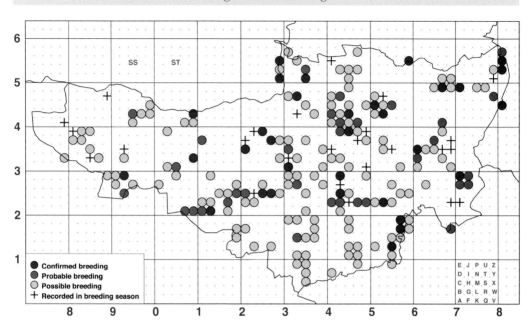

Kingfisher – Breeding

Confirmed breeding
Probable breeding
Possible breeding
+ Recorded in breeding season

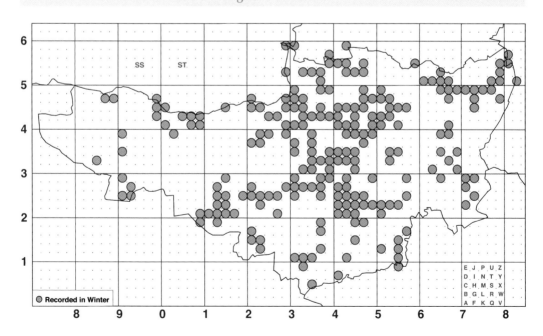

Kingfisher – Winter

Recorded in Winter

GREEN WOODPECKER *Picus viridis*

It has always been considered a common and sedentary resident, and is, or ought to be, a notably conspicuous species. Yet even in areas with ant-rich grassland and old timber its presence may not be obvious, especially as the peak time for the far-carrying call (the 'yaffle' that gives it its old country name) is in March. Atlas results confirm that it is scarce on the Mendip Plateau and across the barer parts of the Levels, where the high water-table is a deterrent to an ant-hunter and there is little timber suitable for nesting. It is missing from more than half of the tetrads on the Brendons and Exmoor, where it is common only in the heavily wooded valleys of the north-east. On the other hand, at least three-quarters of all tetrads across South and South-east Somerset were occupied, though it proved more difficult to confirm breeding, as evidenced by the high proportion of 'possible breeding' records. The noticeable concentration of confirmed and probable breeding records in the Yeovil area (especially ST51) may be due to particularly skilful and diligent searching.

There is a comment in *WA 1981–84* on scarcity in the South West, which was attributed to poor coverage. Winter records ran at about 83% of summer ones, presumably because calling is reduced. Numbers were certainly affected nationally by the hard winter of 1981/82, after which they recovered in four years, and local shortages are likely to have followed the winters of 2009/10 and 2010/11. These can, indeed, be seen in the results for ST63 (the Castle Cary and Bruton area), where most winter coverage was towards the end of the Atlas period, and the number of tetrads with records fell from a summer high of 22 to a winter low of only eight. On the other hand, records received by SOS rose from 199 in 2011 to 299 in 2012, and even if we allow for deliberate Atlas targeting, this must indicate some recovery.

Green Woodpecker sponsored by Liz and David Rayner

Green Woodpecker – Breeding

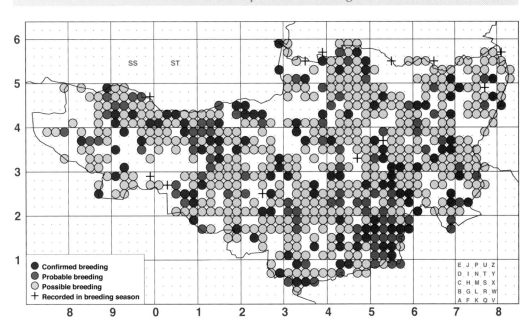

Legend:
- ● Confirmed breeding
- ● Probable breeding
- ○ Possible breeding
- + Recorded in breeding season

Green Woodpecker – Winter

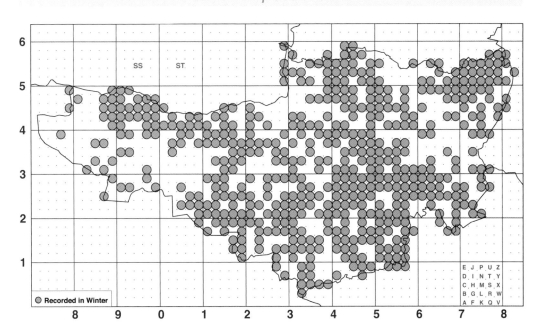

Legend:
- ● Recorded in Winter

GREAT SPOTTED WOODPECKER *Dendrocopos major*

In the early part of the 20th century Great Spotted
Woodpeckers were apparently scarce throughout
the county, but they steadily increased so that by
1940 they were probably universally distributed in
the county except on parts of the Levels, around the
Parrett Estuary, and on Exmoor Forest (which like
similar 'forests' in Scotland is largely bare moorland). This remains the case today; overall, 85% of
tetrads returned records for one or both seasons. We
have no population estimates, but records from Avon
reflect the national trend, suggesting that the population may have trebled there since 1992, though an
estimate of six pairs per tetrad seems high for parts
of lowland Somerset.

The reasons for the population explosion in this
species are probably both varied and complex; they
no doubt benefited from the spread of Dutch Elm
Disease in the 1960s, but by 1990 that advantage
will have been exhausted. The species does not seem
to have suffered from recent hard winters, perhaps
because of the support given by garden feeders
(Smith and Smith 2013), which are useful when
searching for several species. The loss of competition
from woodland Starlings may have provided more
nest-holes (Smith 2005).

A surprising number of coastal migrants have
been recorded in recent autumns, so it seems likely
that there are winter visitors added to the resident
birds, which probably do not wander far.

Great Spotted Woodpecker sponsored by Dave Bodley

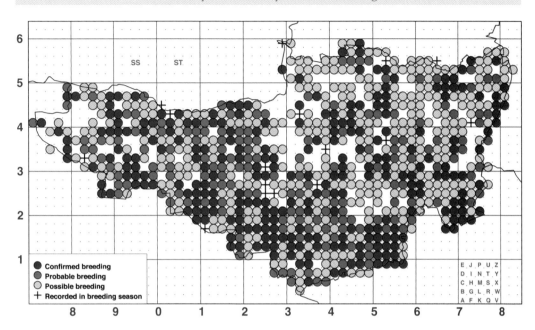

Great Spotted Woodpecker – Breeding

Confirmed breeding
Probable breeding
Possible breeding
+ Recorded in breeding season

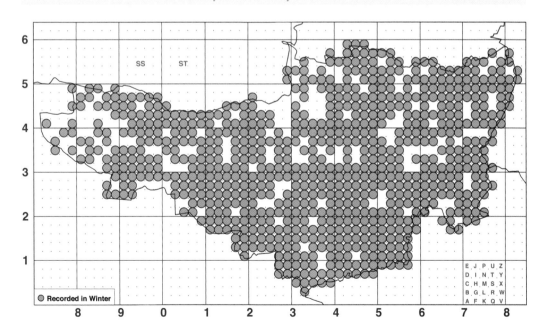

Great Spotted Woodpecker – Winter

Recorded in Winter

LESSER SPOTTED WOODPECKER *Dendrocopos minor*

The Lesser Spotted Woodpecker's story is a sad one. No widespread decline was suggested before *BA 1968–72*, though the species was recorded in only about half the county; except in the west, it was absent from the coast, and also from parts of East Somerset and the Bridgwater area. Ten years later it was found in only nine 10-km squares for *WA 1981–84* and in about the same number for *NBA 1988–91*. By then the disappearance of the high elms which were such a feature of Central and South Somerset until the 1970s was nearly complete, removing many nesting sites and breaking the chains of high timber that enabled birds to move around. Over the last 40 years, the British population has fallen by at least 70%, and it has been suggested that the greatest losses have been in a diagonal belt across southern England where elms were a dominant species. This gap can readily be traced on both the national distribution maps in *BA 2007–11*. An additional factor in Somerset is likely to have been the disappearance of many old cider orchards.

With such an unobtrusive species, it was hoped that more would be found during the intensive effort of Atlas fieldwork. In fact there have been very few: from 2005 to 2007 (before this began), SOS records came from 44 sites, with annual totals of from 15 to 25; in the five years from 2008 to 2012 they came from only 50, most regularly from East Mendip along the Mells River, the Quantocks, and the Horner Valley. Of course the month when they are perhaps most noticeable, calling and drumming, is March and thus outside either Atlas season, but March records from the SOS database do not add to the distribution mapped here.

Breeding was confirmed only at West Camel and in the Horner Valley, but is difficult to prove; probable breeding was recorded in 17 other tetrads, mostly in known areas for the species, and it is reasonable to assume that breeding actually did take place in these tetrads at least once during the Atlas period. As the species is so sedentary, this may also hold true for the 20 tetrads where possible breeding was recorded. Apart from sites already mentioned, these were mainly in the southern lowlands, which were once the heartland of this species' distribution. There could easily be undiscovered populations, and at least one known site (Langford Heathfield) is missing from the map; a confirmed breeding record from 10-km square ST12 was almost certainly from this area, but the tetrad could not be identified.

Lesser Spotted Woodpecker – Breeding

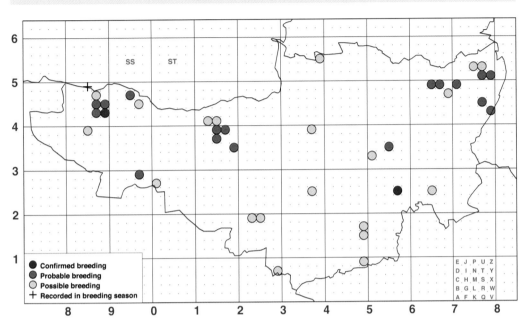

- ● Confirmed breeding
- ● Probable breeding
- ○ Possible breeding
- + Recorded in breeding season

SS ST

E J P U Z
D I N T Y
C H M S X
B G L R W
A F K Q V

Lesser Spotted Woodpecker – Winter

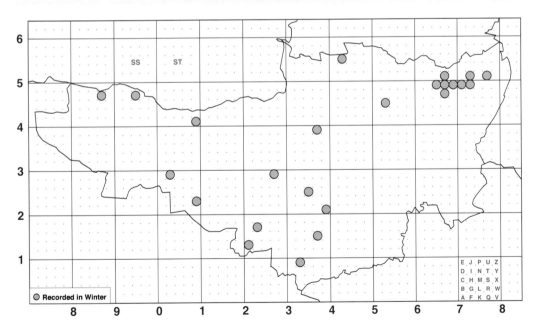

SS ST

○ Recorded in Winter

E J P U Z
D I N T Y
C H M S X
B G L R W
A F K Q V

MAGPIE *Pica pica*

No species is more conspicuous or familiar. Magpies are nearly universal in Somerset, except that they do not breed above the tree limit on Exmoor and the Quantocks; on the latter they seem surprisingly scarce even at lower levels, perhaps because of control by shooting estates. There appeared to be a surge in numbers in Somerset during the 1980s, when roost counts at Berrow sometimes rose to 150. Since then, numbers have generally levelled out, or even decreased, so that there have been no recent reports of over 30. Persecution of this species continues in a number of areas, but it is not clear whether this has caused anything more than very local losses. Magpies seem to have become much commoner in towns, wherever trees have provided nest sites, and any early riser can see how they benefit from road kills. *BA 2007–11* makes it clear, indeed, that the highest densities are urban, and this

can be seen in the abundance map there with regard to Bridgwater, Yeovil, and Taunton. As expected with this essentially sedentary species, the winter distribution differs little from that in the breeding-season map.

Proof, and even probability, of breeding have in all likelihood been understated in some tetrads, perhaps because the large nests, conspicuous in March and April, are much more difficult to see by May. In reality it is highly probable that Magpies bred in all or almost all tetrads in which they were recorded. There are many parties of non-breeders about in summer, and observers have understandably hesitated to assume that they are recent fledglings from the tetrads where they were seen.

Wintering birds were similarly recorded in almost every tetrad in Somerset, as would be expected for this omnivorous species.

Magpie – Breeding

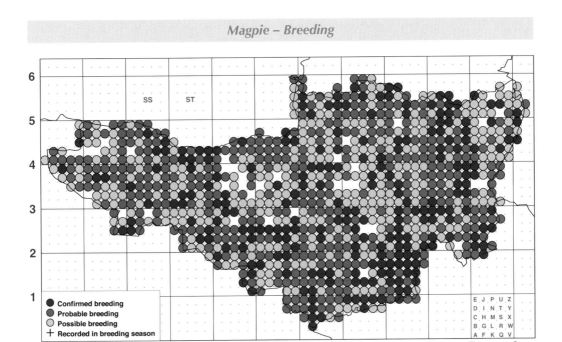

Legend:
- ● Confirmed breeding
- ● Probable breeding
- ○ Possible breeding
- + Recorded in breeding season

Magpie – Winter

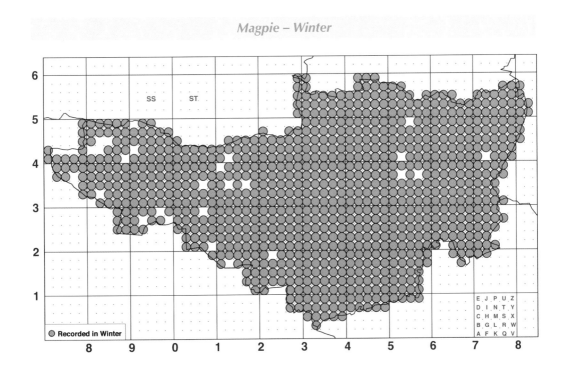

Legend:
- ● Recorded in Winter

JAY *Garrulus glandarius*

Unfortunately, Jays are most obvious and mobile in autumn, when they move more freely between woods in search of acorns. In the breeding season they can be remarkably difficult to find, being heard rather more often than seen; consequently there are very few records of confirmed nesting. Even at the 'possible' level, they were found in only 53% of all tetrads. *BA 1968–72* showed a scarcity over most of the Levels; this was supported by *NBA 1988–91*, in which parts of the south and east and, unexpectedly, also Exmoor and the Brendons, showed presence rather than breeding. A shortage of thick cover and of oaks will mean few Jays, and they are always scarcer where woodland is fragmented, as it is on most of the Levels. All three previous national atlases showed gaps in the Bridgwater area, and the biggest gaps in distribution today are around Bridgwater Bay, on the coastal Levels, and across King's Sedge Moor; areas which are almost without woodland. Even the Western Poldens do not provide a wide enough corridor for Jays in summer, but they are regular in the Avalon Marshes, which afford a lot of suitable cover. Further east they are commonly recorded again in the more wooded areas of Mendip, and in the eastern escarpment of Selwood Forest.

There are occasional invasions in autumn, the most remarkable being in 1983, when very large numbers came from the Continent following the failure of the acorn crop; another occurred in 2012, just after the Somerset Atlas period had finished.

Some national surveys, such as the Common Bird Census and the Breeding Bird Survey (cited by Brown and Grice 2005), have suggested that a 'shallow' decline took place in the last quarter of the 20th century, while *BA 2007–11* records a 15% increase from 1995 to 2010. Jays may still be killed legally on sporting estates, but it seems unlikely that such minor local persecution could now cause a general decline in the county.

This Atlas shows a very patchy distribution in both winter and breeding seasons; this is probably linked to the availability of both nesting and feeding habitats across Somerset. Jays were more likely to be seen in winter, when they occurred in 70% of all tetrads; combined winter and summer results record the species in 79%. They now enter gardens more freely than they once did, as noticed in *NAvA 2007–11* for the Bristol area; Yeovil seems to be fully occupied, even in the summer, but it is hard to explain apparent scarcity or absence around some other towns, such as Taunton and Frome. They are scarce on the western side of Exmoor, where there is little suitable habitat.

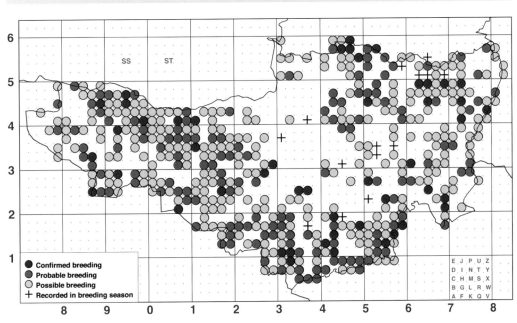

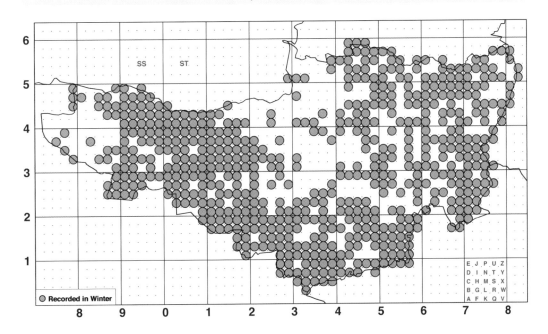

JACKDAW *Corvus monedula*

The Jackdaw has always been a very common Somerset bird, breeding in chimneys, industrial and agricultural buildings, churches, quarries, coastal cliffs, mature deciduous woodland and hedgerow trees, and in fact anywhere that provides suitable holes and crevices, though there seem to be no recent records of colonies in rabbit-holes. It occasionally breeds in rookeries, building open or domed nests. Both *NBA 1988–91* and *WA 1981–84* recorded some strange absences and shortages around Bridgwater and in parts of the south-west. These were probably accidents of coverage, or else infilling has occurred since then; the breeding map here shows few such gaps. In this Atlas Jackdaws are absent as breeding birds from some tetrads, largely on the Quantocks and Exmoor, but also around the Parrett Estuary and across King's Sedge Moor. They are perhaps most commonly recorded among the East Mendip quarries, as is suggested by *WA 1981–84* and by the abundance map in *BA 2007–11*. There is no obvious significance in the lack of confirmed breeding status along the eastern border of Somerset.

It is generally agreed that the British population has increased over the last 50 years; *BA 2007–11* records a growth of 131% from 1970 to 2010. Local proof of this in Somerset is found at Crewkerne, where the 40 pairs of 1975 had risen to 72 by 1998 (Parsons 1999). Outside the breeding season (and sometimes even during it) Jackdaws join Rooks in large flocks to feed communally on rough grassland and arable, and then to roost over the winter in adjacent woods. Others are efficient urban scavengers, and parties are often found in and around the large barns that are now characteristic of upland stock-farming in the west.

Small-scale coastal migration has often been noticed in autumn, especially in October, but most birds are sedentary during the winter within the feeding range of a few tetrads.

The winter map for this species shows a very similar distribution to that for breeding, clearly demonstrating the sedentary nature of Jackdaws: they remain faithful to both site and pair.

Jackdaw sponsored by Rev. Robin Ray

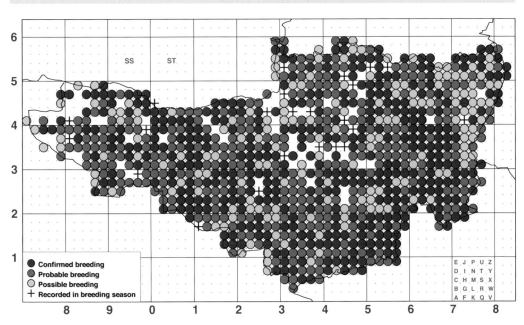

Jackdaw – Breeding

Jackdaw – Winter

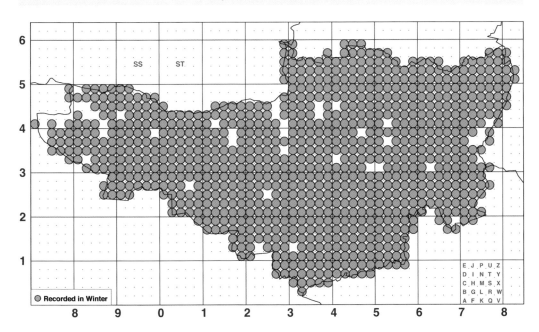

ROOK *Corvus frugilegus*

Surveys by Tucker (1935 and 1936) found 27,000 Rook nests within present-day Somerset, and Cohen (1944) suggested that there had been very little change in numbers or distribution. A BTO survey (Parsons 1976a,b), however, found 19,000 nests in Somerset. The post-war decrease has been attributed to the intensification of agriculture and the widespread use of pesticides, though the 1975 survey also coincided with the epidemic of Dutch elm disease. The population may have stabilised over the last 30 years, or shown a further slight loss. There have been many local variations, since Rooks often move for no obvious reason.

The highest nest counts over the last ten years have been of 305 at Cheddar Head Farm and 210 at Dunster Beach Wood. In Atlas work, only six rookeries of over 100 nests were reported, of which three, including Dunster Beach, were within the narrow coastal strip from West Quantoxhead to Minehead.

As with other corvids, their earlier breeding season militates against proof of breeding during Atlas fieldwork, as nests are less easy to find by mid-May, and some small rookeries may have been missed. Over the last couple of years of fieldwork, however, observers made great efforts to find the more obscure colonies in unvisited corners of farmland, particularly in March, which improved the percentage of tetrads with confirmed breeding considerably.

Over the county as a whole, breeding was confirmed in 53% of all tetrads, and was probable or possible in a further 24%; some possible records may refer to feeding flocks of foraging birds from outside the tetrad. Rookeries are least numerous in much of the urbanised corridor along the line of the M5, from Burnham south to Taunton, in heavy woodland, in areas with little arable, and in the moorland of the west. It is hard to account for the apparently thin distribution in parts of the south-east, as some parts of this area were among the most frequently visited.

An attempt was made to assess the total number of Somerset nests, using the counts of rookeries and applying local averages from these to estimate the likely number of nests in all colonies. This gave a minimum of about 12,500 nests, implying the loss of about a third since 1976, very close to the 34% fall recorded in Avon between 2000 and 2009.

It is still legal to shoot Rooks, and the custom of 'thinning' birds in summer and autumn is still practised in places, particularly where villagers dislike their noise.

In winter Rooks are recorded in nearly all tetrads, except on high ground in the west and around the larger conurbations.

Rook sponsored by DDS Consultants Ltd.

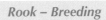

Rook – Breeding

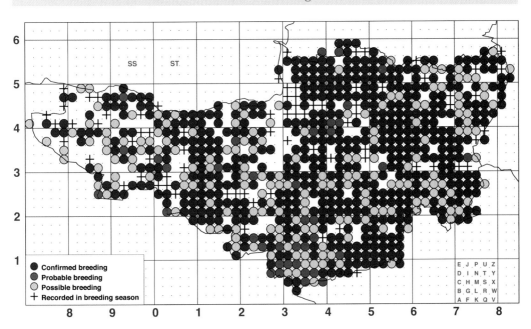

Legend:
- ● Confirmed breeding
- ● Probable breeding
- ○ Possible breeding
- + Recorded in breeding season

Rook – Winter

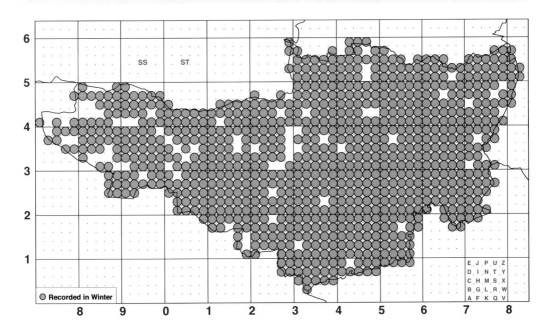

Legend:
- ○ Recorded in Winter

CARRION CROW *Corvus corone*

Researching the history of Carrion Crows in Somerset, Parsons (1978) concluded that in general they had always been common, despite some local populations being reduced by intensive keepering up to a century ago on East Somerset estates.

Presence during the breeding season is almost universal, although confirmation of breeding is somewhat less so, perhaps because Crows are early breeders and nests which are obvious in March and April have been missed in tetrads first visited in May. Observers may then have been reluctant to assign fledged young to a specific tetrad. Specific efforts were made in some areas in the March of both 2011 and 2012 to locate active nests. Although the map still shows a high proportion of 'probable' and 'possible' breeding, it seems likely that at least one pair

of Carrion Crows nested in nearly every tetrad in Somerset during the Atlas period. On the barer parts of Exmoor, they will nest in low beech hedges and hawthorns, even on walls, where nothing higher is available, and along the Bridgwater Bay coast they have occasionally bred in tide-wrack. Electricity pylons have been used since the 1930s.

Carrion Crows hold the rare distinction of being recorded in every single tetrad in winter, even on the barest moorland tops. Large wintering flocks are not merely a modern phenomenon, as sometimes supposed. Congregations of up to 200 are frequent, and up to 1,000 have gathered at roosts. Even in summer, flocks of up to 150 non-breeders have been reported on the coast.

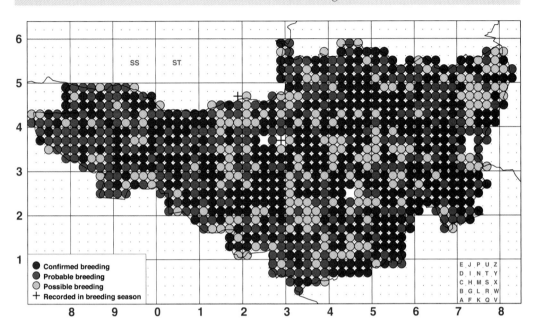

Carrion Crow – Breeding

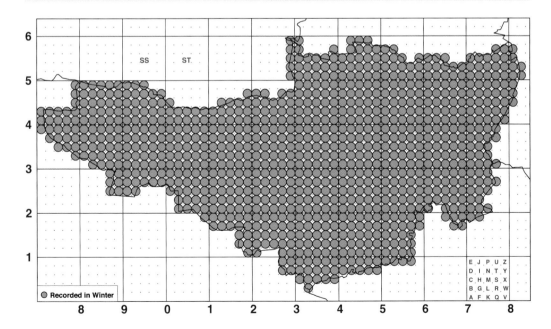

Carrion Crow – Winter

RAVEN *Corvus corax*

At the start of the 20th century, because of persecution particularly by sheep farmers, Ravens were mostly restricted to the uplands, chiefly in the far west of the county. Gradually they spread eastward over the Brendons, where abandoned slate quarries became available, along the Quantock coast, and into the Quantocks and Blackdowns, where they nested in trees. There was no evidence of any further eastward spread between *BA 1968–72* and *NBA 1988–91*, but in the 1990s Ravens at last began to re-occupy tree sites in many areas of the east and south and to lose some of their wariness of humans, though they can still be secretive in the breeding season. On the Levels, pylon sites have proved much to the liking of this lover of high places. The English population probably quadrupled between 1994 and 2005; by 2007 breeding had extended to the eastern edge of Gloucestershire (Kirk and Phillips 2013) and was well into Oxfordshire (Easterbrook 2013), and

BA 2007–11 shows that the eastward spread continued during the Atlas period, one of the avian success stories of modern times. Somerset, which had been in the front line of the advance 20 years earlier, has consolidated its population behind the pioneers.

By 2010, *SB* published records of 47 pairs, and there are recent reports of winter gatherings of up to 150 in game-farming areas on the Blackdowns and the Brendons, both of which show up in *BA 2007–11* as the areas of greatest winter density.

Ravens are often very early breeders, such that the accepted pattern of wintering and breeding maps does not show the real position particularly well. The two maps for this species have accordingly been drawn up differently to the standard format, in that all breeding records, regardless of timing, are on the 'breeding' map with all other records being on the 'non-breeding' map.

Raven sponsored by Eve Tigwell and Terry Gifford

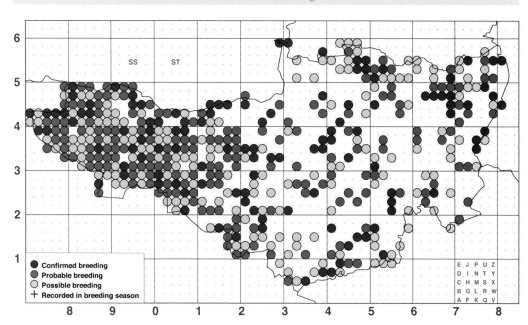

Raven – Breeding

Confirmed breeding
Probable breeding
Possible breeding
+ Recorded in breeding season

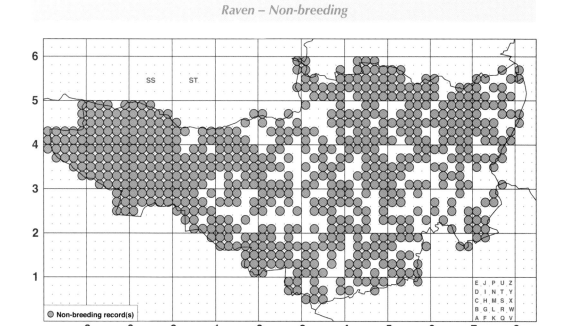

Raven – Non-breeding

○ Non-breeding record(s)

GOLDCREST *Regulus regulus*

As breeding birds, Goldcrests have always been associated with conifers and, with the high availability of this habitat, are probably commoner than ever. Numbers can fluctuate widely from year to year, this being linked to hard winters, but the highest densities are presumably to be found in Forestry Commission plantations, though the species is also found in many quite small areas like old gardens and churchyards, where planted yews and other ornamental conifers provide suitable nest sites. They are also fairly commonly recorded in old sessile oakwoods, and in the Avalon Marshes.

In *BA 1968–72*, Goldcrests were found in all 10-km squares, but only thinly in ST23 (Bridgwater West); in *NBA 1988–91*, they were discovered there but were entirely missing from five 10-km squares in Central Somerset (ST33/34/42/52/53) and were only thinly present in three nearby ones (ST24/32/43). Goldcrests were infrequently recorded over most of the Levels, but they were not entirely absent, being found in 48% of tetrads within these nine 10-km squares, though proof of breeding was hard to come by. They are sparsely distributed around Taunton, and also in the farmland of the Vale of Taunton Deane; in all this area there are relatively few conifers.

Most Goldcrests in southern Britain are thought to be sedentary, unlike Firecrests, although there is passage from late September to late October. The return movement in March and April can be stronger than is commonly realised, as is evident from the numbers ringed over many years at Five Bells, Watchet; some April records for this Atlas may have been of migrants. Local birds can become nomadic in winter, when they join tit flocks and can even be found far up Exmoor combes exploring lichened hawthorns. Winter results show a slightly wider distribution than in the breeding season: 69% of all tetrads as opposed to 62%. Only 20% of tetrads had no Goldcrests in either season.

As noted above, this species is particularly vulnerable in hard winters. There is evidence of a severe population crash in Gloucestershire immediately after the snowfall in the early winter of 2008/09 (Kirk and Phillips 2013): numbers there remained very low over the following winter, but by the winter of 2010/11 they had largely recovered to 2008 levels. It would be reasonable to assume that there will have been a similar pattern in Somerset, only a short distance to the south-west, and given the snowfall and low temperatures experienced in two winters during the Atlas period, but there is little evidence for this. *SB 2011* suggested that increased use of feeders by Goldcrests may have played a part in mitigating the worst effects.

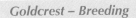

Goldcrest – Breeding

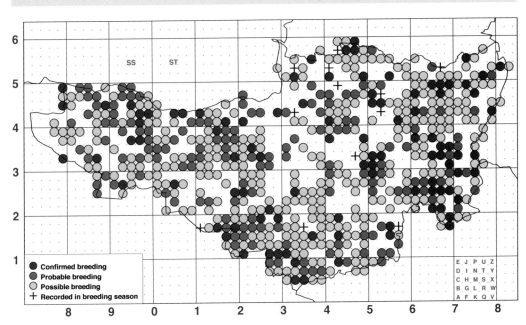

- ● Confirmed breeding
- ● Probable breeding
- ○ Possible breeding
- + Recorded in breeding season

Goldcrest – Winter

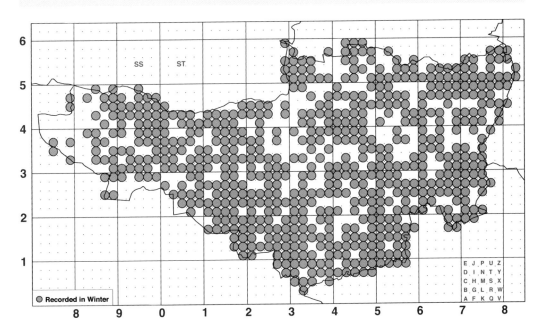

- ● Recorded in Winter

FIRECREST *Regulus ignicapilla*

Formerly recorded as a scarce passage migrant and winter visitor, Firecrests were first proved breeding in Somerset near Alfred's Tower in 1985 (Spencer *et al.* 1988). From then to 2009, up to six pairs were noted in most years there or elsewhere on the Selwood Ridge, but in 2010 there was a sudden surge of records, at least 27 being found from Penselwood north to Gare Hill; some of these were in Wiltshire. From 2007 to 2011 for this Atlas, up to three were recorded on Mendip at Edford Bridge and Harridge Wood, and in the last year a pair bred successfully in Edford Wood and there were two birds at Nettlebridge in May. Prior to the Atlas period there were a number of summer records at other sites, but with no proof of breeding; these may have been wandering or perhaps prospecting individuals.

It is possible that any expansion could have been checked by the two severe winters, but *BA 2007–11* suggests that most Firecrests probably migrate. Few small birds are so easily missed, even by competent observers. There are now thought to be up to 1,000 pairs in England, almost all south-east of a line from Exeter to The Wash, of which a third are in the New Forest (Holling *et al.* 2012).

During the five Atlas winters from 2007 to 2012, a total of 32 birds were recorded, mainly in coastal areas, in the Avalon Marshes or at sewage-treatment works. Compared to the 34 in the single winter of 2004/05, these are low figures, but whether this is due to normal fluctuations in numbers or as a result of hard winter weather is unclear.

Firecrest sponsored by Ken Hall and Dan Lupton

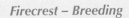

Firecrest – Breeding

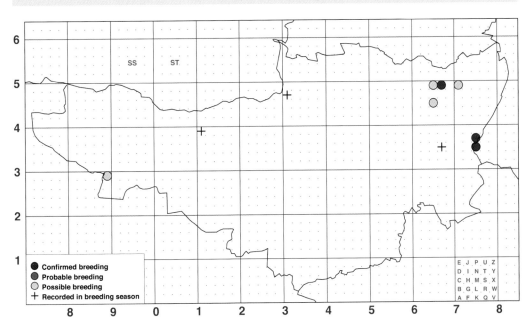

Confirmed breeding
Probable breeding
Possible breeding
+ Recorded in breeding season

Firecrest – Winter

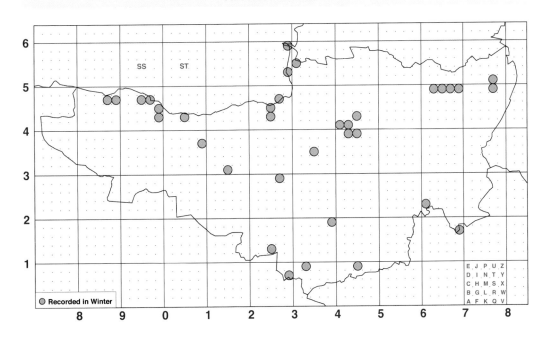

Recorded in Winter

BLUE TIT *Cyanistes caeruleus*

The Blue Tit's natural habitat is broad-leaved woodland, especially oak, but it has spread along hedges and into gardens, where it now frequents feeders all through the year and often takes to nest-boxes. It has thus been greatly helped to survive recent winters by human intervention with apparently very little loss and may well be the most frequently recorded bird in the county as a whole. There are fewer Blue Tits in the uplands, as can be seen for Exmoor in the *NBA 1988–91* and *BA 2007–11* abundance maps, and this Atlas suggests that they do not breed there in a few barren tetrads, although wanderers are found in combes as far as the limit of bushes. *BA 2007–11* shows a stable or increasing relative abundance for Somerset's 10-km squares since *NBA 1988–91*. With such an active, conspicuous and much-loved species, it is not surprising that it was recorded almost universally in both seasons for this Atlas. The proportion of confirmed breeding records is high, which may reflect both its visibility and its frequent use of nesting boxes.

From midsummer, flocks are formed, often with other species in woodland canopy, but ringing recoveries show that almost all birds are sedentary within a defined foraging area. There are certainly winter visitors from the east and north and in some years there have been sizeable flocks on autumn passage, though there has been no major influx since 1985. For this Atlas, Blue Tits were recorded in almost all tetrads in Somerset; the gaps on Exmoor and the mid-county gap on Tealham Moor are probably explained by a lack of suitable wintering habitat.

Blue Tit sponsored by Jim Rosser

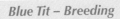

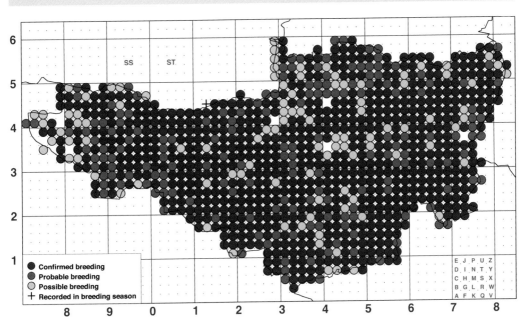

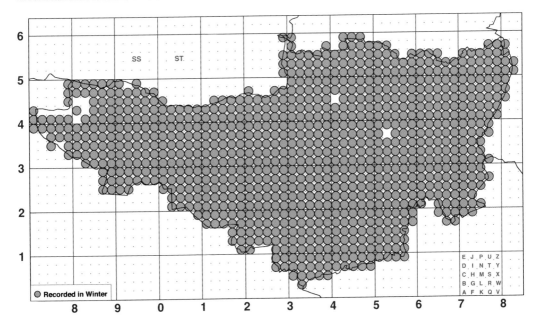

GREAT TIT *Parus major*

This is generally accepted as being the second most numerous tit, and it is scarcely less popular with the general public than the preceding species. It breeds almost everywhere, but is only thinly distributed on the highest ground of Exmoor. Great Tits dominate many a bird feeder and readily occupy nest-boxes. In winter they will join other tits in foraging flocks among the foliage, but they are also ground feeders in good beechmast years.

Breeding was confirmed in every 10-km square in *BA 1968–72*, and in all but one in *NBA 1988–91*. *BA 2007–11* shows an increase in relative abundance

for nearly half of Somerset's 10-km squares since *NBA 1988–91*, mostly in the middle and east of the county. According to *WA 1981–84*, winter numbers were relatively low compared with those in Avon and Wiltshire, with only seven 10-km squares, all in the north-east, reporting day-counts of over 38. Unsurprisingly, this Atlas shows that Great Tits were present and breeding in almost all tetrads in Somerset, probably for very similar reasons as detailed for Blue Tit.

Most are sedentary, but there is some coastal passage in autumn, possibly of Continental birds.

Great Tit – Breeding

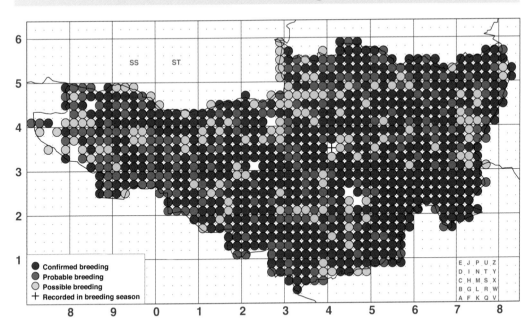

Confirmed breeding
Probable breeding
Possible breeding
+ Recorded in breeding season

Great Tit – Winter

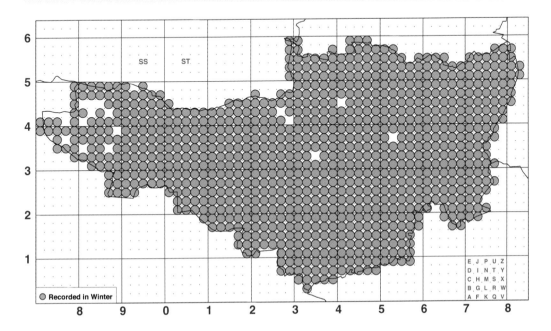

Recorded in Winter

COAL TIT *Periparus ater*

Coal Tits have always been much more local than Blue and Great Tits, and are most frequently recorded in areas with plentiful conifers: the Mendip plantations, parts of the Blackdowns and the East Quantocks, and the Brendons and their northern outliers. For example, on Rowberrow Warren they are reported to outnumber all other tit species (G. Suter *in litt.*). However, they are also widespread, though probably in smaller numbers, in the mature broad-leaved woodland of Exmoor and elsewhere, and in larger gardens, where even a few conifers will encourage colonisation. It was pointed out by Yapp (1962) that Coal Tits were much commoner than Blue Tits in upland woods of sessile oak, where they were present in equal numbers to Great Tits; they were using nesting crevices in rocks at ground level.

In *BA 1968–72* no breeding was found in the two Bridgwater squares of ST23 and 33. In *NBA 1988–91*, Coal Tits were present west of the town, but they were not proved to breed in ST33, and were very scarce or absent on King's Sedge Moor, in the central section of the Poldens, and across a wide belt of South-central Somerset from the Fosse Way west to the Tone Levels. In *WA 1981–84*, they were most abundant in the Quantocks and the East Brendons, and absent not only from most of the summer gaps, but also from the Quantock coastline, these being almost the only gaps in the South West. There are now no 10-km squares in Somerset entirely without this species, except the six tetrads of ST25 along the coast from Brean to Burnham, where they were not reported for this Atlas even at feeders, despite the presence of small stands of conifers in some places. There were few tetrad records for either season in ST33 and ST34 (Lympsham), where woodlands are small or lacking.

The winter status has undoubtedly improved with the widespread provision of feeders. In the 264 tetrads of West and South-west Somerset, Coal Tits were found in only 55% during the breeding season, but in 77% in winter. There were similar results from Mendip. The most striking seasonal difference was in ST22, much of which is the built-up area of Taunton. This has no coniferous woodland larger than a copse, and Coal Tits could be found in only nine tetrads in the breeding season. However, they were found in 18 tetrads in this 10-km square in winter. ST21, which covers part of the Blackdowns, has them in every tetrad, and in winter they presumably descend to make use of the garden feeders to the north. By contrast, the western end of Bridgwater apparently supports no Coal Tits. Some attach themselves to nomadic flocks of other species in deciduous woods, and they have a special fondness for high gorse.

Coastal passage has been sometimes observed in autumn, so there may be occasional winter visitors, but there have been no ringing recoveries to support this suggestion.

Coal Tit – Breeding

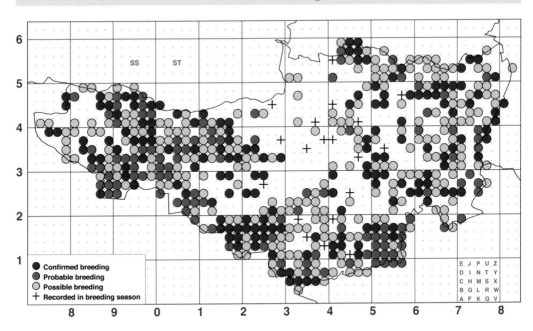

- ● Confirmed breeding
- ● Probable breeding
- ○ Possible breeding
- + Recorded in breeding season

Coal Tit – Winter

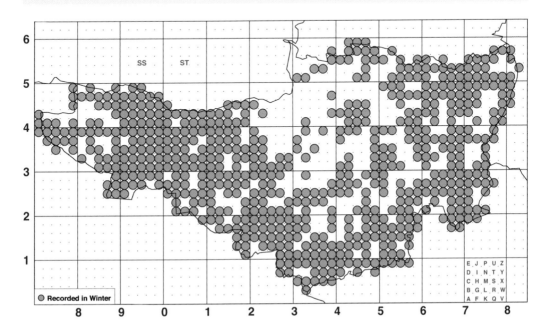

- ● Recorded in Winter

MARSH TIT *Poecile palustris*

Until 1983, Marsh Tits were thought too common in Somerset for their records to be published in *SB*. In fact, their distribution had always been uneven, since they avoid conifers and are not generally found in very small woods, or, despite their name, in the wettest ones. Yet they were certainly far more familiar birds than they are today and were regular at many feeders and in most woodland in South and Central Somerset, as well as in the Exmoor and Brendon oakwoods. On the Poldens, they were in 1960 'the dominant tit' in Copley Woods, where there were autumn counts of up to 50; they are still there today, but with perhaps only five pairs. The text of *BA 1968–72* gave no hint of decline, but the map showed that a large area of the county was almost wholly without Marsh Tits, including six 10-km squares on the lowest ground north and south of the Poldens and around Bridgwater.

They are among the most sedentary of British birds, seldom moving more than a few kilometres, so summer and winter records are of equal importance in showing their distribution. The map in *WA 1981–84* clearly shows a contraction of range: only 11 squares had counts of eight or more, and nine had no records at all; there was a virtual gap between Mendip and East Somerset and the Quantocks, except on the Poldens and around Langport. A similar pattern appeared in *NBA 1988–91*: there were again nine squares with none (including Wincanton and part of the Vale of Taunton Deane) and there were a further ten with no proof of breeding. The relative abundance change breeding map for *BA 2007–11* shows that this species is declining in abundance almost across its whole range, whereas the range itself has changed little over time.

During work for the present Atlas, Marsh Tits were found in 35% of all tetrads (223) in the breeding season, in 43% (274) in winter, and in a year-round total of 53% (334). The general impressions of distribution from the maps covering both seasons are similar, though. Marsh Tits were absent around the coast of Bridgwater Bay, along the M5 corridor and adjacent Levels, and on Exmoor Forest, where there is very little suitable habitat. They are clearly very infrequently recorded everywhere below the 50-metre contour. They are almost universally present throughout the north-east, on the Blackdowns and in ancient woodland on the east side of Exmoor and in the Brendons. They are still widespread in the Quantocks, in the Great Breach Wood complex at the east end of the Poldens and associated woods to the east of Somerton, and in the thin ribbon of escarpment woodland running north-east along the southern edge of West Sedge Moor, as well as in most deciduous woodlands along the Dorset border.

Marsh Tits can easily escape observation, especially if they are not calling, and are more conspicuous around winter feeders than they are in the breeding season. This can be clearly seen in the five main squares of the north-east (ST64/65/73/74/75), where they were recorded in 38 tetrads in the summer, but in 58 in the winter.

Marsh Tit sponsored by Julian Thomas

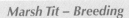

Marsh Tit – Breeding

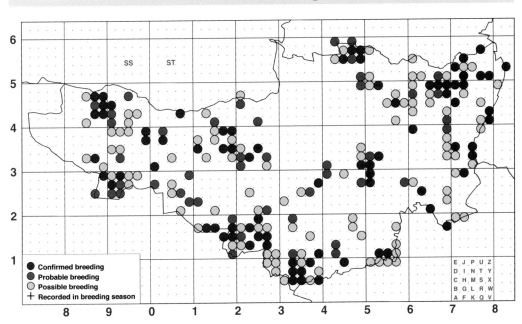

Marsh Tit – Winter

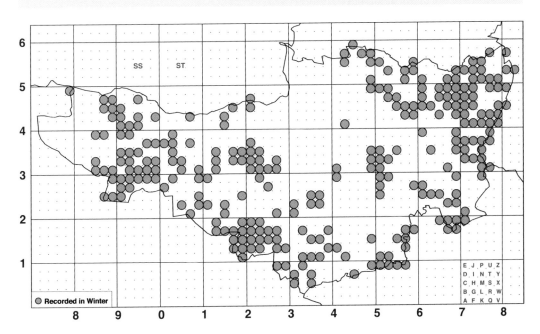

BEARDED TIT *Panurus biarmicus*

In 1974 two pairs of Bearded Tits bred at Berrow Marsh, the first breeding record for the county, and from 1983 a small colony was established there. This has sometimes risen to 15 pairs, though it has fluctuated markedly, and attempted drainage on occasion by the neighbouring golf club has hampered its development. This was an even greater cause for concern because, until not long before the current Atlas period, Berrow was the only breeding site in the county. Then, in 2004, two pairs bred at Ham Wall, and there were up to eight pairs there from 2005 to 2007. In 2005 young were also seen on Westhay Moor. The area of suitable habitat in the expanding reedbeds of the Avalon Marshes gives much more hope for the future of this species in the county.

Nonetheless, during the Atlas period, Bearded Tits at first seemed to be at a low ebb: one pair generally succeeded at Berrow (though not in 2011), but development was apparently slow in the Avalon Marshes, where in 2011 at least one pair bred at Ham Wall, and two males were present at Shapwick Heath. A later study suggested that the population was much larger and more widespread than these records indicate, since a post-Atlas autumn count at Ham Wall in 2012 located 145 birds. Much of this area is normally inaccessible except to reserve staff and volunteers, who monitor the population.

As Bearded Tits are a Schedule 1 species, breeding records are mapped conventionally within 10-km squares. The main breeding sites are well known, and acknowledged here, but outlying or prospecting pairs may still be vulnerable to disturbance.

Outside the breeding season there were records of wanderers at Cary Moor and Wall Common; in previous years erupting birds have appeared at other sites, even by the fort on Brean Down.

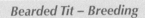

Bearded Tit – Breeding

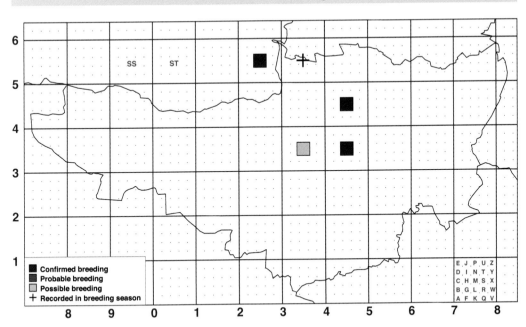

Legend:
- ■ Confirmed breeding
- ■ Probable breeding
- □ Possible breeding
- + Recorded in breeding season

Bearded Tit – Winter

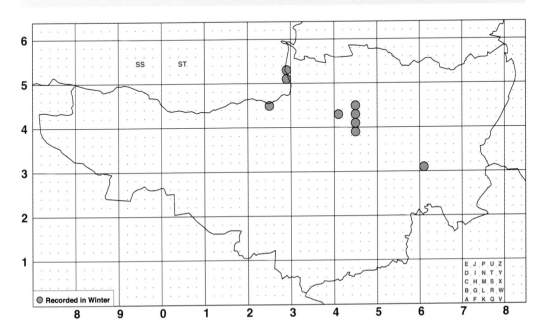

- ● Recorded in Winter

WILLOW TIT *Poecile montana*

The Willow Tit was recognised as a British species only in 1897, and it may never have been widespread in Somerset. From the late 1930s to the 1980s, most records came from the Avalon Marshes, where there was a flourishing population, but others were found on Mendip, in Central and South Somerset, on the Blackdown escarpment and at Langford Heathfield. Further west, there were scattered records from Quantock and Exmoor woodland and regular sightings by Wimbleball Reservoir, where the last was in 2002. A fairly rapid decline means that there is no regular site left, and and a full description is now required supporting any claims of this species, most specifically because Marsh Tits are still present in many of the sites where Willow Tits used to occur.

A number of records were submitted during the Atlas period, but only two were accepted by the Somerset Rarities Committee: one in ST21 (Blackdowns), December 2008, and one in ST02 (Langford Heathfield), April 2009. They are still recorded in North Devon, west of the county border. If the Willow Tit remains a breeding species in Somerset at all, it is maintaining a tenuous toehold at best.

SAND MARTIN *Riparia riparia*

The first hirundines of spring are generally Sand Martins. Research has shown that their arrival date has advanced during the last 75 years from the first week of April to the second week in March. Large numbers pass through the Avalon Marshes in late March and April.

Nationally, there have been much-publicised population fluctuations, including disastrous declines following droughts in their African winter quarters in 1968/69 and 1983/84, and a notable recovery apparent from Breeding Bird Survey records from 1994 to 2000. Colonies in Somerset are very small and scattered, so their fortunes are difficult to connect to the wider picture. Few of the county's rivers have long stretches of soft, sandy banks suitable for breeding colonies.

Sandpits provide good nesting habitat, but there is currently only one extraction site, the ARC quarry at Greenham, which provides an unstable base for up to 30 pairs. Other existing regular sites are subject to collapse, and disturbance by humans and cattle.

During the Atlas period a few natural breeding sites in river banks were located, but none with more than five pairs: on the Tone at East Nynehead; along the Barle, mainly from Sherdon Hutch to Withypool, near Exebridge; and on the Exe at Hele Bridge. Breeding has been suspected on the Frome at Oldford, and birds were present in Lower Weir Water in 2012.

The most regular sites are in man-made drainholes along the Tone and the canal from Taunton to Creech St Michael, and at Ashford Reservoir, which held up to ten pairs. Breeding was also recorded in an artificial bank on Cary Moor and in a peat-mound on Glastonbury Heath.

Breeding attempts by one or two pairs can easily go unrecorded. The map shows a scatter of 'possible' sites, but some of these at least may well refer to migrants. Birds depart unobtrusively in August and September, when passage numbers are much lower than in the spring.

Willow Tit – Combined Winter & Breeding

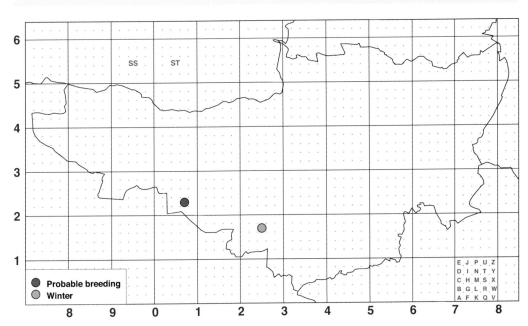

Sand Martin – Breeding

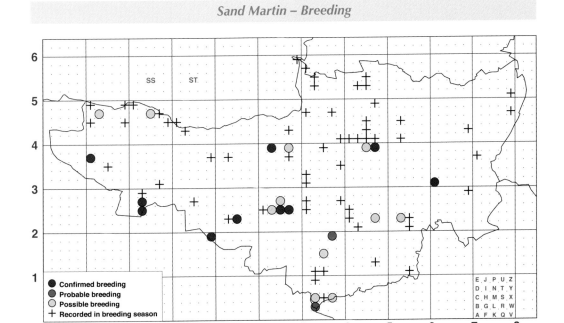

SWALLOW *Hirundo rustica*

Swallows begin to arrive in mid March, but the main passage is in the second half of April. By the end of the first week in May most of our breeders have settled into the breeding sites. Almost all tetrads held breeding Swallows during the Atlas period, but they were generally absent from town centres and were thinly distributed in the western uplands. Swallows may once have used tree-sites, but now breed exclusively in man-made structures: in barns, outhouses, sheds and church porches, or under bridges. On Exmoor Forest, a few sites are in buildings remote from actual farms, such as the open shed at lonely Mole's Chamber. The presence of livestock is always an attraction, as it usually ensures an abundance of insects.

Local increases and losses are often noticed, and there has certainly been some decrease around the edges of towns and villages, where converted barns and closed double garages offer no breeding sites for Swallows, and there may be a reduced amount of insect food. They may even be considered a health risk in milking parlours (R.J.Butcher *in litt.*). Other losses might reflect changes in the wintering areas in Southern Africa.

Even in places where breeding is fairly obviously taking place, conscientious Atlas workers may not have entered it as 'confirmed', since the nest itself may not be visible from public rights of way. For example, in ST12 (Wellington) both Swallow and House Martin were at least probable breeders in every tetrad, but Swallows were confirmed in only 13, whereas House Martins, with their conspicuous nests, were in all 25.

HOUSE MARTIN *Delichon urbicum*

Although a few House Martins may be seen in March, the main arrival of breeders is not until late April or early May, and passage may be strong until much later. Even then, prospectors may arrive, depart for a few days, and then return to settle. Most other summer migrants arrive earlier than they once did, but House Martins' habits have changed little, and their average arrival date may even be later than it once was.

Their special requirements are eaves to support their nests, mud to build them and a good supply of insects. They are usually concentrated in colonies, though these may be dispersed over a village high street, as in Porlock, which has recently hosted up to 67 pairs, or in Coleford and Combwich, which have each had as many as 80. They are, of course, easy targets for Atlas workers seeking proof of breeding. They are not as universally present as Swallows, though they may locally outnumber them; for example, in 118 Exmoor tetrads they were found in only 77, whereas Swallows were in 98. House Martins do not usually find their nesting requirements satisfied by isolated and uninhabited buildings.

House Martins are easily affected by building developments, house painting and an urban passion for tidiness; their nests cannot be legally destroyed while they are occupied, but many a householder sallies out quietly with a long pole in the winter, when they can be removed. Modern developments with tightly packed houses and hardly any gardens may be colonised as long as the houses have broad eaves, which many do not. Twenty per cent of all tetrads showed no positive evidence of breeding during the Atlas period. Figures in *NAvA 2007–11* suggest the loss of at least a quarter of the population in Avon since 1992. The national overview in *BA 2007–11* records losses in the south of England, but considerable gains in Scotland and in the eastern half of Ireland, mirroring the range changes of several other migrant breeders.

Departure is in September or early October, generally somewhat later than most Swallows.

Swallow sponsored by Stephen, Suzanne, Charlie, George and Daisy Moss
House Martin sponsored by Kay and Rob Grimmond

Swallow – Breeding

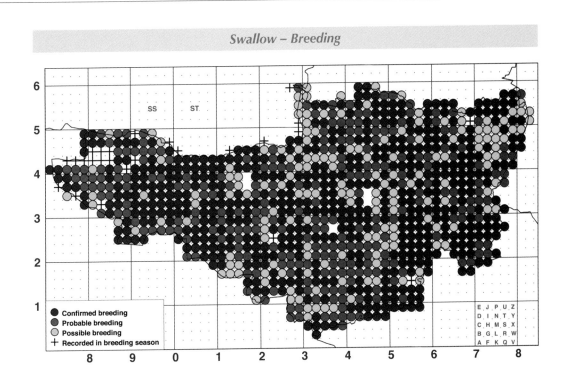

House Martin – Breeding

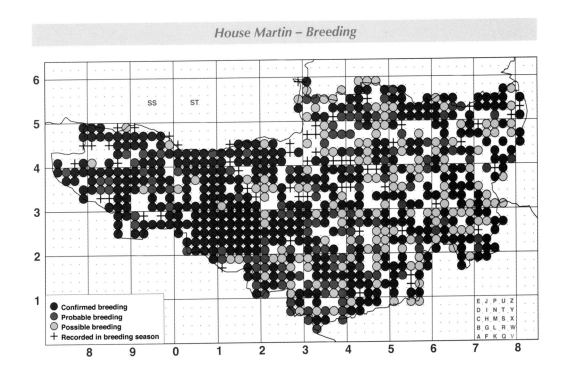

SKYLARK *Alauda arvensis*

There is very little information on its distribution before the 1980s, but Skylarks are likely to have always been commonest in areas of arable or mixed farming, on the Levels and in the uplands. They are very rarely recorded in small fields surrounded by high hedges, so they were probably never numerous in those parts of Somerset with this habitat.

In *BA 1968–72* there were few hints of decline: Skylarks were absent from ST75, north of Frome, and were rather thinly distributed in parts of South Somerset and around Taunton. In the abundance map of *NBA 1988–91*, the highest densities were on King's Sedge Moor. The decline appears to have started in the 1970s; around Crewkerne the 150 pairs in 1975 had fallen to 42 by 2000, but they fared better in the arable around Somerton.

In the last 30 years there has been a marked contraction both in range and in numbers. This has been most obvious in pasture: on one Common Bird Census plot on the Brendons, the flourishing population of 38 pairs on 76 hectares in 1981 had almost disappeared by 2002. The conversion from traditional hay to silage has often been disastrous, since Skylarks have no time to rear a brood between cuts. Breeding success is higher in arable areas, but even there, where stubbles have been ploughed immediately after harvest and reseeded with winter grain, Skylarks are deprived of their traditional winter source of nourishment. The culture of maize and oilseed rape has helped them; so has setaside, but the policy that funded that has now changed. They may still be quite common on coastal farmland: in a survey of 57 tetrads from Clevedon (North Somerset) to Steart, Archer and Forecast (2001) found 250 pairs, but there are few more recent records from that area. Inland, there were high counts of 130 on Western Mendip in 2007 (Archer 2008) and of 183 on West Sedge Moor in 2009.

The moorland of the Quantocks and Exmoor remains a refuge, but even there we have perhaps seen a decline: on the former, 250 territories in 1992 had shrunk to 78 by 2000, but recovered to 136 in 2012. The most recent Exmoor survey (including Devon Exmoor) in 2008 found 2,470 territories. They are certainly commoner on tussocky grass moorland than on heather, but the increased sward height resulting from smaller numbers of stock has probably worked against them. They prefer some bareness, which regular swaling provides. Like some other moorland birds, they have tended to lose numbers on outlying and coastal sites and have concentrated on favoured areas such as the flatter tops of the South Forest. In this Atlas they generally followed the pattern of known suitable habitat, with concentrations on Exmoor, the coast, and most tetrads across the Southern Levels and farmland to the east in ST32, 42, and 52.

On high ground Skylarks are generally absent from September to at least the end of January. Except in hard winters, song is frequent on sunny days in February, even on exposed sites, when their arrival precedes that of Meadow Pipits. They frequent any sites where they can find grain and weed-seeds: game-crops, stubbles, fodder rape, germinating cereals, setaside, warm coastal fields, *Salicornia* and so on. In the cold winters during the Atlas years, flocks arrived from the north or east, or passed by on their way to Ireland, the highest counts being of 820 at Steart on 18 February 2009 and 550 at Knighton on 24 December 2010, though these hard-weather movements are small compared with those recorded in the 1970s and 1980s. In the winter map, the concentration of numbers far inland and on the Levels is interesting; it may be influenced by birds searching for unfrozen ground in two hard winters.

Skylark sponsored by Val Anderson

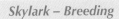

Skylark – Breeding

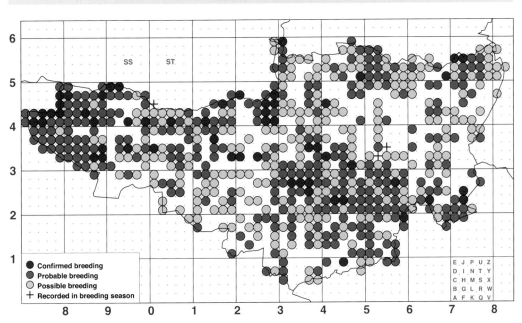

Confirmed breeding
Probable breeding
Possible breeding
+ Recorded in breeding season

Skylark – Winter

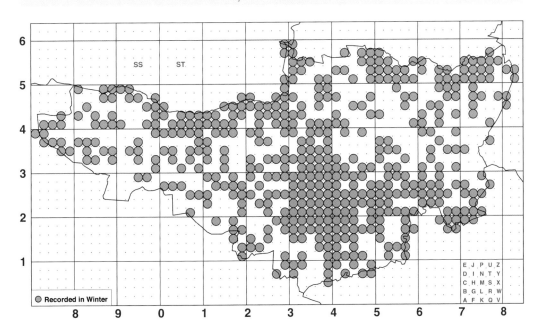

Recorded in Winter

CETTI'S WARBLER *Cettia cetti*

The first British record of a Cetti's Warbler was in Hampshire in 1961, and by 1973 the species was breeding in Kent. The first two Somerset birds were identified in 1968 and 1976. Cetti's Warblers expanded across the county during the 1980s, including to the developing reserves of the Avalon Marshes which are now their stronghold, holding at least 220 singing males by the start of the Atlas in 2007. The males are often polygamous, so the number of nesting females may exceed population estimates based on the former.

Their ideal habitat is reedbeds and ditches with a liberal addition of scattered scrub, often bramble. Outside the Avalon Marshes, most regular breeding has been in four areas: from Berrow to the Brue Estuary and up the Huntspill River; from the Bridgwater clay-pits up the canal to Taunton; on the western part of King's Sedge Moor; and along the Steart to Stolford coast. Odd birds have appeared at many other sites, including Cary Moor. They are skulkers, but the males are always betrayed by their disproportionately loud song.

Cetti's Warbler is a Schedule 1 breeding species, but in this case the size of the Somerset population is such that the risk associated with disclosing breeding sites is considered to be low, and breeding-season records are mapped at tetrad level.

During the Atlas period the winter distribution differs little from that for breeding, apart from a scattering of winter wanderers across the south-east. Recent cold spells must have had some effect on numbers: in 2009 there were 110 records submitted to SOS from 26 sites, but there were only 77 from 24 in 2011 and 71 from 20 in 2012. Though these records provide an interesting comparison between years (assuming a similar amount of observer effort), they are clearly incomplete, as in 2011 the RSPB counted 83 in song at Ham Wall. In the same year, Avon Breeding Bird Survey results showed a sharp fall in numbers on their side of the border.

Cetti's Warbler – Breeding

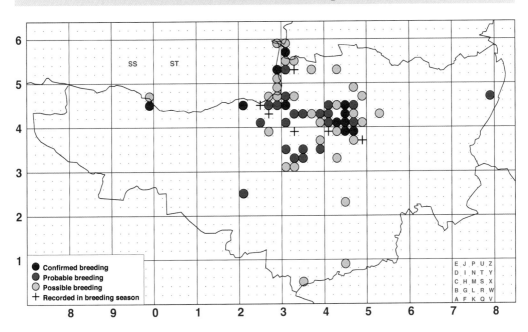

- ● Confirmed breeding
- ● Probable breeding
- ○ Possible breeding
- + Recorded in breeding season

Cetti's Warbler – Winter

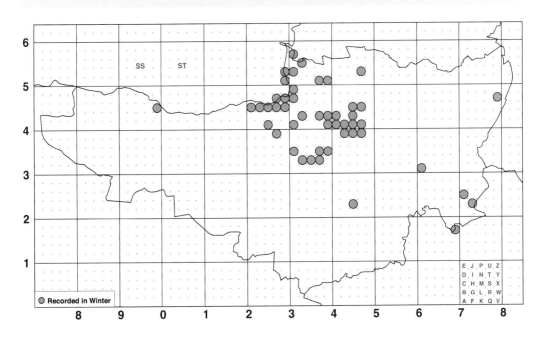

- ● Recorded in Winter

LONG-TAILED TIT *Aegithalos caudatus*

A glance at *BA 1968–72* and *NBA 1988–91* might suggest that Long-tailed Tits are evenly distributed over the county, but *WA 1981–84* shows a less regular picture, which is supported by the abundance map in *NBA*. In *WA* there were hardly any records around Bridgwater Bay, none at all in ST33 (Bridgwater East), and few in parts of the south-west. *NBA* found the greatest abundance to be in the Quantocks, where there is much deciduous woodland and scrubby marginal land, and there are many suitable gardens. During this Atlas there were records from all but one of the 25 tetrads of ST13. On Exmoor, and especially on the Forest, there is very little suitable habitat, and the 26 Somerset tetrads of SS73 and 74 had records from only ten at either season, though autumn parties may wander up combes to the limit of bushes.

Long-tailed Tits are early breeders. Spring is the only season when they are not in family or larger groupings and, although they are not particularly shy, they are much more easily seen in autumn and winter, especially along hedgerows. This is reflected in some Atlas data: of the 265 tetrads on or west of the Quantocks there were records in 176 in winter, but in only 137 during the breeding season. Current results show them to be almost universally distributed, however – they are generally sedentary within a fairly small area, and if summer and winter records are combined, Long-tailed Tits were found in 90% of all Somerset tetrads, the exceptions being parts of Exmoor already mentioned, some areas of the Levels and on the Mendip Plateau. On the last, there is an interesting discrepancy between the results obtained for *NAvA 2007–11* and those for this Atlas: both show an almost complete absence in summer, and *NAvA* confirms this for the winter months, whereas this Atlas shows a number of records at that season, perhaps because of the inclusion of the extra, and milder, winter of 2011/12.

The species has suffered greatly in hard winters in the past. Those of 1916/17, 1939/40 and 1962/63 resulted in short, but dramatic, declines and some local extinctions. Long-tailed Tits are almost wholly insectivorous (though they have also taken to fat-balls at garden feeding stations) and they find it hard to survive prolonged frost-glaze on trees. Yet the two hard winters during the Atlas period seem to have had relatively little effect. There have been many reports of flocks of between 20 and 40, and even one of 67 on North Hill in June 2009.

A few coastal records have suggested possible autumn immigration, which is supported by over 100 having been recorded on Lundy (Davis and Jones 2007).

Long-tailed Tit sponsored by Robin Levien

Long-tailed Tit – Breeding

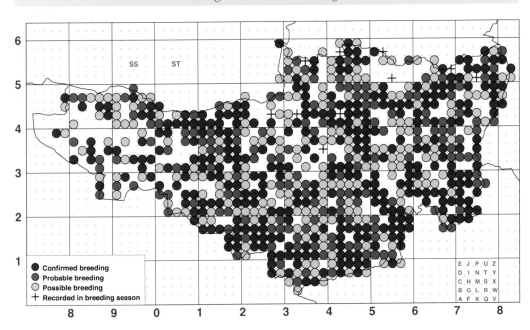

- ● Confirmed breeding
- ● Probable breeding
- ○ Possible breeding
- + Recorded in breeding season

Long-tailed Tit – Winter

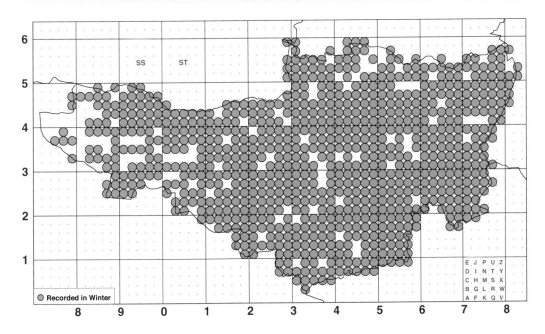

- ○ Recorded in Winter

YELLOW-BROWED WARBLER *Phylloscopus inornatus*

This is a late-autumn migrant from the east, still scarce, but nationally far more numerous than formerly. The first Somerset record was in 1970. From then to January 2007 there were 30, followed by 18 during the Atlas period, 11 of them in the October months. Of the seven others mapped, four were in November (and probably better thought of as late migrants) and three from December to February. This species can wander widely, so some duplication of records is impossible to eliminate.

Wintering in the mild South West is an increasing habit, though numbers are small. Fraser (2013b) showed that from 2004 to 2007 total British numbers exceeded 1,000, mainly along the east coast, but in 2007 including about 200 in Cornwall and Scilly. However, wintering birds, from January to March, never exceeded 18 in any year. They often favoured sewage-treatment works.

Yellow-browed Warbler sponsored by Tim, Ellie and Tristan Farr
Wood Warbler sponsored by Frankie Macrow

WOOD WARBLER *Phylloscopus sibilatrix*

Wood Warblers chiefly arrive from about 20 April to 5 May, when a few may sing briefly at sites where they will not stay to breed.

For breeding, the species prefers a closed tree canopy and sparse shrub layer. These conditions are found widely in West Somerset, usually in sessile oakwood, but sometimes in beech. There is some evidence that the population has always fluctuated widely, even in the most favoured sites. Some of these have been regularly monitored in recent years. In the 1980s, numbers were much higher than they are today, and the range was somewhat wider. Since then, every national and local indication has been of decline; according to *BA 2007–11*, up to 65% of the population has been lost. However, many suitable woods are remote, private, and difficult to survey effectively. Wood Warblers are single-brooded and are in the UK for no more than three months, so they could have been missed entirely in some tetrads.

The most regular sites are now almost all in the west. On the Quantocks, they are largely confined to the north-eastern combes, though there are a few along the south-western escarpment. The number of singing males averaged 24 during the Atlas period. In Horner Woods there has been a long-running programme of ringing, which has proved that many birds are site-faithful, with up to 50 pairs nesting. Breeding birds may be found in the Barle Valley, from Withypool to Dulverton, and along the Exe Valley, along the steep coast from Porlock Weir to Glenthorne, and, in the Brendons, from the Avill Valley west to Weir Wood, and around Wimbleball Lake. In the east of Somerset, Selwood Forest, including Alfred's Tower, still holds a few breeding pairs. There were relatively few records from Mendip, and from the Blackdowns, where most recent records have been from the north-facing escarpment woodland from Castle Neroche to the Wellington Monument.

Wood Warblers become inconspicuous in late June, and then leave in July on a generally south-easterly course (Simms 1985). Very few are reported on autumn passage.

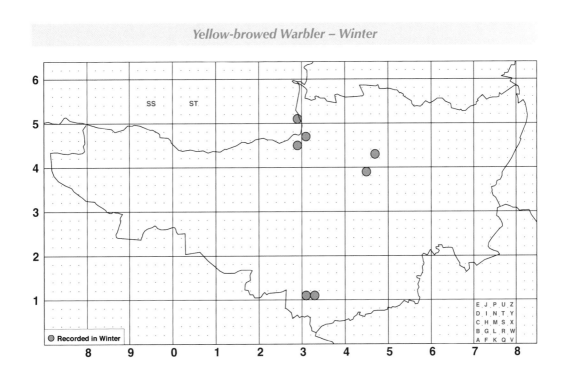

Yellow-browed Warbler – Winter

○ Recorded in Winter

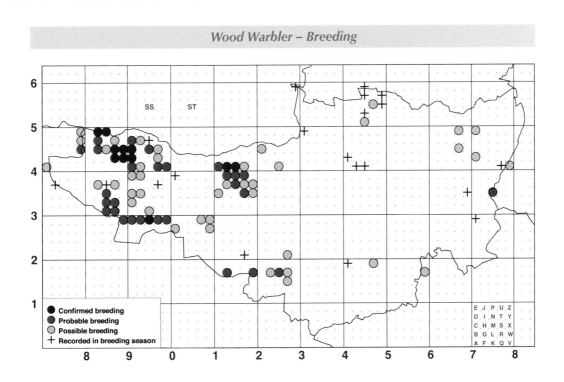

Wood Warbler – Breeding

● Confirmed breeding
● Probable breeding
○ Possible breeding
+ Recorded in breeding season

CHIFFCHAFF *Phylloscopus collybita*

Chiffchaffs are in general the first summer visitors to arrive, from early March. They need a combination of trees for foraging and song-posts, with scrub or rough corners for nesting. The species nests in larger gardens, and even in intensive farmland there is often enough cover for breeding. Chiffchaffs are found in almost all tetrads in Somerset, but are scarce on the western side of Exmoor, where they do not nest above the tree-limit in combes. They are also sparse on the Mendip Plateau and on the barer parts of the Levels. In some 10-km squares, breeding was rarely confirmed, since territories could easily be estimated from the conspicuous song. No change in distribution was found between *BA 1968–72* and *NBA 1988–91*. The abundance maps in the latter, and in *BA 2007–11*, show a universally high figure, except in the far west; this is part of a generally strong population in South-west England. The impression, supported by statistics from national surveys, is that Chiffchaffs have increased in Somerset over the last 30 years, and that the Quantocks hold the densest populations, this being a species that has adapted well to conifers.

Breeders leave, or at least fall silent, in July and August. In some years there is a considerable passage up to late September. Wintering birds were first noted in 1880, but not annually until the 1950s. They can now be found among nomadic tit flocks, in scrub and willow near water, and at many small sewage-treatment works, but chiefly near the coast or on lower ground. They appear to have been scarcer in the two very cold recent winters, when they either failed to survive or retreated southward.

Some winter visitors have been of the Siberian race *Ph. c. tristis*; about eight were reported over the Atlas period. These were at scattered sites, but often with birds of the nominate race around filter beds. Birds of the Scandinavian race *Ph. c. abietinus* also probably occurred, but are very difficult to identify with certainty.

Chiffchaff – Breeding

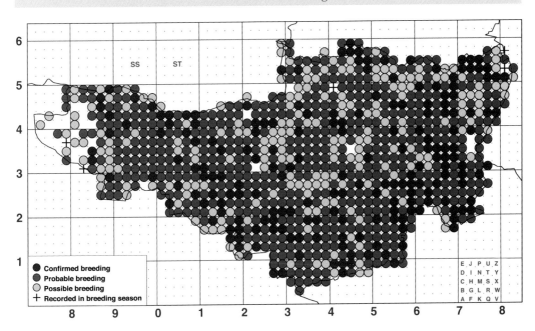

- ● Confirmed breeding
- ● Probable breeding
- ○ Possible breeding
- + Recorded in breeding season

Chiffchaff – Winter

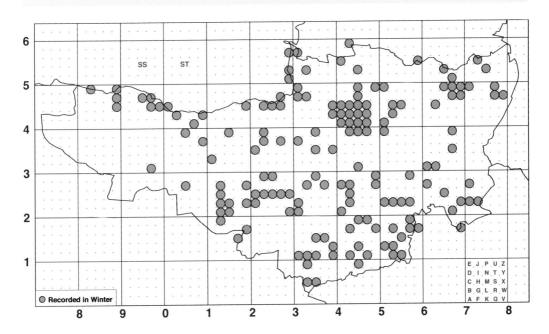

- ○ Recorded in Winter

WILLOW WARBLER *Phylloscopus trochilus*

Willow Warblers begin to arrive in late March, and are widespread by mid April. Until the 1980s they bred extensively in the lowlands, but habitat changes meant that by the 1990s there were population declines and local extinctions on the Levels and in the south. These losses accord with the national picture: a widespread decline in South-eastern and Midland England, but substantial increases in Scotland and Ireland.

The Breeding Bird Survey Index for the South West fell by 56% between 1994 and 2004. However, the RSPB/EMP Exmoor survey in 2008 found 958 territories, including on the Devon part of Exmoor. Many Willow Warblers nest outside the actual moorland, using rough woodland edges, scrubby patches and verges of beech-hedged enclosure roads. The difference between the hills and lowland farmland is shown in the Atlas results for West Somerset. Most 10-km squares on or beyond the Quantocks showed hardly a gap among their tetrads; ST02, along the Devon border and the Upper Tone, had blanks for a third of its total; but ST12, the western end of the Vale of Taunton, largely cereal land, had only seven tetrads occupied. About 60% of Mendip tetrads had Willow Warblers, mostly concentrated in the plantations of Stock Hill and Rowberrow or on the heathland of Black Down. Distribution has always been patchy across the Levels and in the farmland of the south and east, but the present map is perhaps deceptive: many 'possible' entries are likely to have been of non-breeding transients.

Most breeders probably leave in July or become locally nomadic. Passage numbers in late summer have been very variable and may have decreased recently, apart from occasional 'falls' on the coast.

GARDEN WARBLER *Sylvia borin*

This species has always been reported irregularly: its plumage is inconspicuous; it is obvious for only about six weeks, from late April to mid June; and it is hard to separate from the Blackcap by its song alone. The authors of *BA 1968–72* encouraged observers to see singing birds to clinch identification. Garden Warbler is a skulking species, which mainly sings from a thick cover of brambles, hazel or willow; it is often along the edges of woods or around clearings. The habitat is more widespread in West Somerset, and on higher ground, but Garden Warblers are also found in parts of the Avalon Marshes, where Gibson (2009) counted 38 singing on Westhay Moor. Birds are attracted by the abundant growth of willow and other scrub around old peat diggings.

In *BA 1968–72* they were probably under-recorded on Exmoor. Only one or two were found in four squares (ST32/33/34/41), from Crewkerne north to Huntspill, the largest gap in Southern England, and very few on the Quantock coastline, where they have always been scarce, but national numbers were low at the time, following the Sahel drought. They had recovered by the time of *NBA 1988–91*, when the main shortages were in East-central Somerset. These differences may reflect uneven coverage in some areas.

Nationally, *BA 2007–11* shows declines in the east and in the South Midlands, but some increases in Wales and Scotland. In Somerset, birds were found in half the 261 tetrads westward from the Quantocks, the highest numbers being across the Brendon Hills from Haddon Hill to Minehead, where they were in 47 out of 60; by far the lowest numbers were in the Vale of Taunton, where the species was found in only a fifth of tetrads. They are fairly commonly recorded in the Blackdowns, but are scarce in the south and largely absent from the Levels south of the Poldens, though they occur in escarpment woodland. In the east and on parts of Mendip there are few records; these are widely distributed, grouped in the few suitable sites, such as Rowberrow Warren. There are small concentrations of tetrads holding birds in Selwood Forest and in the Yeovil area.

Few are seen after mid or late June; but departure is presumably from then into July or August.

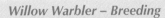

Willow Warbler – Breeding

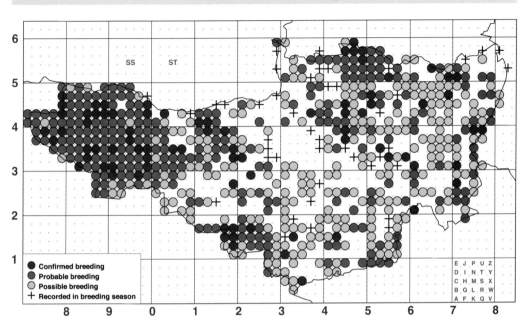

Garden Warbler – Breeding

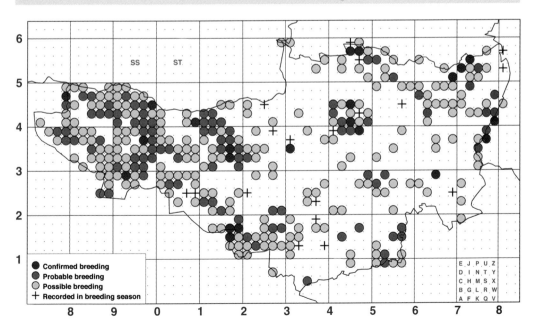

BLACKCAP *Sylvia atricapilla*

Most Blackcaps arrive in April. It is now usual to find a few forerunners from early March, but some of these may be wintering birds returning towards Central European breeding grounds.

Blackcaps have always been widespread in the county, but only thinly and locally distributed on the highest ground, where they are sometimes outnumbered by Garden Warblers. They need some ground cover, but it need not be very thick or extensive and they can be surprisingly common even in lowland farmland, where they can find stretches of untrimmed hedge and small corners of woodland or scrub. *BA 2007–11* shows that the English population has doubled in the last 15 years, and there have been much greater increases in Ireland and Scotland. In Somerset, Blackcaps have certainly increased over the last 30 years, even on the higher ground in the west. On the Levels, the 144 territories found by the Lower Brue Survey (McGeoch, 1985) had doubled by 1997. Many birds winter around the Mediterranean and in North Africa, thus avoiding the hazards of a Sahara crossing or the climatic problems further south, both

of which have sometimes wrought havoc with other migrant passerines.

The breeding map shows that Blackcaps are widely recorded across Somerset, with some gaps on the higher and wetter areas of the county. Confirmation of breeding is not always easy with this species, so it is likely that many probable records could be regarded as tantamount to confirmed.

Breeding Blackcaps disperse in July. The first wintering bird was recorded in 1885, but they did not become regular and numerous until the 1970s. On arrival, they congregate to feed on berries, especially on the sea-buckthorn of the Berrow dunes. In late autumn they begin to visit feeders and bird-tables. They are seldom or never found in winter above 150 metres; other gaps in winter distribution may be attributed to low-level differences in habitat. From ringing returns, wintering birds are generally thought to be from Central Europe, but a juvenile ringed at Watchet in June 2001 was retrapped there in the following December, so some of our breeders evidently prefer residence.

Blackcap sponsored by Di Gorringe

Blackcap – Breeding

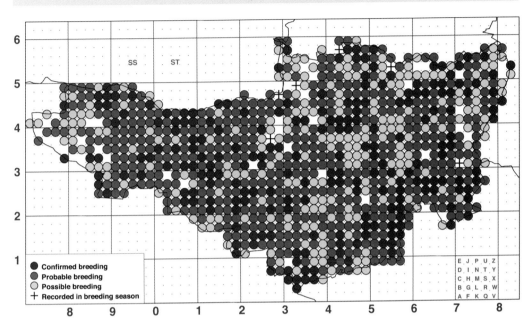

- ● Confirmed breeding
- ● Probable breeding
- ○ Possible breeding
- + Recorded in breeding season

Blackcap – Winter

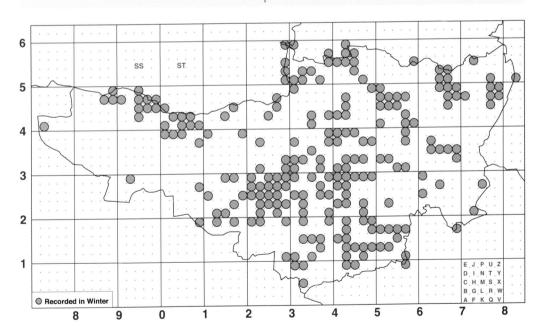

- ● Recorded in Winter

LESSER WHITETHROAT *Sylvia curruca*

This is a species of lowland hedgerows and scrub, on the north-western frontier of its wide Palearctic range. Fluctuations are therefore to be expected, even though it should have been unaffected by the Sahel droughts, since its winter quarters are further east. However, there was a drop in numbers in 1969, at the same time as the Common Whitethroat disaster. Recovery was slow, and there was a further setback about 1990, after which even populations on low ground north of the Poldens, identified in *NBA 1988–91* as the area of greatest abundance in Somerset, have been at a low ebb. By 1990, the frontier had fallen back eastward, apart from one or two pairs along the Quantock coast. In the west, Lesser Whitethroats have in the past penetrated as far as the Porlock Vale, and they were found in *BA 1968–72* in all the four north-eastern Exmoor 10-km squares

(SS83, 84, 93, and 94), though only in small numbers. In recent years they have not appeared west of Watchet and Williton, and *BA 2007–11* shows an abrupt western frontier, with few records for Devon or Cornwall, though South Wales has been recently occupied.

Lesser Whitethroats were recorded in far fewer tetrads than their fellow migrants, but were found in a reasonable proportion of tetrads through the central and eastern parts of Somerset, together with a noticeable concentration around the fringe of Bridgwater Bay. They are essentially low-country birds and even where the habitat may seem suitable very few have been recorded above about 80 or 90 metres.

Most arrive in late April or early May, when singing transients may have added to the 'possible' records, and they presumably depart in August.

Lesser Whitethroat sponsored by Alison Everett
Whitethroat sponsored by Geoff Suter

WHITETHROAT *Sylvia communis*

Fifty years ago, Whitethroats were considered so common that almost all the printed records in *SB* were of Steep Holm migrants. Yet there must always have been local variations; for example, they were never numerous on Exmoor, except in some gorse patches. In 1969, while *BA 1968–72* was in progress, there was a population crash caused by drought in the Sahel wintering grounds. Numbers have never entirely recovered: the low point nationally, in 1974, indicated a fall of 77% from the pre-crash peak, and there were further crashes in 1984 and 1991. We may still have less than half of the pre-1969 population, despite a further recovery in the late 1990s. In Britain as a whole *BA 2007–11* reports a 43% increase from 1995 to 2010. Some evidence can be obtained from the numbers of singing males reported to SOS: from 2005 to 2009 these ranged from 262 to 475. In 2010, a sudden peak of 570 reflected Atlas work, especially in the farmland of the south and east, though the last Atlas summer, in 2012, was a poor one, with only 210 singing males recorded. However, on Mendip, there was a marked increase from 2010 to 2012 on Black Down, where they moved into territories previously occupied by Dartford Warblers (G.Suter *in litt.*).

Whitethroats arrive from the third week of April to mid May. They are mainly hedgerow birds, where they have cover and launching pads for their song-flights, but are also found in scrub, in the early stages of plantations, and in heathland gorse. In the western hills and on the Blackdowns they are uncommon or absent in farmland, and they are also scarce on the barer parts of Mendip.

The abundance maps in the national Atlases do not reflect wide local variations, though they emphasise that Whitethroats have always been commonest in the lowlands from the south-eastern end of the Poldens to Steart and north to the southern slopes of Mendip. Irregularities are well shown by the map: in the west and south-west they were present in 73 of 140 tetrads, but in only three of the 13 tetrads in SS73 and in only 11 of the 25 in SS93. Of the 124 tetrads covering the East Brendons, the Vale of Taunton and the Quantocks they were present in 105, including almost all in the last two areas. In lowland Somerset as a whole they were found in about three-quarters of all tetrads, though they were scarcer in parts of the east, where there is extensive mature woodland.

Breeders presumably depart from August to September, but few are seen after July.

Lesser Whitethroat – Breeding

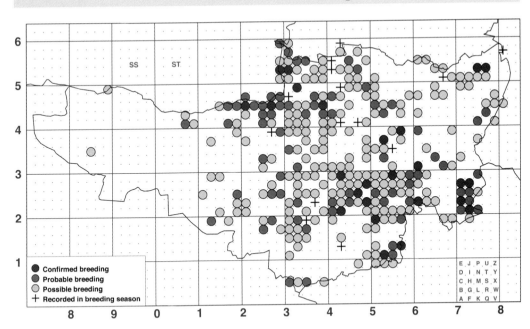

- ● Confirmed breeding
- ● Probable breeding
- ○ Possible breeding
- + Recorded in breeding season

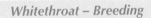

Whitethroat – Breeding

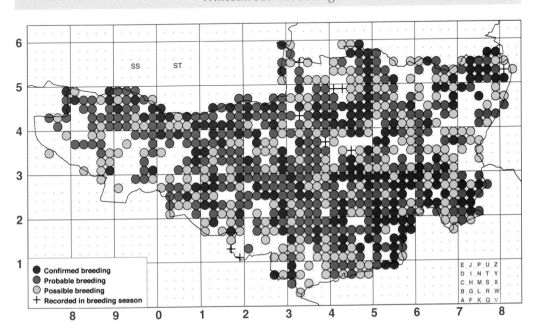

- ● Confirmed breeding
- ● Probable breeding
- ○ Possible breeding
- + Recorded in breeding season

DARTFORD WARBLER *Sylvia undata*

The first confirmed Somerset records of Dartford Warblers were of ten single vagrants at coastal and moorland sites from 1974 to 1982. After a gap, breeding pairs were found at two Quantock sites in 1989/90, on Black Down in 1993 and on Dunkery in 1995. A succession of warm winters enabled a rapid extension into many suitable areas of mixed gorse and long heather, and even to young plantations on Rodhuish Common and Croydon Hill. The national survey in 2006 found 126 Somerset territories (Wootton *et al.* 2009). By 2008, the first Atlas summer, there were probably more than 150 pairs recorded: 11 on Black Down and Rowberrow Warren; two at Sampford Point, on the Blackdowns; at least 20 on the Quantocks; and at least 110 on the Somerset side of Exmoor, where breeding had extended from the coastal heaths as far as Withypool Common and Brady Moor. The colonisation has been described in detail by Packer and Knight (1997) and Hill (2003).

The heavy snow in early February 2009 changed all this; they were hit badly elsewhere even on lowland heathland, but in Somerset, where all the suitable habitat is on higher ground, the effects were particularly severe. There were no more than about a dozen pairs remaining: three on the Quantocks and about nine on Exmoor. While the connection cannot be proved beyond doubt, the sites where they survived generally had large stands of tall gorse, which may have provided both shelter and snow-free feeding areas. The last were seen on Mendip, where the suitable sites have less tall gorse, in the autumn of 2008. In 2010 there was only one Quantock record, but around Exmoor at least two pairs continued to breed on the North Hill–Hurlstone ridge, and possibly one or two on Crawter Hill and Dunkery. The breeding map published here therefore largely represents the 2008 situation and overstates considerably the breeding distribution as it stands currently.

There was no improvement in 2011, though very small numbers persisted on these Exmoor sites. In 2012, there was some evidence of a slight increase between North Hill and Hurlstone, where breeding was successful and 16 were counted in November. Yet there has been no recovery elsewhere, though one sang on the North Quantocks. A 2014 survey on Exmoor should show whether any others have returned. Further west, in North Devon, they have vanished from the high moorlands between Lynton and Combe Martin, but have survived on the low promontory of Baggy Point (P. Madgett *in litt.*).

There have been occasional autumn and winter records elsewhere, most frequently at coastal sites. Records in the central and eastern parts of the county have always been rare, and are likely to remain so at least in the near future.

SAVI'S WARBLER *Locustella luscinioides*

Savi's Warbler is a rare visitor to Somerset, with the first record as recently as 1970; nationally it is an extremely rare breeder, barely maintaining a toehold and perhaps not currently breeding annually. Of the 13 county records to date, the twentieth-century records were mostly around the Bridgwater claypits, but the development of the Avalon Marshes has provided much more habitat for this reedbed reeler, and almost all recent records have been of singing males from this area. There has never been any evidence that a breeding attempt has taken place, but the habitat is ideal and breeding difficult to prove, so we can but hope that colonisation might take place at some point. That said, there was only one record in the Atlas period, of a singing male at Ham Wall RSPB reserve on 23–29 June 2010. (No map.)

Dartford Warbler – Breeding

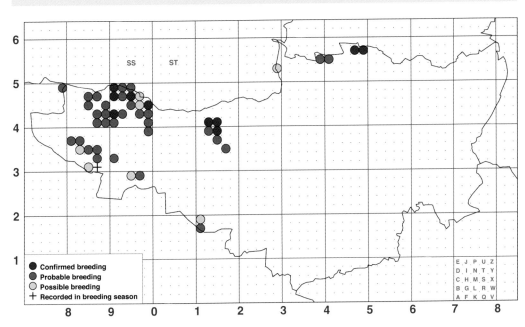

Legend:
- ● Confirmed breeding
- ● Probable breeding
- ○ Possible breeding
- + Recorded in breeding season

Dartford Warbler – Winter

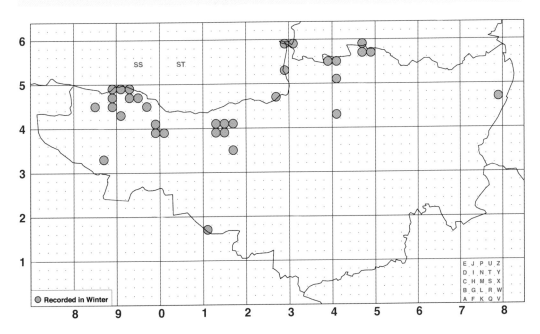

○ Recorded in Winter

GRASSHOPPER WARBLER *Locustella naevia*

Little is known of the history of this species before 1920, which may be partly because of its crepuscular habits. As observers became more mobile Grasshopper Warblers were found in many different habitats, from the peat moors to the young fir plantations and the heather or tussock grassland of Black Down and Exmoor. The indefatigable Wells collector, Stanley Lewis, once found nine nests in a morning on the Cheddar Moors, a much-changed habitat today.

On Exmoor, the earlier full breeding surveys found few territories: 15 in 1978 and 52 in 1992. In 2008, however, there were 235 on the Somerset side. This result was largely achieved by starting work just after dawn, but one may also suspect that the figures include some passage birds. The Mires Survey (Boyce 2012) found many songsters. The Atlas map confirms the belief that Grasshopper Warblers in Somerset have largely moved to the hills, while at the same time they have declined seriously in the lowlands, disappearing from many areas on the Levels. This is perhaps because of an increase in sward height, particularly on Exmoor, as upland grazing has declined, while 'improvement' of the lowland grass moors has made those areas much less attractive, though they cling on, much reduced, in and around reserves. In recent years there has been little conifer planting, so that habitat has now almost vanished, which may help to explain the relative paucity in other upland areas. Some at least of the 'possible' records away from the two main clusters are perhaps as likely to have been passage migrants as territory holders.

Breeding birds presumably leave in July or August.

SEDGE WARBLER *Acrocephalus schoenobaenus*

Until the 1970s there were few records of this species' numbers, or even of its habitat, in the county; it regularly figured in *SB* in the list of species for which no details were thought necessary. It has always been a common bird of the lower and wetter areas, breeding widely along rivers and rhynes, and almost entirely avoiding high ground. In 1969, its national numbers crashed after the Sahel drought with those of the Whitethroat, but this escaped all notice in Somerset and the *NBA 1988–91* map shows that any long-lasting shortfalls were confined to marginal areas.

Counts at key sites did not begin until 1976/77, when the first comprehensive survey of the Levels found 415 pairs (Round 1978). The second major failure of rainfall in the Sahel was reflected when this figure was halved (Weaver and Chown 1983), though recovery followed this. Recent counts are mainly from West Sedge Moor, the most profitable single site, where there were 146 singing males in 2010 and 229 in 2011, but only 86 in 2012. In the Avalon Marshes, the expansion of reedbeds means that Sedge Warblers are now far outnumbered by Reed Warblers, but they remain the commoner species along thickly vegetated rhynes in some grass-moor areas of the Levels, especially where there are occasional willows. As the map shows, a few are also found outside those areas, for example in the Blackmoor Vale, on Cary Moor, along rivers in the south, and on the coast as far as Dunster Hawn. A relatively isolated group of records appears along the Upper Barle on Exmoor, where Sedge Warblers frequent dense willow. The colonisation of oilseed rape fields, first observed in the early 2000s, may be more extensive than has yet been shown.

The main arrival is in the second half of April, but a considerable passage continues into May, and migrant songsters heard early in the season may have inflated the number of possible breeders, especially away from core areas. Breeders disperse from July.

Grasshopper Warbler sponsored by Walter John Stone

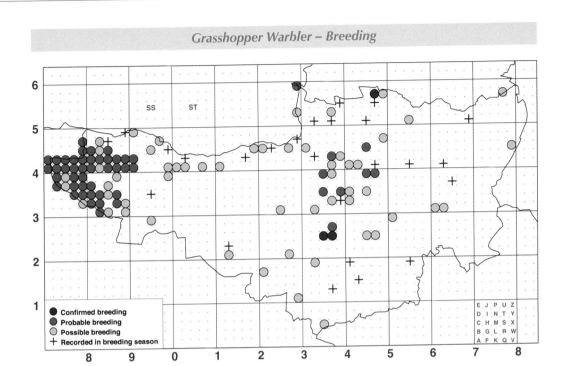

Grasshopper Warbler – Breeding

Confirmed breeding
Probable breeding
Possible breeding
+ Recorded in breeding season

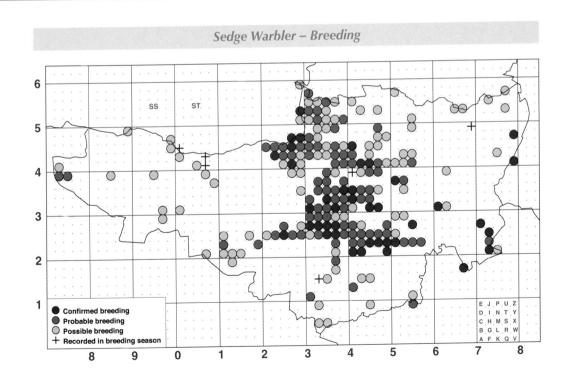

Sedge Warbler – Breeding

Confirmed breeding
Probable breeding
Possible breeding
+ Recorded in breeding season

REED WARBLER *Acrocephalus scirpaceus*

Reed Warblers are closely associated with beds of *Phragmites australis*, and therefore with lowlands, but they are also found in nearby withies and shrubs. They probably entered Somerset with the digging of 'borrow' pits along the railways and the flooding of brick-pits around Bridgwater, and then slowly penetrated to a number of similar sites and to the margins of park lakes. Until the development of the wetlands on the Avalon Marshes they were very local and far outnumbered by Sedge Warblers. They did not reach the far west until the 1940s; they are still common around Minehead Marshes but have had to retreat from Porlock Marsh, which is now too brackish. The apparent decrease noted on the change map in *NBA 1988–91* may have been affected by coverage.

Reed Warblers have greatly increased in England over the last 30 years and have also colonised many sites in South Wales and South-east Ireland. A huge expansion accompanied the development of reedbeds in the Avalon Marshes. Two full surveys there found 534 in 1996 and 1,170 in 2002 (D.J. Chown *in litt.*).

Some counts are available for large parts of the major sites: in 2006 there were 307 territories on Ham Wall and 337 on Shapwick Heath NNR (excluding Canada Farm Lake); by 2011, the Ham Wall figure had risen to 415. They are widespread elsewhere: on Cary Moor; at Berrow and in other coastal reedbeds west to Hinkley Point; on the Huntspill River, now a major site, with up to 75 pairs; on reservoirs with reedy margins; across King's Sedge Moor and adjacent Levels; on the South Levels; on the Yeo near Yeovilton; and along the Bridgwater–Taunton Canal. Even small reedbeds, such as those at Kilve Beach and Rodden Nature Reserve (Frome) provided breeding records during the Atlas.

As with other migrants, arrival dates have crept earlier in the year, but most still arrive from late April to mid May. They probably leave in July and early August, but a few are still feeding young up to early September. In late summer, many pass through the coastal reedbeds, where a long-established ringing programme has been conducted.

WAXWING *Bombycilla garrulus*

Waxings have always been irregular visitors this far to the south-west, even in irruption years. During the five Atlas winters these Fennoscandinavian invaders were recorded in only two: there were five birds from December 2008 to March 2009, but a major influx of between 220 and 270 from November 2010 to February 2011, including parties of up to 40. The map probably shows some duplication and overlap among the records as these highly mobile flocks ate their way through berries. The maturing of trees and shrubs in ornamental plantings by supermarkets and local authorities has led to Waxwings being more conspicuous during their incursions, to the delight of many observers.

The 2010/11 influx was the second-largest since records began in 1850, and came only six years after the largest, in 2004/05, when there were over 400, including flocks of 80 to 100 in Frome and Taunton, perhaps trebling the total number of Waxwings previously recorded in Somerset.

Waxwing sponsored by Roger Musgrove

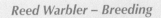

Reed Warbler – Breeding

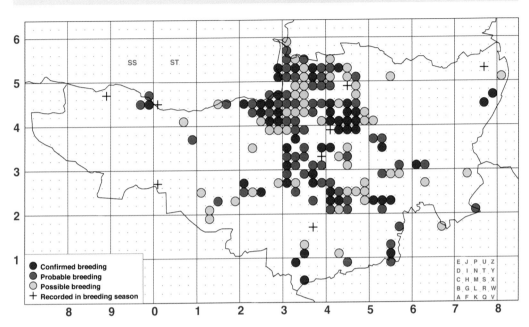

Legend:
- ● Confirmed breeding
- ● Probable breeding
- ○ Possible breeding
- + Recorded in breeding season

Waxwing – Winter

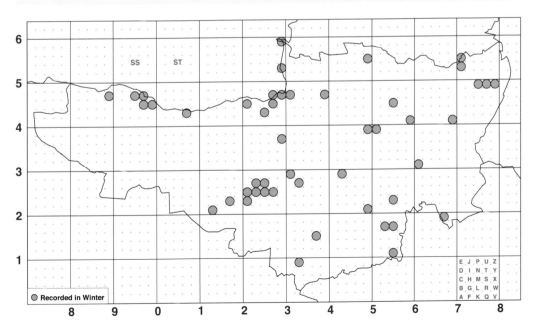

Legend:
- ◉ Recorded in Winter

NUTHATCH *Sitta europaea*

Nuthatches require large, old timber, both for nesting and for foraging. Woods are not always essential, as can be seen in parts of south-west Somerset, where Nuthatches are found in the abundant hedgerow oaks as well as on garden feeders. They have always been scarce on the Levels and along the coast of Bridgwater Bay. During the last century local absences elsewhere were sometimes reported, even in apparently prime territory. Adult Nuthatches are extremely sedentary, so gaps in the range are not swiftly filled, but *BA 2007–11* shows that juveniles can colonise empty areas, as they have done recently in Northern England and in Scotland.

The previous Atlases were at one in displaying the absence, or rarity, of Nuthatches in the four 10-km squares around and to the east of Bridgwater. They are still very scarce here, and further north in ST35, which in Somerset is largely the floodplain of the Axe and relatively devoid of trees. However, the more thorough coverage now achieved shows that no 10-km square is entirely without them in both seasons, apart from the urban and duneland coastal strip of ST25, from Highbridge to Brean Down. Both *WA 1981–84* and *NBA 1988–91* showed further gaps in Central Somerset (ST42/52); these 10-km squares which include the South Levels, Yeovilton airfield and some rather barren farmland, still have very few breeding Nuthatches, despite thorough searches. The loss of elms (*Ulmus procera*) may have been the main cause of local extinctions. Such gaps extend over the entire Levels, though there are Nuthatches in the escarpment woodland. By contrast, taking summer and winter records together, about three-quarters of all the 264 tetrads west and south-west of the Quantocks are occupied, and every one in ST13, which covers most of those hills. Of 69 Somerset Mendip tetrads, 54 have Nuthatches. There are also many along the Wiltshire border and on the Blackdowns.

This species is often easier to find in winter, both at feeders and in woodland, and can be noisiest in early spring, before the breeding season.

Nuthatch sponsored by Blake Veterinary Group

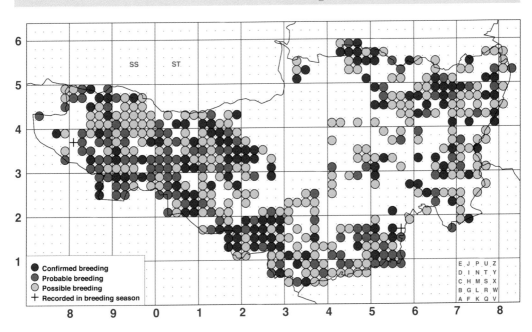

Nuthatch – Breeding

SS ST

- ● Confirmed breeding
- ● Probable breeding
- ○ Possible breeding
- + Recorded in breeding season

E J P U Z
D I N T Y
C H M S X
B G L R W
A F K Q V

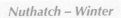

Nuthatch – Winter

SS ST

- ● Recorded in Winter

E J P U Z
D I N T Y
C H M S X
B G L R W
A F K Q V

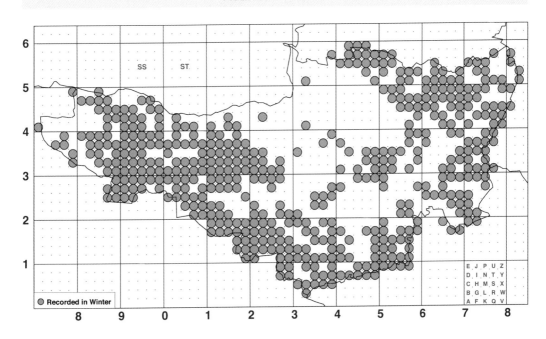

TREECREEPER *Certhia familiaris*

Of all the fairly common diurnal species, this has given most trouble to Atlas observers, unobtrusive as it is. There are few species where recording can be so dependent on the persistence of observers in their awkwardly vertical and often vain searches of tree trunks. The song period is short, and the high notes are not readily picked up by all observers. Away from well-watched areas resident observers will have a much better chance of detecting Treecreepers than casual visitors surveying a tetrad. When nest-finding was a more widespread hobby 'up to seven nests were found in a day of normal Atlas fieldwork', according to *BA 1968–72*. Attitudes have changed towards such potentially intrusive practices, however, and it is an unlikely achievement nowadays. In *BA 1968–72*, Treecreepers were recorded in every 10-km square in Somerset. By contrast, in *WA 1981–84* they were absent from four (around Bridgwater and on the Brendons) and scarce in many others, especially along the coast and in Central or East Somerset. A similar picture was given by *NBA 1988–91*, where none were recorded in four 10-km squares, and very few in ten others, largely across the same areas.

In the current Atlas, taking the breeding and winter records together, Treecreepers were found in every 10-km square except in the six relatively tree-less tetrads of ST25, along the Burnham coast. However, on the lowest ground, and on the western part of Exmoor, they were very scarce, appearing in no more than a quarter of the tetrads. A comparison between summer and winter records is instructive: the species was recorded in 393 tetrads in summer and in 448 in winter, but overall in a total of 570. In Britain Treecreepers are largely sedentary, so such a relatively low degree of overlap between the seasons says much about their 'detectability'. It seems fair to regard them as present in about 60% of the county. In tetrads that were visited in the last two years of fieldwork, Treecreepers may have suffered cold-weather losses before they could be surveyed.

Treecreeper sponsored by DJEnvironmental (Tim Davis and Tim Jones)

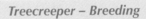

Treecreeper – Breeding

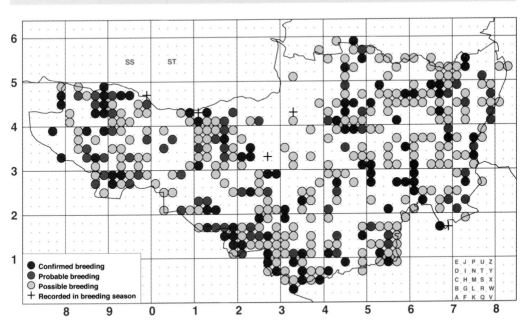

- ● Confirmed breeding
- ● Probable breeding
- ○ Possible breeding
- + Recorded in breeding season

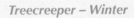

Treecreeper – Winter

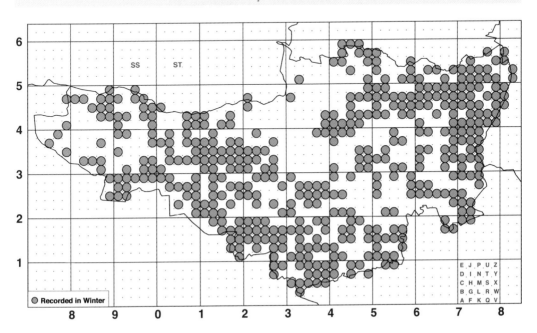

- ● Recorded in Winter

WREN *Troglodytes troglodytes*

Although *BA 1968–72* and *NBA 1988–91* both had an unbroken display of occupied 10-km squares, and the abundance map in the latter showed a high level of population throughout most of Somerset, *WA 1981–84* told a slightly different tale, with low counts of up to only a dozen birds in 12 tetrads, mostly around Bridgwater, on Exmoor, and in parts of the south and east. The cold winter weather of 1981/82 may have played a part in these results.

Wrens are one of the UK's commonest bird species, being ubiquitous and relatively abundant in most habitats. In Somerset they can be found from sea-level up to the long heather on Dunkery, Exmoor, and in any habitat that can provide a little cover, including areas of farmland with some gardens. There is some vertical movement, the highest sites often being deserted from November to February. Wrens are hard to miss once song has started, so this is one of the easiest species to survey with a high degree of accuracy for both presence and breeding activity. They suffered during the cold winters of the latter two years of fieldwork, but losses had perhaps been made good by the spring of 2012. Wrens probably breed in every tetrad, except one or two coastal fragments, but no winter birds were found in 24 tetrads on Exmoor.

Wren sponsored by Thomas G. Bartlett

Wren – Breeding

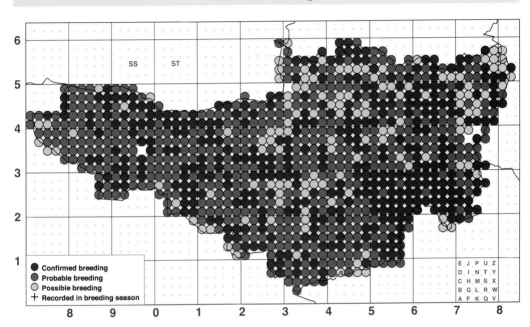

Confirmed breeding
Probable breeding
Possible breeding
+ Recorded in breeding season

Wren – Winter

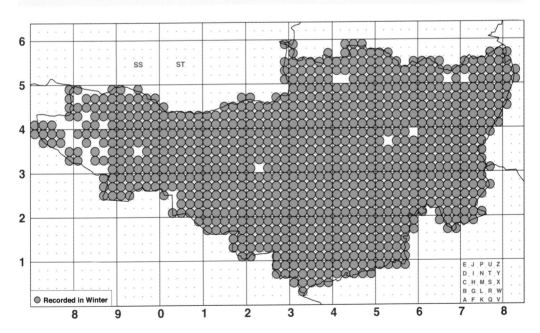

Recorded in Winter

STARLING *Sturnus vulgaris*

Familiar as they now are, and a source of wonder in their winter millions, Starlings were not widespread in the South West until after 1850. At the beginning of that century, the pioneer ornithologist Colonel Montagu, presented with a juvenile at Kingsbridge, named it as a new species of thrush. By 1890, however, they were probably breeding in woods and buildings throughout the county. Even in *NBA 1988– 91*, there was no hint of a decline, although the abundance map showed a wide variation in density, with the highest numbers along a partly urban band from Weston-super-Mare to Chard, where Starlings can find abundant nest-sites in buildings and use adjacent grassland for feeding. By contrast, Exmoor was thinly inhabited, and most breeding birds there were probably in ancient woodland.

From 1995 to 2005 a slight decline was noticed, especially in western villages such as Porlock, where daily records for a garden fell dramatically in 2004, and have not recovered (Vaughan and Vaughan 2007). The latest Atlas shows that similar decreases must have taken place over wide areas of the west: in 177 tetrads of Exmoor and the Brendons breeding attempts were found in only 30, most of which were on the thickly inhabited coastline, and no woodland colonies seem to remain. At the other end of the county, on Mendip, Starlings are still present in three-quarters of Somerset tetrads, and are absent only on the barest section of the plateau, in ST55. In *NAvA 2007–11*, Mendip tetrads were found to have the lowest population in summer, but, conversely, the highest in winter. Starlings are still quite common on the Blackdowns.

In most of lowland Somerset about 70% of tetrads are now occupied, with a lowest score of 11 in ST43 (King's Sedge Moor) and almost complete presence throughout the south-east (ST41/42/51/52), though they are curiously scarce in ST62 (Cadbury) and along the Wiltshire border. Research has shown that the decline, which is less marked in urban areas, is in part at least due to a loss of invertebrates in permanent pasture, hayfields and winter stubbles. On the national scale, *BA 2007–11* shows contractions in range for Devon and West Wales and a fairly general decline in numbers over England, except in parts of the east and south-east. In Wales as a whole, there was a 67% decline between 1995 and 2010 (Risely *et al.* 2012), which has been most marked in rural and upland areas (Brenchley *et al.* 2013).

Starlings disperse quickly in flocks over the countryside near their urban breeding grounds, so some records of presence in later summer may distort the 'possible' breeding statistics. The mass of winter immigrants from Eastern Europe usually begin to arrive in the second part of October; in November and December huge roosts develop in the Avalon Marshes, and have become the spectacular focus for ecotourism. In 2002, there were estimated to be eight million birds roosting at Shapwick Heath, perhaps the largest roost recorded in England; most recent estimates have not exceeded one million. There have been other sizeable roosts at Yeovil Crematorium, Chard Reservoir, and the Obridge Viaduct in Taunton. Though now without summer Starlings, Exmoor grasslands in winter attract many thousands, which are known to have used several woodland roosts, notably near Sandyway and in Allcombe Water, but sometimes move over the Devon border.

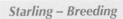

Starling – Breeding

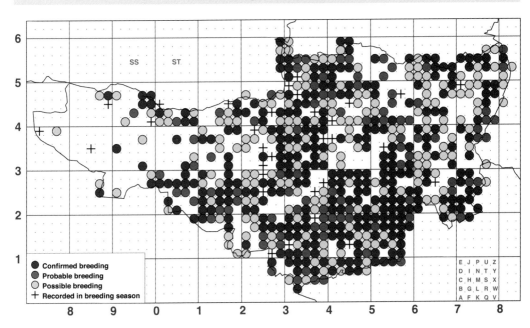

Legend:
- ● Confirmed breeding
- ● Probable breeding
- ○ Possible breeding
- + Recorded in breeding season

Starling – Winter

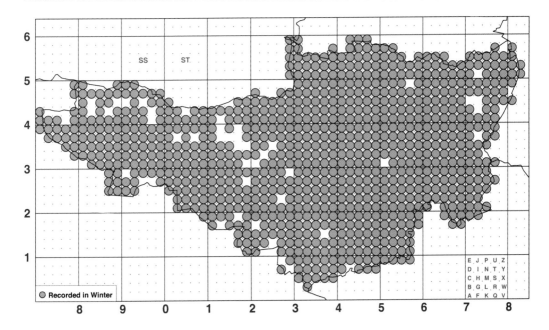

Legend:
- ○ Recorded in Winter

DIPPER *Cinclus cinclus*

Dippers are far simpler to find from January to April, when they are very active and singing, than in high summer when the vegetation has closed over the smaller streams. Most Somerset Dippers live along the larger rivers of the west, especially on Horner Water, Badgworthy Water, and the Barle, with their tributaries, and they are commonest in the wooded middle reaches. Local observers in the west believe that they are not quite so numerous as they once were, with numbers down by perhaps a third since 1945. Dippers can be victims of mink, and suspicion also falls on the many stock barriers now inserted across streams, where heavy timber may present less danger than less-visible wire. They are generally scarce along the upper sections of rivers, as on the Exe above Westermill or the Barle above Cornham Ford, partly because of a shortage of nest-sites. They breed on most of the larger tributaries, such as Pennycombe Water and the Quarme, and on the northward-flowing streams of the Brendons. In slower waters, they may be found near weirs and old mills.

Outside the western hills, the Atlas has helped to give us more complete knowledge of their range. In the south-east, they were not recorded around Yeovil, but are on the upper Cale near Wincanton. In the north-east there are a few pairs on the Brue and the Alham, quite a strong population in the wooded reaches of the Mells River from Nettlebridge down to Frome, and some on Nunney Brook. They also breed on Wellow Brook, but only a short stretch of its banks are in Somerset. Dippers occur on the Sheppey, even in Shepton Mallet and in the outskirts of Wells, and there are pairs on the Mendip Axe near Wookey Hole and on the Cheddar Yeo. In the far south they are present on the Axe, on the upper Isle and on streams around Chard. They were found on the headwaters of several Blackdown rivers. There are small numbers along the Tone from Clatworthy to Greenham and then here and there through the Vale down to Bradford-on-Tone, but most recent records below East Nynehead have only been in winter. There are even one or two secretive winterers on the Taunton streams, though they were not found in summer.

Dippers breed here and there between the Quantocks and the Brendons, but sightings depend very much on chance encounters at bridges. Here, as in many other places, by no means all of the course of a stream is publicly accessible, which hinders searches. The small eastern streams of the Quantocks have only a few pairs, but there are probably more to be found, for up to 12 were once discovered here in a little-known study in which farmland streams were extensively searched (White, Baker, and Baker 1987).

Dippers are mostly sedentary within their breeding territories, but there is some vertical movement during hard weather and dispersal up and down streams after breeding.

Dipper sponsored by Roger and Ann Butcher

Dipper – Breeding

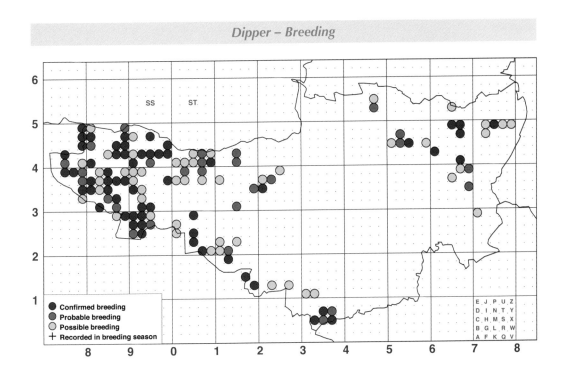

Dipper – Winter

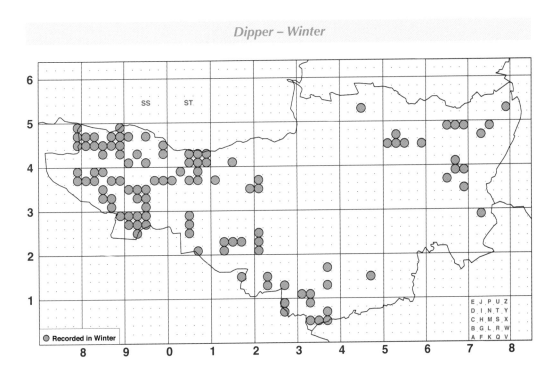

BLACKBIRD *Turdus merula*

Blackbirds are almost universal breeders, except in a few tetrads on Exmoor Forest which lack suitable cover. Some have advanced up the combes into the steep gullies that once belonged to Ring Ouzels. The abundance maps in *NBA 1988–91* and *BA 2007–11* show that Exmoor is the only area where Blackbirds are in general less numerous than in the rest of the county. Blackbirds are thought to have been originally birds of tall forest, but their highest densities are in parks and large gardens, and they can be scarce in tight modern developments. Yet some small towns support large numbers: back in 2000, there were 250 pairs within a half-mile radius of Redstart School in Chard. However, the population has declined over the last 30 years in Crewkerne, where few young seem to be successfully fledged.

Somerset breeders are in general residents, though perhaps not on the highest parts of Mendip, the Quantocks and Exmoor. This Atlas shows fewer probable and confirmed breeding records in those areas, although some eastern parts of Somerset were similar. There is some evidence of dispersal to the north-west, as shown by previous recoveries of Somerset birds in Wales and Ireland. In most winters, the residents are joined in late October and November by many birds from further north or east, which either remain in small parties or flocks for the winter or pass on towards Ireland and France. There may also be cold-weather movements into the county, one of which led to the record Somerset count of 161 on Westhay Moor in November 2007.

RING OUZEL *Turdus torquatus*

The decline of the Ring Ouzel as a breeding species on Exmoor began around 1970. Breeding was last proved there in 2002, despite much searching since, including by Atlas observers and the Exmoor Monitoring Project; the RSPB survey of 2008 found just a single bird. It remains a scarce passage migrant, and during the Atlas period was recorded in April and early May in a number of scattered locations, chiefly at upland and coastal sites. Birds were recorded at a number of former breeding sites, but few lingered and unfortunately there was no evidence of breeding.

Autumn passage peaks in the latter half of October. Two 'winter' Atlas records, from Brean Down in 2008 and well inland near Marston Magna in 2009, were both in the first half of November, and are better considered as late-autumn migrants. (No map.)

Blackbird sponsored by Paul Bovett

Blackbird – Breeding

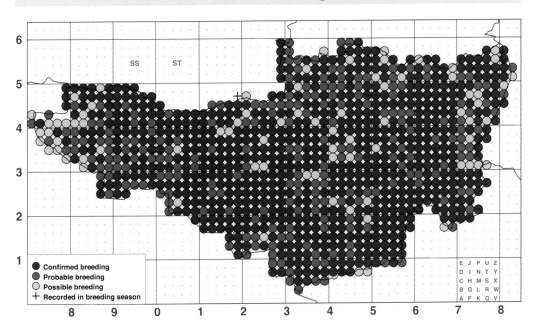

Blackbird – Winter

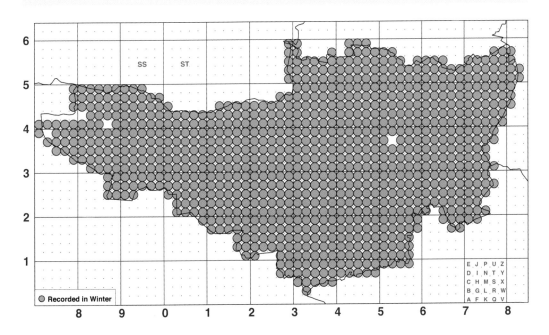

FIELDFARE *Turdus pilaris*

Fieldfares begin to arrive from Fennoscandinavia in the second half of October, on average slightly later than the Redwings with which they are often found. They then feed largely on autumn fruits. When these have been exhausted, they may turn to fallen apples, which become important to them in hard weather, and to invertebrates in farmland. They generally remain in wary, nomadic flocks, and are

found throughout the county, even on the highest ground, but are most numerous on the Levels. *WA 1981–84* showed a curious absence in the Bridgwater area, where they were missing from three 10-km squares; the only such areas in Southern England east of Cornwall. That may have been due to coverage levels, though the more intensive recording for the present Atlas still shows some gaps west of Bridg- water and in the north-east of the county. Fresh numbers may arrive from the north after New Year, under pressure of weather. Counts of up to 2,000 are frequently made, but much higher numbers have sometimes occurred at favourite foods, such as sea- buckthorn, which at Berrow has attracted up to 15,000, or at roosts, as in the Stock Hill plantations, which have provided shelter for up to 35,000 Field- fares and Redwings. Such numbers, however, were not reported in the recent Atlas period.

The return movement starts in late February. Flocks may pass through the county well into April, and these account for the few breeding-season Atlas records, which have not been mapped.

REDWING *Turdus iliacus*

Redwings arrive from early October, usually a few days in advance of Fieldfares. They come from Fennoscandinavia or Russia, and presumably also from Iceland. Like Fieldfares, they are very widely spread across the county, perhaps even more so: there are relatively few tetrads (away from bare moorland) where neither was recorded, as can be seen from the maps. Large numbers pass along the coast towards Ireland, or southward on a broad front, where they are often heard over towns at night. They feed at first mainly on hedgerow fruits and are highly mobile, shifting ground when they have exhausted local food supplies. There have been heavy concen- trations in the sea-buckthorn of the Burnham and Berrow coast.

In late autumn and winter they generally become less common on higher ground, or at least less con- spicuous, since they disappear into deciduous wood- land, where they feed in leaf-litter or on ivy berries. In hard weather they may enter gardens, and many can fall victim to intensely cold weather. Very large numbers were once counted at Mendip roosts, but

wintering flocks of more than 500 are now unusual anywhere in the county. In *WA 1981–84*, Somerset showed a complete blank in two Bridgwater and Quantock squares, the only one in all Southern England. This Atlas shows a winter distribution very similar to that for Fieldfare.

The return passage begins early, and by March Redwings can be scarce, April stragglers appearing in early breeding-season results much less frequently than Fieldfares.

Fieldfare and Redwing sponsored by Nigel Cottle

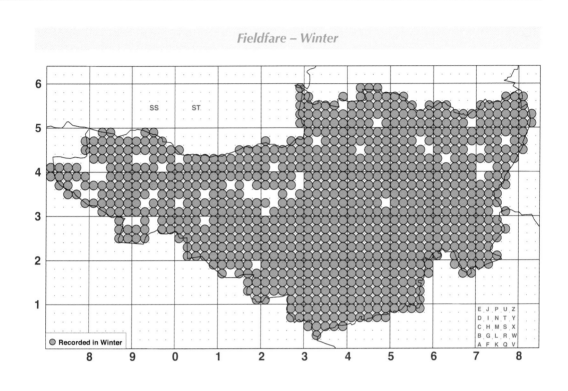

Fieldfare – Winter

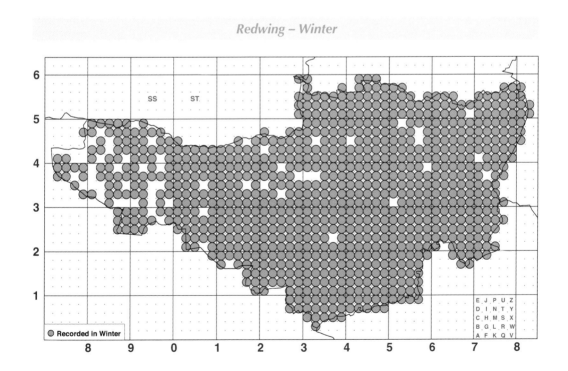

Redwing – Winter

267

SONG THRUSH *Turdus philomelos*

Before the 1970s, no concerns were expressed about the numbers of Song Thrushes. In *BA 1968–72*, there were no gaps in 10-km squares or obviously weak populations. The widespread national decline does not seem to have affected the South West until the 1980s, when it was noticed in lowland farmland and in gardens. There was certainly a severe drop in numbers during the 1990s, with the halving of populations of 100 in the Lower Brue Valley and of 90 in the parish of Crewkerne. There may then have been some recovery, even in the suburbs: in Chard there were 58 singing males within half a mile of Redstart School in 2000. However, later observers have commented on the apparent lack of breeding success in towns.

As *BA 2007–11* shows, the decline was most obvious in Eastern England and may therefore have received disproportionate publicity. Various causes have been suggested, especially the widespread use of molluscicides in suburban gardens and the loss of winter fallows. In Somerset, Song Thrushes are still common woodland birds, especially in the west, where they also often breed in dense gorse, and were present in 240 out of 264 tetrads. From 2006 to 2010, there were thought to be between 70 and 90 singing along the Barle from Withypool to Dulverton, and in June 2012, a two-hour walk at Combe Florey found 13 in song around the village. There is also a strong population on Mendip, where 82 out of 86 tetrads were occupied.

The breeding-season map here shows that Song Thrushes are still widespread birds, with relatively few gaps in their distribution. The gap on the higher parts of Exmoor is as expected for an essentially woodland species. The map suggests that little breeding has recently been proved over King's Sedge Moor and the South Levels, or in the higher farmland east of Glastonbury. Numbers are undoubtedly low in parts of the Levels, and once population falls below a certain total, and singing birds are far apart, observers may struggle to count adequate numbers in a day's tetrad visit to justify entering a 'T', and thus promoting the breeding status to 'probable'. This problem may have also affected recording in the east and south-west.

Autumn passage is less obvious than with Field-fares and Redwings, but birds can often be seen in mixed flocks with other thrushes. These may pass on to Ireland or Iberia. Several Scandinavian birds ringed in Somerset have been recovered in the following summers.

The winter distribution is similar, though Song Thrushes were recorded in more tetrads in winter – this may be partly because of their greater visibility then, and partly because of wintering birds from further north boosting their numbers. The hard winters during the Atlas period sometimes brought high numbers to the unfrozen coast, though counts never reached those in 1981, when every field in the Porlock Vale was full of them. They are generally scarce on high ground in winter, especially on Exmoor Forest.

Song Thrush sponsored by Imogen Savage

Song Thrush – Breeding

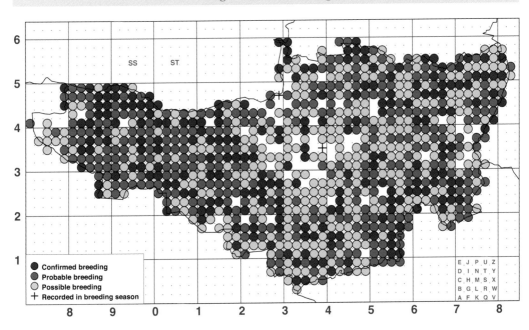

Song Thrush – Winter

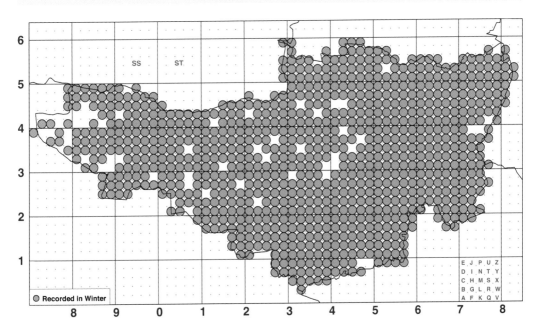

MISTLE THRUSH *Turdus viscivorus*

Mistle Thrushes have always presented the compilers of Atlases with problems. Even where they are fairly common, individual territories are perhaps four or five times larger than for Song Thrush; song is far-carrying, but strongest from December to April, so early visits are necessary to record definitive evidence of breeding. Observers were encouraged to record singing males in March, which helped to further fill in the picture.

Little information can be gathered from the older atlases. In *BA 1968–72*, birds were breeding in all 10-km squares, but in *NBA 1988–91* they were scarce or absent over a wide area of East-central Somerset. They are scarce in the lowlands around Bridgwater Bay and over much of the Levels (and always have been), probably because the tall trees that they favour as song-posts are often lacking there beyond the adjacent escarpment woodland. In *BA 2007–11*, this general area shows up on the abundance map as having the lowest population in Southern England. From the River Parrett to Cornwall, the upland woods hold far higher numbers than the lowlands.

The British population is thought to have halved over the last 40 years, an estimate which accords with evidence presented in *NAvA 2007–11* for Avon, though probably not for the Somerset section of Mendip which is also covered there; once again, the uplands have more records of Mistle Thrushes than the lowlands.

Small coastal movements have often been noted in late autumn, but it seems likely that Somerset breeders are resident, or are nomadic only over a small range. In Somerset as a whole, there were records from 60% of all tetrads in the breeding season and from 66% in winter; if these are combined, the total is as high as 80%. However, the picture is not uniform: on the western part of Exmoor there were winter records from only about half the tetrads where the species was present in summer, suggesting significant movement to lower ground. It is unlikely that there is enough food on the higher ground to sustain anything but a very thin population of Mistle Thrushes; those that do stay will often defend food sources such as holly.

Recent counts of late-summer flocks suggest some decline in the numbers of juveniles, though without a contraction of range. A flock of 72 at Williton in June 2011 was exceptional.

Mistle Thrush sponsored by Andrew Pugsley

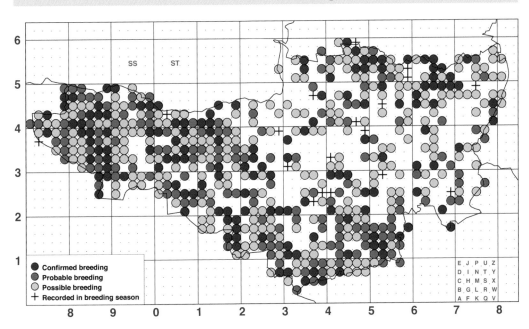

Mistle Thrush – Breeding

● Confirmed breeding
● Probable breeding
○ Possible breeding
+ Recorded in breeding season

SS ST

E J P U Z
D I N T Y
C H M S X
B G L R W
A F K Q V

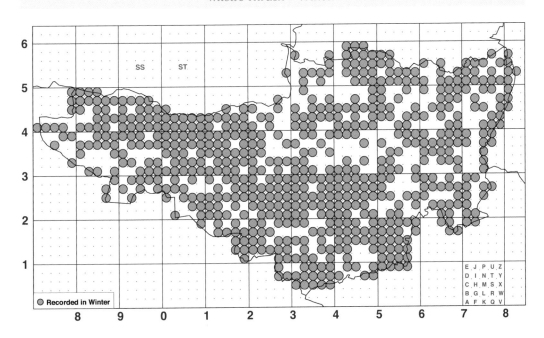

Mistle Thrush – Winter

● Recorded in Winter

SS ST

E J P U Z
D I N T Y
C H M S X
B G L R W
A F K Q V

NIGHTINGALE *Luscinia megarhynchos*

Across England the Nightingale population has declined by 90% since 1970; the remaining birds are almost all concentrated in a few prime sites south of a line from the Severn to the Wash (*BA 2007–11*). Major national BTO surveys were carried out in 1976, 1980, 1999, and 2012, the data from the last being included in this Atlas. Somerset has always been at the extreme north-western tip of the Nightingale's breeding range, but the 1980 survey, in what was obviously a good year, found 169 singing birds in 36 10-km squares. The repeat in 1999 could find only 116 in 17, however, and in 2012, there were only 35, in 14 tetrads, though the weather was almost unremittingly poor.

As the map shows, the species' range within Somerset is now largely confined to a limited area of the south and south-west: the stronghold is Merryfield airfield, a Ministry of Defence site, but there are seemingly stable populations in the escarpment woodland along the southern edge of the Levels and in several woodlands on the north-eastern corner of the Blackdowns. The Atlas probably records the last days of the small population around Hinkley Point, remnant of a once-flourishing population in the lowland copses between Combwich and Watchet, and the Avalon Marshes, another former stronghold, now has few records. On the plus side, however, fieldwork for the Atlas and the 2012 BTO survey has discovered a number of singing males in the east of the county.

Nightingales arrive in the second or third week of April and are seldom seen once they stop singing in mid June.

Nightingale sponsored by Roger Dickey
Spotted Flycatcher sponsored by Dan Lupton

SPOTTED FLYCATCHER *Muscicapa striata*

Fifty years ago Spotted Flycatcher usually figured in *SB*'s annual list of the commonest birds, on which commentary was unnecessary. It frequented large gardens, churchyards, parkland, and open woodland, and was perhaps most numerous in the warm, stone-walled villages of the south and west. There were no gaps in *BA 1968–72*, but according to a more recent survey (Baillie *et al.* 2012), the British population declined by 86% between 1966 and 2010. In Somerset, the main losses seem to have been in farmland, and especially on the Levels, in parts of which Spotted Flycatchers suddenly became rarities around 1990. The worst decline came probably in the late 1990s, when numbers fell drastically even in prime habitat. Although there have been apparent increases since then, this is now a bird to be looked for, rather than casually noticed.

Various causes for the decline have been suggested, of which the most significant are likely to be repeated periods of drought in their winter quarters in West Africa and a shortage of larger insects during the breeding season, especially in farmland; it is mainly on these that the young are fed. The weather in some breeding seasons also has been unfavourable.

In the present Atlas there was some evidence for breeding in exactly half of all tetrads. In the north, Spotted Flycatchers were already very scarce in *AvA 1988–91*, when only 27 of the 87 Somerset tetrads recorded contacts; the latest results appear similar, but have been enhanced by an extra year of targeted searches. Elsewhere, the lowest numbers are in coastal areas, across the more open Levels such as the Cheddar Moors and King's Sedge Moor, in parts of East Somerset, and on Western Exmoor, where there has never been much suitable territory. Many observers have reported the arrival of birds which have failed to find mates, even in the most favourable domestic sites. Woodland birds, which are often less well recorded, may have been more successful, and there was a good concentration of positive tetrads in the Avalon Marshes, where insect prey is abundant.

Spotted Flycatchers generally arrive from the second to the fourth week in May, or even in early June, and depart in August or early September. Traditionally, they are double-brooded; August fell outside the Atlas recording period, so there are few records from that month.

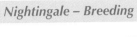

Nightingale – Breeding

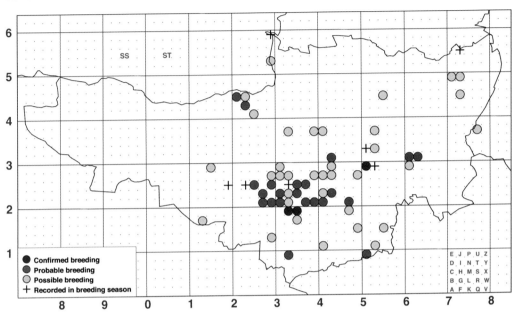

Spotted Flycatcher – Breeding

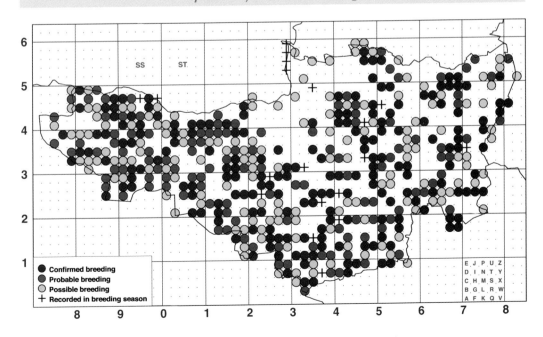

ROBIN *Erithacus rubecula*

Robins were recorded at both seasons in nearly every Somerset tetrad, apart from one or two on the barren and houseless upland of Exmoor Forest. The few isolated gaps in the lowlands are probably due to random chance, though the lack at either season in ST44C (part of Tealham Moor) may be real, as it too is almost treeless and Robins, if present, must be at very low densities. Confirmation of breeding is missing in a surprising number of tetrads, but when the maps for both seasons are looked at together it can reasonably safely be assumed that Robins in fact do breed in all or nearly all the tetrads in which they were recorded. The abundance map in

NBA 1988–91 showed the greatest densities to be largely in the western half of the county. In winter, they are often the only birds visible in woodland, foraging in leaf-litter and sheltering in holly and other evergreen species.

Most Robins are apparently faithful to an area within a few kilometres of their birthplace, but a few may seek lower ground or even move south-west to winter in Iberia or south-west France. Some Continental birds pass through in autumn, bound for these places or for Ireland, and moving mainly by night, but there is no published evidence that they winter in Somerset.

Robin sponsored by Katharine Balmforth

274

Robin – Breeding

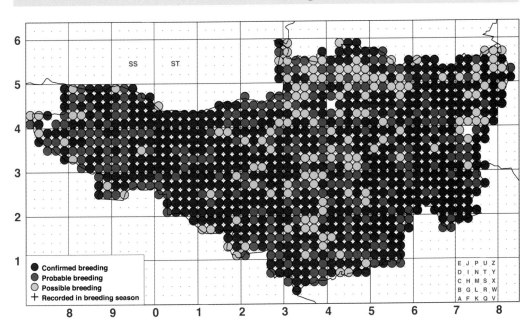

Legend:
- ● Confirmed breeding
- ● Probable breeding
- ○ Possible breeding
- + Recorded in breeding season

Robin – Winter

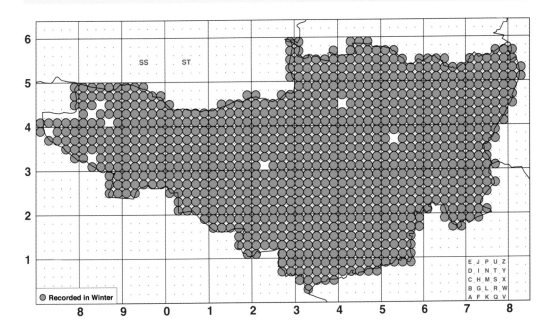

Legend:
- ● Recorded in Winter

PIED FLYCATCHER *Ficedula hypoleuca*

Nationally, Pied Flycatchers have a well-known preference for 'hanging' woods, predominantly of sessile oak (*Quercus petraea*). Therefore it is no surprise that the strongholds for Pied Flycatcher in Somerset are the wooded combes of the Quantocks and the fringes of Exmoor and the Brendons. Some sites in the latter areas, such as Horner Woods and Haddon Hill, are well visited, but in the Barle, Quarme, and Exe Valleys a full survey has never been carried out, since many of these steep and ancient woodlands are private, and the Atlas maps therefore will understate this species' distribution for the county. Natural nesting sites are abundant in these areas, both in oak and in ash. It is likely that the total population exceeds 100 pairs, although, as the *Migration Atlas* points out, it is being held at an unnaturally high level by nest-box provision. One or two pairs also usually breed on the Blackdowns, and there was a summer record from Ash Priors Common.

National records showed a decline of over 50% since 1995, perhaps because of a mismatch between the arrival times of Pied Flycatchers and the abundance of the emerging caterpillars on which they feed (Both *et al.* 2006, based on an experiment in the Netherlands). However, the annual study of Exmoor NHS nest-boxes indicated an improvement since a low point in 2008: in 2011 there were 29 breeding successes (White 2012), not including Barlynch Wood, which is the subject of a long-term study by the University of Exeter and which had 23 nesting attempts the same year.

Males arrive first, usually in the second week of April, and by mid June the young have begun to disperse.

BLACK REDSTART *Phoenicurus ochruros*

Black Redstarts are mainly passage migrants, and more than half of all records are in October or November. Some of the 'winter' records mapped here may refer to late-autumn migrants, but a few regularly remain to winter, usually at favourite coastal sites such as Brean Down and the sea wall between Hinkley Point and Stolford. During the Atlas period there was also a wide scatter of records inland, in towns and on industrial buildings. It is not clear whether this is a new phenomenon, or an existing one that has now been discovered by the more intensive coverage for the Atlas.

The very few breeding-season records (not mapped here) almost certainly refer to migrants on spring passage. A pair nested at Hinkley Point power station in 1996, but there has been no indication of a repeat since.

Pied Flycatcher sponsored by Rob Daw
Black Redstart sponsored by Andrew Grinter

276

Pied Flycatcher – Breeding

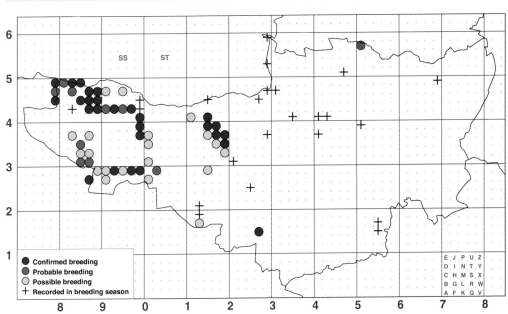

- ● Confirmed breeding
- ● Probable breeding
- ○ Possible breeding
- + Recorded in breeding season

Black Redstart – Winter

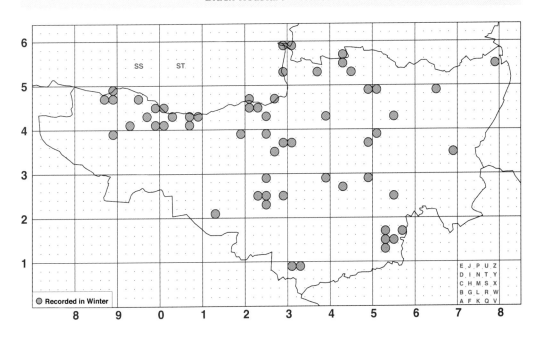

- ○ Recorded in Winter

REDSTART *Phoenicurus phoenicurus*

A century ago this was a familiar summer visitor to gardens and to the many mature orchards of Somerset, especially where there were old buildings, where it could breed in holes and forage along rough headlands. By the start of the Atlas, however, Redstarts were largely confined to the uplands, particularly Exmoor and the Quantocks, but with populations also on Mendip and the Blackdowns. There are three scattered confirmed breeding records from the lowland south and east of the county, but it is not clear whether these are regular sites or isolated instances.

On Exmoor Redstarts still breed regularly in a number of farm buildings and find insects around cattle pens. They are particularly associated with old beeches, often in overgrown hedges, and this habitat is characteristic in Brendon Hills enclosures. In these surroundings they are much less conspicuous than in open woodland or moorland edge. Many new sites were found during Atlas work in ST03 (East Brendons), where two-thirds of the tetrads held Redstarts.

On Exmoor proper, there is some confusion in the published survey figures. In 2002 the RSPB team found 131 territories, including those in Devon, but in 2008 there were only 86. It is thought that in 2002 singing birds were sometimes counted beyond the strict boundary of the moorland, in adjacent woodland. However, it is possible that 'moorland' birds, often dependent on hawthorns, really have withdrawn within the woods. In a number of places nestboxes are used, but their presence has a much smaller effect on numbers than with Pied Flycatchers.

Redstarts arrive in mid or late April. In midsummer, families and individuals disperse widely along hedges and woodland edge, often moving in a seaward direction and presenting the same problem for the Atlas worker as other species that do likewise: are they in their natal tetrad?

WHINCHAT *Saxicola rubetra*

The distribution map shown here would have looked very different 50 years ago. Until the 1980s Whinchats still bred widely on the Levels, where Round (1978) found 153 pairs, mainly south of the Poldens. These lowland birds rapidly disappeared over the next 20 years, and the last confirmed breeding was on Kennard Moor in 2004; the practice of taking earlier silage cuts has generally been blamed for their extinction. The small Mendip population had reputedly disappeared by 2003, and even in the Quantocks, where there were 62 territories 20 years ago (Street 1992), breeding-season records were received for only six tetrads.

There is a very different story on Exmoor, where the first RSPB survey, in 1978, found at least 450 pairs, and perhaps as many as 600; there were still 448 in 1992, of which 358 were in Somerset. Ten years later, in a poor summer, these had fallen to 292, and Whinchats had largely retreated to central and western parts, where grass moorland and large areas of bracken seem more attractive than heather. By 2008, numbers here had revived to over 400 pairs. There have been local losses since then, but Whinchats still were confirmed to breed on Exmoor in at least 24 tetrads, with probable breeding recorded in another 24. The sample surveys in the Exmoor Monitoring Project suggest that the population is remarkably stable, varying over the eight years from 2006 to 2013 only between 82 and 115 singing males on the 14 selected routes, though some of these are wholly or partly in Devon.

Whinchats arrive in the last third of April or in early May, and leave in July or early August. On autumn passage, small numbers still frequent their old haunts on the Levels: like Wheatears they seem particularly fond of recently cut hay and silage fields.

Redstart sponsored by Dave Helliar

Whinchat sponsored by DJEnvironmental (Tim Davis and Tim Jones)

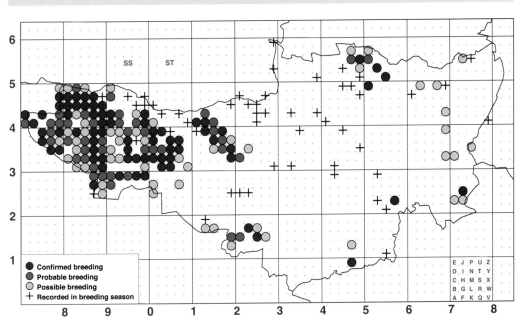

Redstart – Breeding

- ● Confirmed breeding
- ● Probable breeding
- ○ Possible breeding
- + Recorded in breeding season

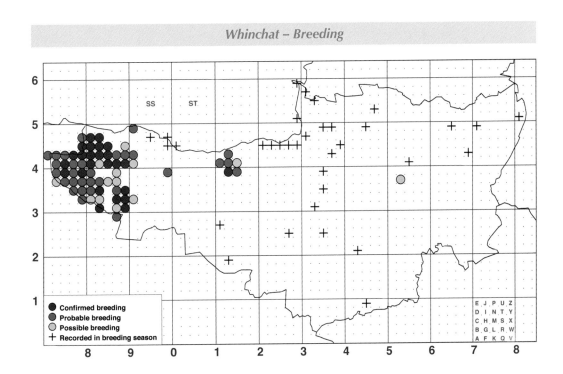

Whinchat – Breeding

- ● Confirmed breeding
- ● Probable breeding
- ○ Possible breeding
- + Recorded in breeding season

STONECHAT *Saxicola rubicola*

Over the last century Stonechats have been generally confined to heathland, with gorse and shrubs; perhaps 90% of the summer population is found in this habitat on the Quantocks and Exmoor, the remainder being on rough Mendip grassland and along the coast. From the 1980s they began to breed more frequently on the Levels, where Whinchats were rapidly declining, and by 2000 there were over 40 pairs, mainly on King's Sedge Moor. Some of these persisted into the early part of the Atlas period: in 2008, up to 25 males were present on Somerton Moor but they then vanished in the wake of two severe winters, and in the last two years of the Atlas there were only one or two records.

The upland birds have been regularly surveyed. Over the 20 years before the period of the present Atlas their numbers rose very fast: Exmoor (including Devon) held 289 territories in 1997–2000, 468 in 2002, and 442 in 2008; the Quantocks held 63 in 1992, 128 in 2000, and 132 in 2012. Stonechats have at least two broods and large numbers of young, so that even the much-documented losses from hard winters can be swiftly made good. Fortunately most tetrads where Stonechats were likely to be encountered were covered for the Atlas in 2008 or 2009, before the losses in the hard winters of 2009/10 and 2010/11; casual records and those from the Exmoor Monitoring Project suggest that Stonechat numbers then fell by about a quarter. Numbers on Mendip and along the coast are by comparison very small. The only Blackdowns site is Sampford Point, where breeding pairs have not always been on the Somerset side of the border.

Stonechats arrive on upland breeding grounds in March or early April, and remain until September or October. The maps show a distribution much as expected, including a general preference for high ground for breeding in Somerset, with a few records from less usual habitats, then wintering in the lowlands and on the coast, but with a general scatter over most of the county. Some breeders migrate over long distances: one ringed at Wimbleball Lake in 1995 was recovered in Morocco in 1997.

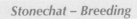

Stonechat – Breeding

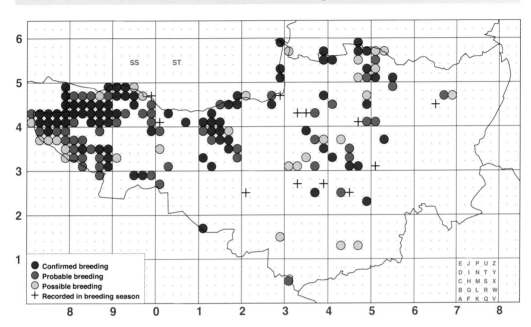

Stonechat – Winter

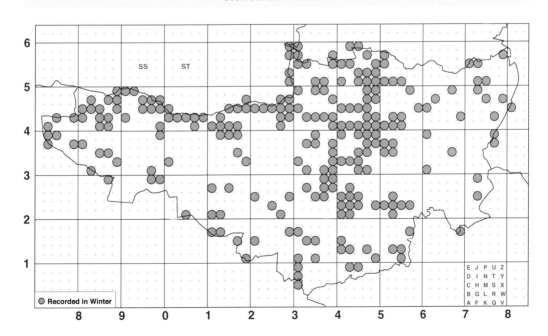

WHEATEAR *Oenanthe oenanthe*

Wheatears are familiar birds on passage, especially on coasts and moorland in early spring, but also across the Levels, and most of the crosses on the map must refer to migrants passing through. The breeding population is small, and has declined, perhaps by a half, in recent decades. Two nests were found on Mendip in 2011, the first recorded instances of breeding there since about 1990. Apart from occasional breeding attempts at Stolford and on the North Quantocks, and an isolated probable breeding record from the Blackdowns, most other recent records have been from Exmoor, which still holds at least 25 pairs, with confirmed breeding in 16 tetrads. The most regular sites are Hurlstone Point (up to four pairs)

and Upper Hoaroak Water (up to ten pairs); in most years there is a scattering of pairs in Chalk Water, in Long Combe, around the headwaters of Badgworthy Water and down the Barle from Goat Hill Bridge to Landacre Bridge. The large Greenland birds are late migrants, and their frequent presence on Exmoor in May or June could cause observers to overestimate the local breeders. Almost all nesting sites have rocky outcrops or stone walls and areas of short sward. The reduction in sheep numbers outside enclosures, with the consequent longer sward, may have had an effect on Wheatears breeding.

Breeders leave in July or August. The autumn passage is prolonged, from late June to late October.

GREAT GREY SHRIKE *Lanius excubitor*

Despite the decline in North European populations, Great Grey Shrikes have been seen more regularly in Somerset in the last 15 years, perhaps because of increased coverage by observers. The map presented here, combining as it does records from five winters, and both short-staying late-autumn migrants and long-staying overwintering birds, inevitably overstates the distribution in any one year.

It is representative, however, in that West Mendip and Exmoor are particularly favoured areas; there and on the Quantocks single Great Grey Shrikes can remain for some weeks in congenial habitats, where they can find rough grass or heather with scattered bushes. There are also several records in recent years from the Levels north of the Poldens, where birds can hunt over rough pastures, though in the winter of

2010/11 one favoured the scattered willows within the reedbeds of Shapwick Heath. Coastal records tend to be of migrants in late October and November, and none fell within the Atlas months during the period.

Single birds may range over a wide area, and some duplication of records must occur. The cluster of dots on the Blackdowns, for instance, probably all relate to a single returning (and particularly wide-ranging and elusive) individual, and a number of other repeat records suggest that some individuals are faithful to sites from year to year, though there is no ringing evidence for this in Somerset. Long-staying birds usually leave in February or March.

There are three old spring or summer records, but there were none during the Atlas period.

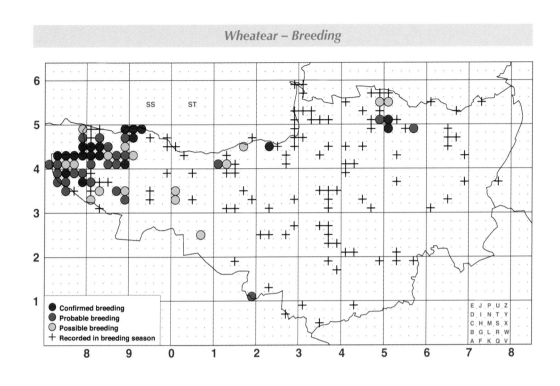

Wheatear – Breeding

Legend:
- ● Confirmed breeding
- ● Probable breeding
- ○ Possible breeding
- + Recorded in breeding season

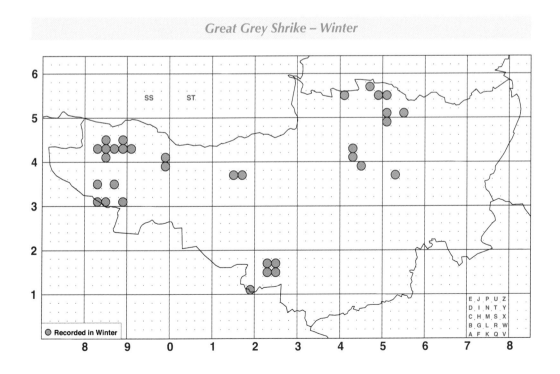

Great Grey Shrike – Winter

Legend:
- ● Recorded in Winter

DUNNOCK *Prunella modularis*

Dunnocks are almost ubiquitous in both summer and winter, the most noticeable gaps at either season being in a small number of upland tetrads, especially on Exmoor Forest. Indeed, the Exmoor records for this Atlas suggest that vertical movement takes place in winter, at least in some years.

While not shy, this is an unobtrusive species, and easy to miss if not vocalising even in areas where it is known to occur. Dunnocks may be at low densities or even absent from treeless and hedgeless parts of the Levels, for example on King's Sedge Moor. It is harder to account for the lack of records from elsewhere, notably in the east towards the Wiltshire border. Dunnocks, though widespread, are seldom abundant and breeding birds in shrubby corners of farmland may be relatively isolated. *NAvA 2007–11* found the highest densities were in urban tetrads, which is reflected in the national trend.

Confirmation of breeding was another matter, and the number of tetrads where possible breeding was the highest level of evidence recorded must be higher for Dunnock than for any other comparably common species.

Taking all of that into account, Dunnocks remain one of our commonest birds and given their sedentary nature, it is likely that the species bred at some point during the Atlas period in all or nearly all tetrads in which the species was recorded.

Dunnock sponsored by DJEnvironmental (Tim Davis and Tim Jones)

Dunnock – Breeding

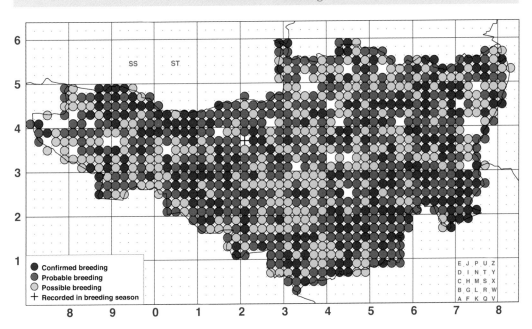

Confirmed breeding
Probable breeding
Possible breeding
+ Recorded in breeding season

Dunnock – Winter

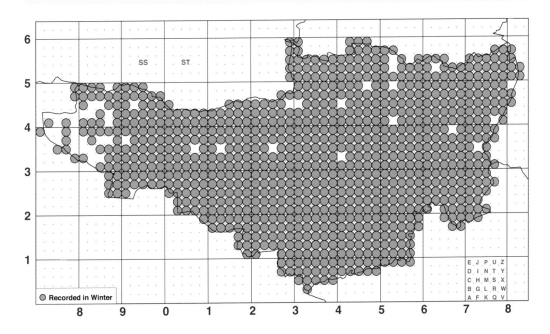

Recorded in Winter

HOUSE SPARROW *Passer domesticus*

House Sparrows do not wander much, so the maps for both seasons probably show their distribution fairly accurately. They were not recorded in 65 tetrads. Of these, 36 were in the western hills, mostly in areas without farms or houses; in others there may be only one small colony centred perhaps on a single bush beside the farmhouse. Where there are horses, there will nearly always be House Sparrows. Away from the west, they were not discovered in some coastal and estuarine areas, on treeless and houseless Levels, on barren Mendip slopes and tops, and in a few tetrads where the only birds may be around inaccessible private property.

The national population has shrunk by about 70% over the last 40 years, but the range, locally and nationally, has altered little. Colonies are on the whole smaller than they once were, and counts of over 100 are confined to areas of predominantly arable farming, such as the Quantock coast and the North Brendons. The only quantitative evidence on town populations in relatively recent times comes from Crewkerne, where the 300 pairs of 1975 had shrunk to 165 by 1998 (Parsons 1999). The point is made in *NAvA 2007–11* that in large urban areas some rough ground is needed for them to flourish. In general, *BA 2007–11* shows the greatest abundance in the south-east third of the county, where every farm seems to have its own small colony, and the lowest on Exmoor, where remote farms sometimes have Chaffinches, but no House Sparrows.

House Sparrow sponsored by Dr Denise Wawman

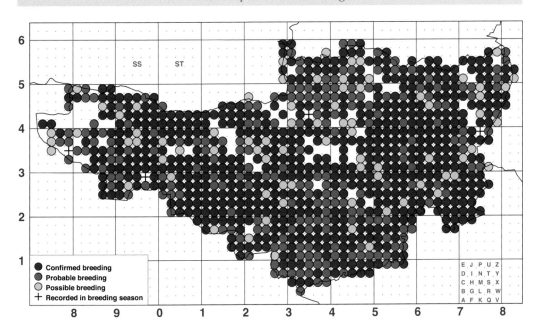

House Sparrow – Breeding

- ● Confirmed breeding
- ● Probable breeding
- ○ Possible breeding
- + Recorded in breeding season

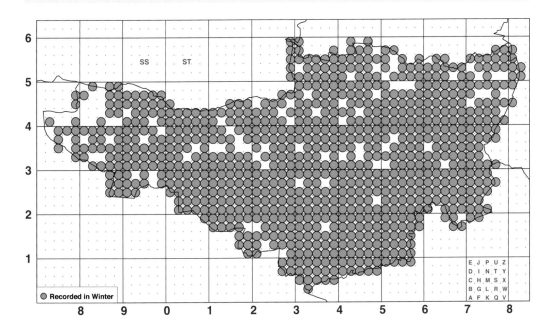

House Sparrow – Winter

- ● Recorded in Winter

TREE SPARROW *Passer montanus*

It is worth remembering that this species, treated as a local rarity, has a vast range across the Old World, and that this county, the western extremity of that range, has experienced surges and retreats a number of times.

By the time of the first Atlas breeding season in 2008, the tide had turned on a recent upsurge: only one flock was known to be still present, though much reduced, at Green Ore, and there was no evidence of successful breeding. However, some winter visitors remained at other sites, notably at Cary Moor where much effort has been made to provide winter forage for this and other seed-eating species, and in both seasons observers found small numbers that had not been previously known, particularly on the Blackdowns and on the fringes of known haunts in East Somerset and on Mendip. In the Atlas period, breeding was proved not only at Green Ore, but also at a number of sites to the north and east of Shepton Mallet suggesting a small-scale upswing; there may even be isolated pairs in the area yet to be discovered.

Tree Sparrow sponsored by Richard Downes

Tree Sparrow – Breeding

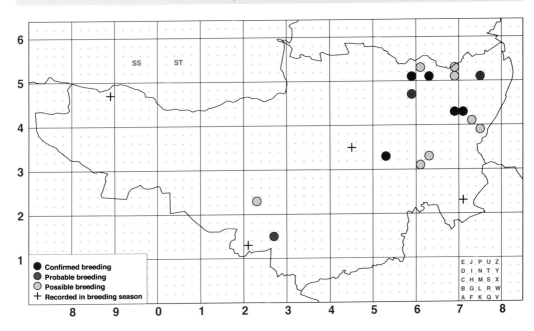

- ● Confirmed breeding
- ● Probable breeding
- ○ Possible breeding
- + Recorded in breeding season

Tree Sparrow – Winter

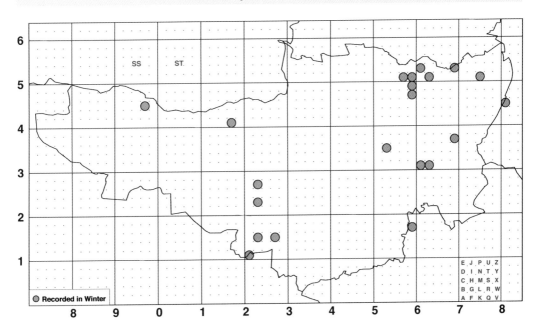

- ● Recorded in Winter

GREY WAGTAIL *Motacilla cinerea*

In summer, Grey Wagtails need fast-running water of good quality, some rocks and shingle, and usually, though not always, adjacent or overhanging insect-rich deciduous woodland. Their greatest density is therefore on Exmoor rivers and streams below the barer moorlands. The summer distribution shown on the Atlas map was mostly obtained in the first two years of the survey; two cold winters appear to have greatly affected their numbers, in a manner that had not been noted in earlier years. Since most appear to leave the higher ground from November to February, the freeze-up must have caught them even at lower levels. This must also imply that most do not migrate south, though some British birds may do so – there are records of a few birds coasting round Bridgwater Bay in autumn, and Portland Bird Observatory records small numbers passing through at the same season. Their absence in summer, even at familiar sites, was widely noticed in 2011, and was still apparent in 2012. Both nationally and locally, Grey Wagtails had done well over the last half-century, especially in parts of Eastern England, and it is to be hoped that they will have mild winters to recover any lost ground. They breed early, and many pairs are double-brooded.

In the five western squares of Exmoor they were found in the breeding season in 61 of the 81 tetrads, but in winter in only 17. On the eastern side of Exmoor and in the Brendons, the summer and winter figures for SS93/94 show them as present in 15 in summer and 17 in winter. Elsewhere in West and South-west Somerset they were found on average in only a quarter to a third of the 124 tetrads, the summer and winter totals being almost the same.

There is a scattering of breeding pairs along the Blackdown streams and across South Somerset at mills and weirs, by reservoirs and locks, and there are also a few on the upper reaches of rivers in the east and on Mendip. A number of 'new' pairs were found by Atlas work in the lowlands, although doubtless, as with Dippers, many were missed on private land; they will sometimes breed on farm ponds. Of the 86 Somerset tetrads which fell within the Avon allocation, mainly on Mendip, they were noted in only 19, about the same result as that obtained for *AvA 1988–91*. Here, they were twice as common in winter.

Grey Wagtails are suddenly on the move in September and October, when they appear around farms and on roofs. Some of these birds, probably from further north, may move on to the south-west or overseas, but others remain or arrive to spend the winter on the lower ground, where they are fond of small sewage-treatment plants and reservoir edges. By February, moorland birds are again taking up territories along wooded rivers.

Grey Wagtail sponsored by DJEnvironmental (Tim Davis and Tim Jones)

Grey Wagtail – Breeding

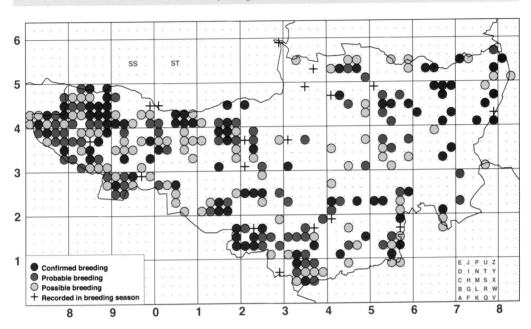

- ● Confirmed breeding
- ● Probable breeding
- ○ Possible breeding
- + Recorded in breeding season

Grey Wagtail – Winter

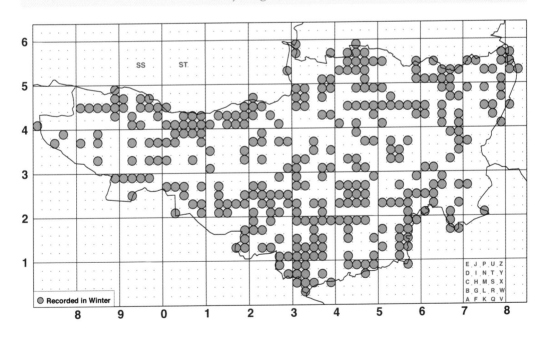

- ● Recorded in Winter

PIED WAGTAIL *Motacilla alba yarrellii*

Pied Wagtails are such familiar birds that one can easily assume that they are as universally distributed as Blackbirds or Robins, but this is not quite so, though they are still widespread. West from the Quantocks they were found breeding in 80% of all tetrads, but almost all birds are there attached to farms, and especially those with cattle. They appear to be absent from houseless areas, on the Quantocks as well as on Exmoor. In the lowlands they occur around villages and farms, and they are often attracted by horse paddocks. There is vertical migration, as with Grey Wagtails: in the western half of Exmoor, where 58 out of 79 tetrads were occupied in summer, only 42 had winter Pied Wagtails. The birds' liking for prominent perches and frequent calling makes presence easy to establish, but figures for confirmed breeding are low. In many cases, however, pairs probably nest on private land within farm enclaves; confirmation, where it came, was often by watching fledglings being fed on an outbuilding roof.

Most of Somerset's breeders are probably sedentary, but there is a strong southerly movement by northern birds in autumn and a corresponding return in early spring. Some of these pass through on their way to the Mediterranean or North Africa, but others probably winter in the county. In cold weather they look for warm and secure roosts: office blocks, large industrial buildings, shopping centres or supermarkets, or even municipal Christmas trees. As recently as October 1999, 1,650 Pied Wagtails roosted overnight at one supermarket in Glastonbury. Since then there have been a number of reports of local declines, especially in the south, and winter roost figures have not approached that peak. Pied Wagtails can be seriously affected by prolonged cold, but these declines had begun before the two recent freeze-ups.

The Continental and Icelandic race *M. a. alba*, the White Wagtail, is a fairly common migrant, especially on the coast, at both seasons, though more easily identified in the spring. Most Atlas records indeed referred to spring migrants, and there was no evidence that White Wagtails bred in Somerset during the Atlas period, even as part of mixed pairs, so all records mapped here refer to Pied Wagtails. The assumption has been made, however, that all records entered as indeterminate Pied/White were also to be treated as being Pied. If any were in fact White, they will be so few as not to affect the overall picture to any great extent, and less so than excluding indeterminate records would do.

Pied Wagtail sponsored by DJEnvironmental (Tim Davis and Tim Jones)

Pied Wagtail – Breeding

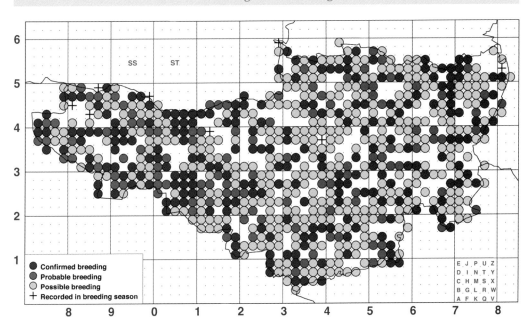

- ● Confirmed breeding
- ● Probable breeding
- ○ Possible breeding
- + Recorded in breeding season

Pied Wagtail – Winter

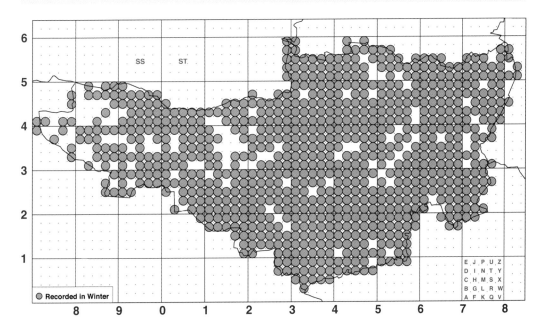

- ● Recorded in Winter

YELLOW WAGTAIL *Motacilla flava flavissima*

Until the 1960s, this was a widespread summer visitor to damp meadows across the county, though commonest on the Levels. The first large-scale survey of the Levels (Round 1978) found 231 pairs, though some areas were not covered. This total was swiftly reduced by drainage in the following decades, so that by the first Atlas year, in 2008, there were probably fewer than 50 pairs, almost all on the Levels south of the Poldens in well-watched reserves or areas with some control over water-levels. In 2011 there were about the same number, more than half of them on West Sedge Moor, but the widespread floods of 2012 destroyed many sites. The other population centre is in the damp pasturelands around the lower reaches of the Parrett. As the national map in *BA 2007–11* makes clear, the Somerset population is now detached from other breeding areas in the Midlands and the north-east.

Passage numbers are much smaller than they once were, probably because of declining numbers in north-western England. However, small flocks still occur at regular coastal sites which have no breeders, and at reservoirs.

Blue-headed Wagtail *Motacilla flava flava*

During the Atlas period there were between two and five records annually of this Continental race, or of intergrades between it and *flavissima*, a variant often now termed 'Channel Wagtail'. Most were migrants, but a mixed *flava/flavissima* pair fledged young on Wet Moor in 2011. A male Channel Wagtail, presumed to be the same bird returning, was noted on Tealham Moor in four consecutive years, and appeared to be paired with a female *flavissima* in two of those years, though breeding was not confirmed in either case.

TREE PIPIT *Anthus trivialis*

A century ago, Tree Pipits were commonly found over a much wider range of sites than they now occupy, both nationally and locally. It has often been observed that apparently suitable habitat, along wood edges, in clearings and on scrubby slopes, is not regularly occupied every year. There seems no good reason why the population should not be much higher than it now is. The answer possibly lies in the species' African wintering areas or along the migration routes, though one prime habitat, young conifer plantations, is now much scarcer than it was in the middle of last century, especially in the south and east. Since the mid 1990s, Somerset Tree Pipits have largely withdrawn into the uplands, particularly the western strongholds of Exmoor and the Quantocks, where they are found mostly in heathland, in some steep 'cleaves', and in the overgrown lines of beeches along the hedges of Western Exmoor. They are still recorded along the Selwood Ridge, around Mendip plantations and on the Blackdowns, but the Poldens and the Avalon Marshes are now deserted.

On Exmoor, the 2008 RSPB moorland survey found 180 territories, a higher figure than expected, especially as actual woodland areas were not included; all but ten of these territories were on the Somerset side. The Quantock survey of 2012 found about 40 males. In the west as a whole, including the Quantocks and the Brendons, the species was present during this Atlas in 86 tetrads, but in only 18 tetrads elsewhere.

They usually arrive, and a few pass through, from the second to the fourth week of April. They are much harder to find after song ceases in July, though the majority of return passage birds recorded are in September.

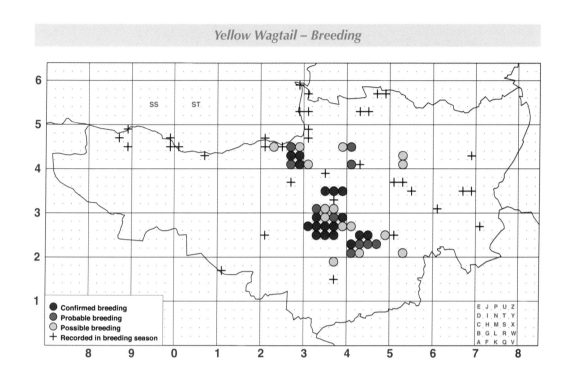

Yellow Wagtail – Breeding

- ● Confirmed breeding
- ● Probable breeding
- ○ Possible breeding
- + Recorded in breeding season

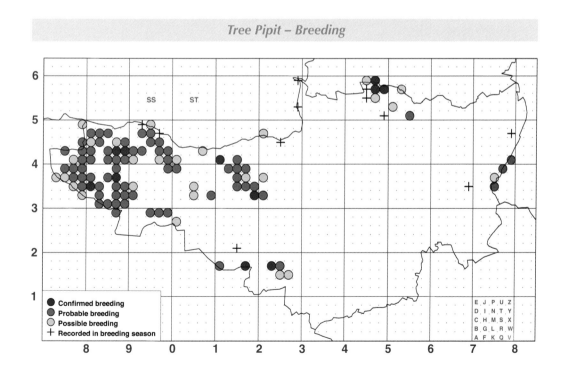

Tree Pipit – Breeding

- ● Confirmed breeding
- ● Probable breeding
- ○ Possible breeding
- + Recorded in breeding season

MEADOW PIPIT *Anthus pratensis*

This is another species which once had a wider distribution than it enjoys today. It is still the commonest bird on the western moorlands, where the 2008 RSPB survey found about 2,500 territories on Exmoor, including Devon areas; there were 202 in the Quantock survey of 2012. Forty years ago, in *BA 1968–72*, it bred in all but three 10-km squares, one around Taunton and two in the north-east; by the time of *NBA 1988–91* it was missing from a further seven. Today, it is widespread only in the western areas mentioned and on the higher parts of Mendip. In the lowlands, it is still found in small pockets of rough grassland in many parts of the Levels, and on the south coast of Bridgwater Bay, but the main concentration is on West Sedge Moor. Meadow Pipits have presumably suffered from the 'improvement' of grass and the switch from hay to silage. They were recorded for this Atlas in only 20 tetrads for East, South and South-west Somerset during the breeding season.

Most upland birds are present from late February or March to October. A few stay out the winter in sheltered combes with hawthorns and warm springs. The rest probably descend to farmland or migrate south-westward to France or Iberia, and others pass along the coast or on a broad front inland. Small flocks (and sometimes gatherings of up to 200) become widespread in farmland; thus, birds were recorded in the south-west in 22 of the 48 tetrads of ST02/12, in the south in all but five of the 66 tetrads of ST30, ST31, and ST32 and in 61 of the 86 tetrads along the northern border from East Mendip to the sea. They are quite thinly spread in the pastures of the south-east, and numbers recorded were usually small. The winter distribution given in *WA 1981–84* showed Meadow Pipits as missing from two 10-km squares and very thinly represented in many others, but this may be partly due to coverage; there were fewer gaps evident in 2007–12.

Meadow Pipit – Breeding

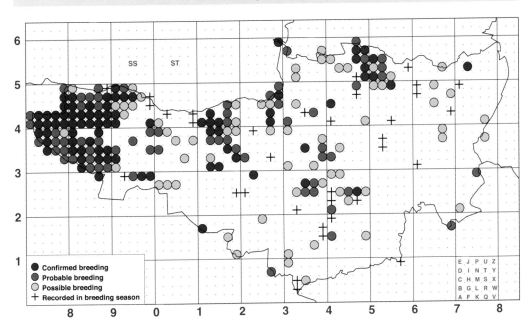

- ● Confirmed breeding
- ● Probable breeding
- ○ Possible breeding
- + Recorded in breeding season

Meadow Pipit – Winter

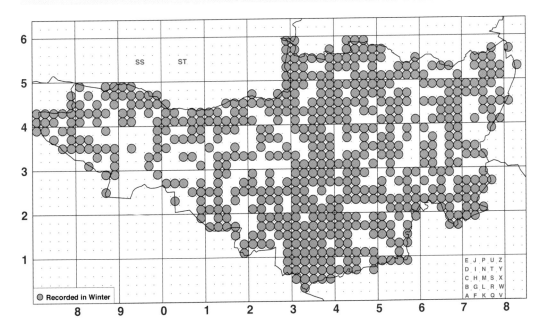

- ○ Recorded in Winter

ROCK PIPIT *Anthus petrosus*

The maps amply demonstrate the preference of Rock Pipits for the coast, especially rocky shores. However, despite their very limited nesting and foraging habitat, systematic counts of the total Somerset population are hard to come by. In most years, 25 to 35 pairs probably breed from Brean Down to Glenthorne, but this is a very rough estimate, with low confidence as to its accuracy. Some areas of suitable habitat, particularly the rocky coast west of Porlock Weir, are difficult to access without a determined effort. For similar reasons, confirmation of breeding was difficult to obtain from this and some other occupied areas.

In winter, the birds spread out along the more accessible coast of Dunster Beach and Porlock Marsh, and may be joined by some visitors from Fennoscandinavia, which cannot be separated until they assume their spring plumage. It is probably these birds that account for the few inland records at reservoirs, which during the Atlas period all fell outside the November to February date-limits.

WATER PIPIT *Anthus spinoletta*

This winter visitor from the mountains of Central Europe was not recognised as a full species until 1986. During the Atlas period there were about 70 birds recorded, mostly on the coast of Bridgwater Bay, the estuaries of the Brue and Parrett being particularly favoured, and on the Avalon Marshes, where muddy margins of pools and recently cut areas of reeds have provided most recent records. Elsewhere in southern England they often prefer watercress beds and sewage-treatment works. The highest count was of 14 together at Huntspill Sea Wall on 18 January 2010.

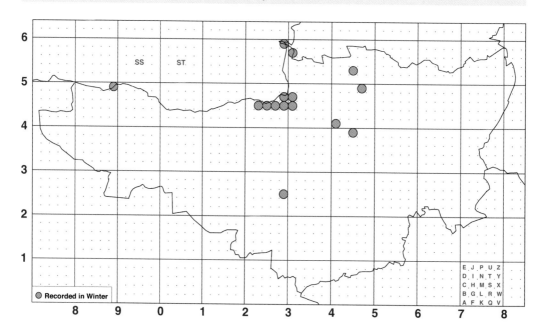

Water Pipit – Winter

298

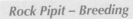

Rock Pipit – Breeding

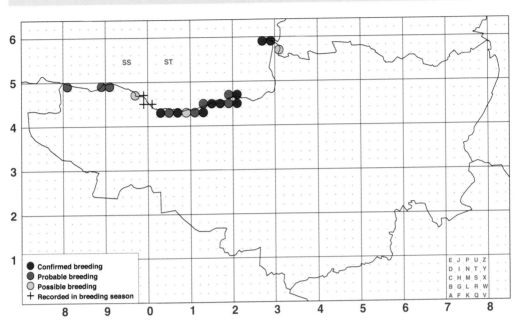

Rock Pipit – Winter

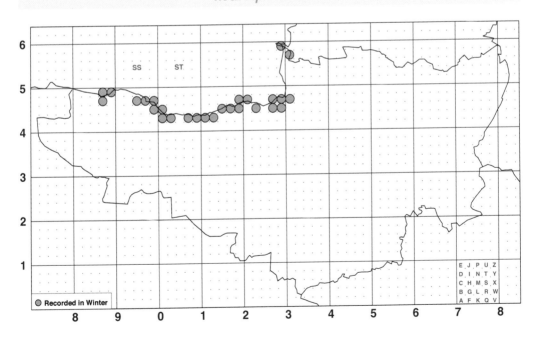

CHAFFINCH *Fringilla coelebs*

This is the only species to be recorded in the breeding season from every Somerset tetrad, apart from coastal edges with little land. Confirmation of breeding is another matter – pairs are easy enough to find, but fledged juveniles are confusingly similar to adult females and may have been overlooked. However, given its ubiquity, it can be safely assumed that, even in the tetrads listed only as possible breeding, at least one pair bred at some point during the Atlas period. Chaffinches even breed up Exmoor combes, as far as the limit of rowans and hawthorns.

We have not attempted to assess abundance in this Atlas, but results in *NAvA 2007–11* raise some questions: despite a slight national increase over the last 20 years, the Avon Breeding Bird Survey registered a decline of 43% from 1998 to 2011. We cannot say whether this effect has also been felt in Somerset.

In late autumn, large numbers pass westward and southward, of which many remain to winter. They are especially common in the western hills, where they feed on fallen beechmast along the roads. In winter Chaffinches are not quite as completely ubiquitous as in summer, as they were not found on the largely treeless Kennard Moor or in four of the highest and bleakest tetrads on Exmoor.

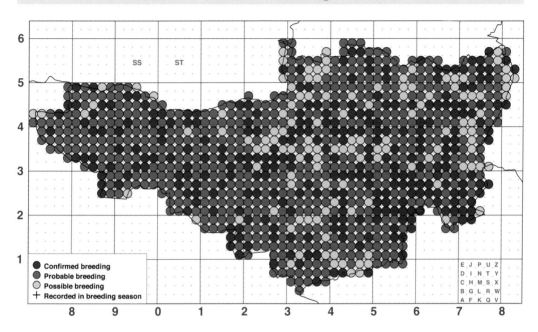

Chaffinch – Breeding

Confirmed breeding
Probable breeding
Possible breeding
+ Recorded in breeding season

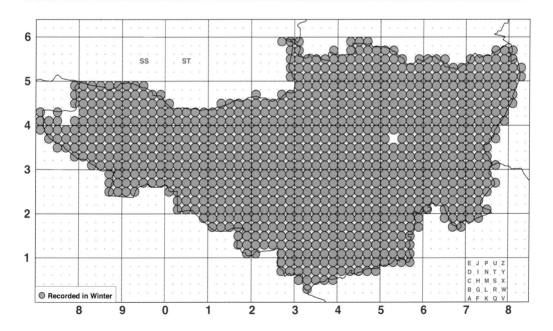

Chaffinch – Winter

Recorded in Winter

HAWFINCH *Coccothraustes coccothraustes*

This elusive bird seems to have been a regular breeder in Somerset, mostly in the east of the county, between the world wars, but has declined since then. Breeding may have continued around the southern end of the Quantocks up to about 1990, but was never confirmed, and it may also have taken place in the Avalon Marshes in 1994. The nearest populations of any size are in the Forest of Dean, which is thought to hold 150 to 200 pairs (Kirk and Phillips 2013), in nearby Gwent, and in the New Forest.

In the last 20 years Hawfinches have been erratic passage migrants and winter visitors. As such, this Atlas cannot hope to offer anything more than a compilation of records, and the map cannot be taken as representative of the species' distribution in the county in any one year. The largest invasion of recent years took place in the late autumn of 2005, when there were counts of up to 30 around Bruton and a number of coastal migrants. At the beginning of the Atlas period, in January 2008, there were four on the Quantocks. In the following autumn and winter there was another influx, including about 20 records of up to ten birds; a few remained through March, and there was even a late-April record of one at Rodhuish, in the Brendons. The last three years of the Atlas produced only five autumn and winter records, of which three were in October.

There were single birds at Fyne Court in April 2010 and at Penselwood in June 2012, the same month in which one with a brood-patch was trapped at Williton; the latter bird was retrapped near Dolgellau (Meirionnydd), a well-known breeding area, in the following March (E. Newman *in litt.*).

Most recent wintering birds have been feeding on yew berries, a habit which has made them conspicuous in the churchyards of Bruton and Norton Sub Hamdon; a colour-ringed bird in the latter came from Gwent (B.J. Widden *in litt.*).

For a general review of Hawfinches in Somerset, see Hill (2013).

Hawfinch sponsored by Brian Hill

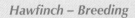

Hawfinch – Breeding

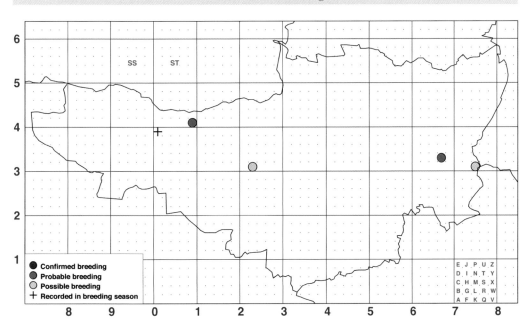

- ● Confirmed breeding
- ● Probable breeding
- ○ Possible breeding
- + Recorded in breeding season

Hawfinch – Winter

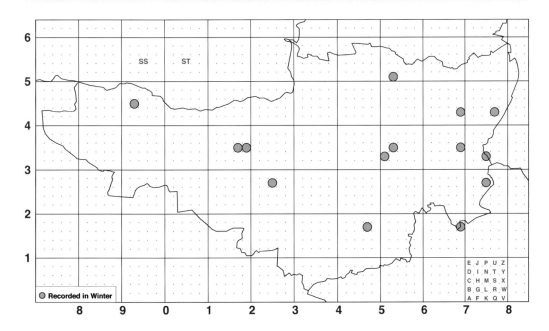

- ● Recorded in Winter

BULLFINCH *Pyrrhula pyrrhula*

Bullfinches are unobtrusive, with quiet calls and an even quieter song. They therefore present a particular challenge to Atlas observers. Many contacts were brief encounters with single birds or pairs, or with late-summer families, and were often from vehicles along deep-hedged lanes. In winter, *WA 1981–84* showed them as absent from three 10-km squares, but coverage may have been a factor. Both *BA 1968–72* and *NBA 1988–91* showed Bullfinches as present in all 10-km squares, but with some scarcity on treeless parts of the Levels.

The greater resolution of this tetrad Atlas gives us a better picture. Bullfinches were found in 68% of all tetrads in summer and in 74% in winter, when wanderers may appear almost anywhere. In ST33/43, extending from Glastonbury to Bridgwater, they were seen in twice as many tetrads in winter as in summer. Only a third of the tetrads of Western Exmoor are occupied in the breeding season, and there are gaps on the Mendip Plateau. In the centre of the county there is a large area with relatively little woodland, poor hedges, and a growing urban and industrial sprawl, where Bullfinches occur in only between 20% and 40% of all tetrads. This is a belt about 15 kilometres wide, running from Taunton and the Tone Levels north to Brean Down and the Avon border, and extending eastwards over King's Sedge Moor, though broken by the line of the Poldens, which have more suitable territory. They remain widely distributed in the east, though there are some gaps, perhaps in part reflecting the relatively high proportion there of mature woodland with little understorey.

Bullfinches like patches of thick scrub, and the general tidying and flailing that began in the 1960s thinned their numbers in farmland across South Somerset, as did the felling of old orchards, where 'hoopes' were common but disliked because of their fondness for fruit-buds. The greatest concentrations of records are in the west: in the block of 10-km squares which includes South-west Exmoor, the Brendons, the Quantocks and the Vale of Taunton, a total of 147 tetrads, Bullfinches were present in summer in 130 and in winter in 119. They do not breed far up Exmoor combes, but they visit them on nomadic forays in search of heather and ling seeds, even in snow. They are perhaps more frequent at garden feeders than they used to be.

There may have been no contractions in range, but data published in *SB* suggests that there has been a considerable fall in numbers: during the Atlas period there was no count of over 25, and most were of fewer than ten, whereas in 1964 one record was of 120 on buddleia in a Quantock quarry. This is in line with a British decline of 39% since 1967, reported in *BA 2007–11*.

Some coastal movement may occur, and there were four records in January 2010 of the larger and brighter Northern birds *P. p. pyrrhula*. One of these, a male at Shapwick Heath, gave the 'toy-trumpet' call indicative of a bird of Russian rather than Scandinavian origin.

Bullfinch sponsored by Colin Ryall and Penelope Fleming

Bullfinch – Breeding

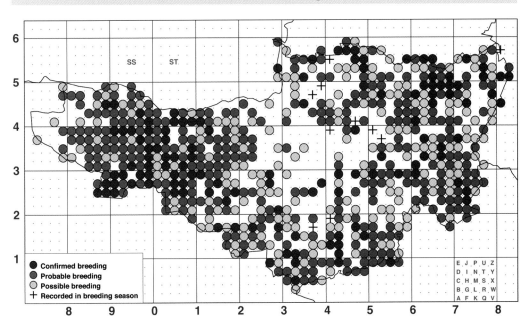

- ● Confirmed breeding
- ● Probable breeding
- ○ Possible breeding
- + Recorded in breeding season

Bullfinch – Winter

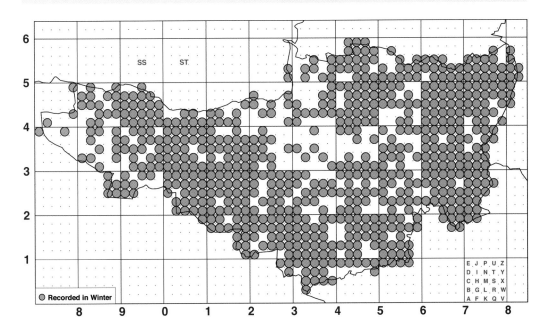

- ○ Recorded in Winter

GREENFINCH *Chloris chloris*

The statement by Mead (2000) that this was the one finch species 'that looks as if it might be coping rather well with the modern world', well-founded at the time, now appears too optimistic. Throughout the Atlas period, Greenfinches were suffering from a severe outbreak of trichomonosis, a disease transmitted from bird to bird by a parasite in saliva; it was first noticed in Somerset in 2006. Many local populations have disappeared and others have been seriously depleted, though in 2011/12 there were some signs of recovery.

In general, this is a species of farmland and woodland edge that has successfully moved to suburbia, where it has found its seed demands satisfied by shrubberies and bird feeders, and where it can breed in friendly conifers, especially the infamous *leylandii*. It was indeed doing very well and made itself conspicuous by perching in dead elm-hedges.

While there were no obvious gaps in Somerset distribution at 10-km square resolution in *BA 1968–72* and *NBA 1988–91*, this tetrad-level Atlas has detected some on the high ground of the west. These may always have existed, but also may have been enhanced by the effects of the disease: thus, of the 79 tetrads of Central and Western Exmoor half were unoccupied in summer and only 22 held wintering birds.

Over the rest of Somerset, the limited data available from other sources suggests that numbers have fallen drastically, but some presence has been maintained in almost all tetrads at both seasons, although most feeding flocks are much smaller than they once were, even at favoured coastal sites. In the last Atlas winter, of 2011/12, the highest count was of only 31, feeding in yews at Bruton. There are presumably also winter visitors, though a recent decline in ringing recoveries of birds from Eastern England suggests that these have diminished.

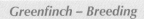

Greenfinch – Breeding

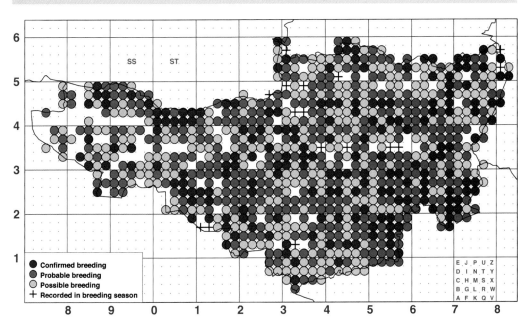

Confirmed breeding
Probable breeding
Possible breeding
+ Recorded in breeding season

E	J	P	U	Z
D	I	N	T	Y
C	H	M	S	X
B	G	L	R	W
A	F	K	Q	V

Greenfinch – Winter

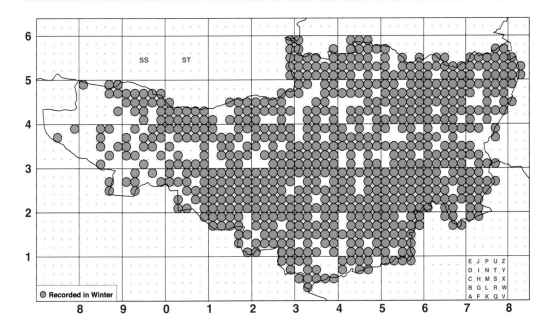

Recorded in Winter

E	J	P	U	Z
D	I	N	T	Y
C	H	M	S	X
B	G	L	R	W
A	F	K	Q	V

LINNET *Linaria cannabina*

Linnets were present in good numbers in almost all 10-km squares in *BA 1968–72* and *NBA 1988–91*, but the abundance map in the latter clearly shows them as commoner towards the coast. Though we have not attempted to assess abundance in this Atlas, it is generally accepted that numbers have declined since about 1970, affected by the elimination of weeds, the varied seeds of which are important for feeding the young (*BA 2007–11*).

In the uplands they are common in gorse, at least in summer: the 2008 Exmoor Moorland Survey found over 400 pairs (including many in Devon), and there would have been others outside the strictly moorland area. The 2012 Quantock survey revealed a flourishing population of about 200 pairs.

In summer, Linnets were present in three-quarters of all tetrads, but in winter in only a third. Linnets may feed in flocks even in the breeding season, but this habit is more marked in the winter, when they may be dependent on finding the limited sources of weed-seed in a large area, for example in game-crops, in unharvested linseed, or on recently disturbed ground. They have profited locally from the spread of oilseed rape; several large winter flocks around Williton and Watchet were found exclusively in stubbles of this crop (J.D. Holmes *in litt.*). In *WA 1981–84*, they were absent from eight 10-km squares. Some of these can now be shown to have a small number of records, but the highest ground is almost entirely deserted: in the five squares of central and western Exmoor Linnets were found in only six tetrads, as against a summer range of 71, and the picture appears to be similar for the Blackdowns and the higher parts of Mendip. This is partly because the flocks concentrate on sources of food, but also because some head south; a Watchet-ringed bird has been recovered in winter near Madrid. It is not known whether winter flocks in Somerset contain birds from the north or east, but there is substantial westward movement along the coast in autumn.

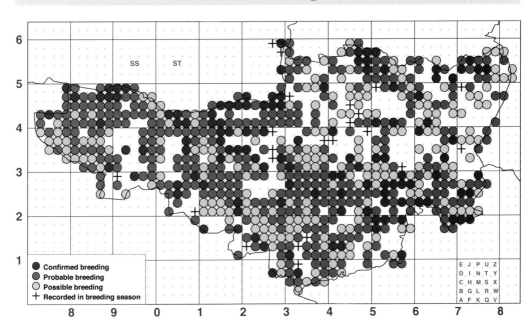

Linnet – Breeding

- ● Confirmed breeding
- ● Probable breeding
- ○ Possible breeding
- + Recorded in breeding season

Linnet – Winter

- ○ Recorded in Winter

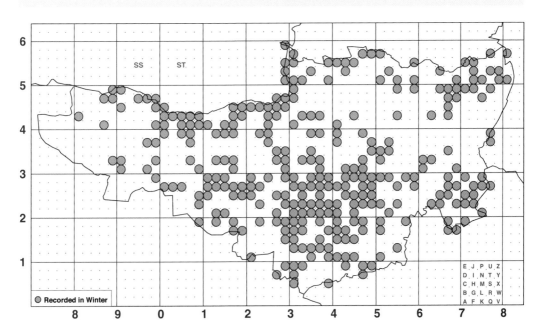

LESSER REDPOLL *Acanthis cabaret*

From a low point between the world wars when Lesser Redpolls almost disappeared as breeding birds in the county, they recolonised parts of the west and have bred annually since. Redpolls have in the past favoured young conifer plantations, and have often been linked with birches, but in its present range the species is more likely to be connected with gorse.

As the map shows, the bulk of our breeding population is on Exmoor; birds were found to have occurred in 60 out of the 140 tetrads on and around the moor. The 2008 Exmoor Moorland Survey recorded the surprisingly high total of 145 territories. Redpolls usually develop small colonies, many of which are based on large areas of gorse, a habitat hardly mentioned in the literature; some of these sites are in barren combes of Exmoor Forest, though Winsford Hill and the neighbouring Room Hill are perhaps more regularly used sites. Most birds must be summer visitors; in the winter there were records from only 15 of these tetrads.

The population on the Quantocks appears to be stable, but further east there were very few breeding-season records from the Mendip Plateau, and the only confirmed breeding record was one from Great Breach Wood, on the Poldens. There were only two contacts in the Blackdowns, where breeding has not been proved in recent years.

There is some coastal passage in autumn. Wintering flocks of up to 50, or more rarely up to 100, are most frequent in the alders and birches of the Avalon Marshes, when they may accompany Siskins. *WA 1981–84* found them distinctly uncommon in the South West as a whole, and largely absent west of the SS/ST north/south grid line. Twenty-five years or so later, as the map shows, there were concentrations in the north-east and in the Avalon Marshes, and on higher ground on the Blackdowns, the North Quantocks and the eastern slopes of Exmoor; in all these, the presence of birch is important, but they also forage in alder and larch.

MEALY REDPOLL *Acanthis flammea*

Since 2001, the Lesser Redpoll has been regarded as a separate species from its European congener, *A. flammea*. During the Atlas period the official BOU name for this species was (confusingly) Common Redpoll, which is correct over the vast majority of its large range, but not of course in Britain, and a number of records had to be reassigned to Lesser Redpoll during validation. The BOU has since adopted the name long used in the field for this form, and it is now officially the Mealy Redpoll.

It is a rare bird indeed in Somerset, though it was perhaps previously overlooked, and there were only two records in the Atlas period, both in 2011: a wintering bird at Westhay Moor, 1–6 January, and two spring migrants on Brean Down, 9 April. (No map.)

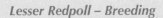

Lesser Redpoll – Breeding

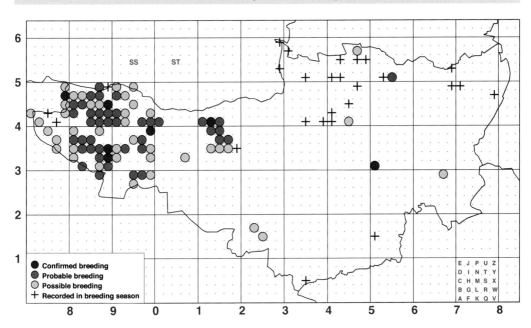

- ● Confirmed breeding
- ● Probable breeding
- ○ Possible breeding
- + Recorded in breeding season

Lesser Redpoll – Winter

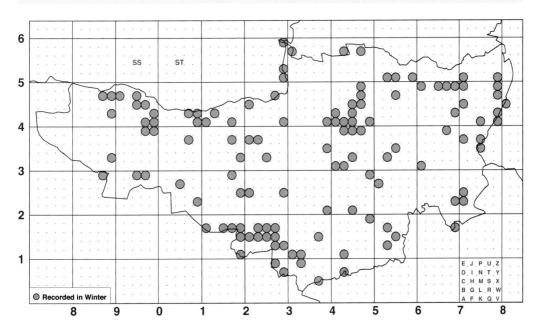

- ◐ Recorded in Winter

CROSSBILL *Loxia curvirostra*

The general pattern of Crossbill records in Somerset over the last 100 years has been of occasional late-summer invasions from the east, generated by local shortages of spruce cones in the forests of Northern and Eastern Europe. Such influxes have increasingly been followed by breeding (confirmed or suspected) in the following winter in favoured sites: along the Selwood Ridge, at Stockhill, in the North-east Quantocks, on Croydon Hill, and on the fringes of Exmoor at Selworthy and Webber's Post. Though they are far more regular than they once were, and observers would now expect to see Crossbills in the county in most years, if not every year, numbers still fluctuate markedly. It chanced that the years of *WA 1981–84* were poor ones for Crossbills in Somerset, for instance.

In the five Atlas years, there were major summer invasions in 2009 and 2011. In the latter year over 350 were reported, ten times the number in 2010. During the tetrad visits in late winter and spring, it became increasingly clear that permanent populations have now been established in some of these areas, though they are presumably reinforced in years of influx and may briefly disappear in years of a poor cone crop. There were records from many sites: in the east on Gare Hill; on Mendip at Stockhill and Rowberrow Warren; on the Blackdowns in North Down Plantation and on Staple Hill; in the Quantocks, around Triscombe Stone and Staple Common, and in Cockercombe and Rams Combe; and in the west on Haddon Hill and on the Croydon Hill, Hopcott Common and North Hill massifs.

A traditionally early breeder, often on eggs in February and with juveniles fledged by the end of April, it does not fit well with the normal Atlas seasons. The maps for this species are unusual, therefore, in that the 'breeding' map covers all breeding records, regardless of date, and the 'non-breeding' map shows all other records.

Crossbill sponsored by Barrie Widden

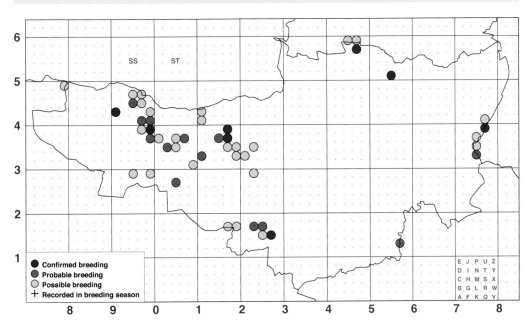

Legend:
- ● Confirmed breeding
- ● Probable breeding
- ○ Possible breeding
- + Recorded in breeding season

Crossbill – Non-breeding

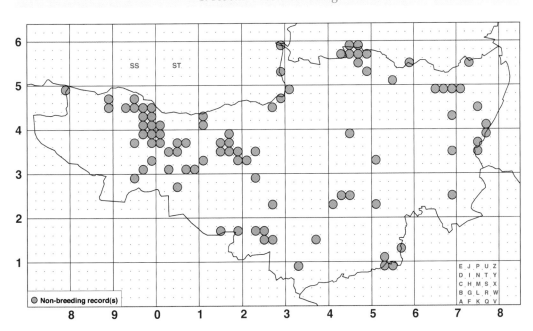

Legend:
- ○ Non-breeding record(s)

GOLDFINCH *Carduelis carduelis*

Goldfinches depend largely on tall weeds, such as thistles and ragwort, and profit from wide verges and odd unkempt corners, which are most abundant in summer in the western parts of the county and on the Blackdowns. They are nearly ubiquitous, though there are areas in the north-east and the south-west, for example, where distribution and proof of breeding on the breeding-season map are patchier. This may reflect the fact that coverage, while adequate, was less intensive perhaps than in some other areas.

Neither *BA 1968–72* nor *NBA 1988–91* registered local weaknesses, but the winter distribution shown in *WA 1981–84* was much more limited, with no records from seven 10-km squares and very small numbers in a dozen others. It was previously thought that 80% of all British Goldfinches move to south-west France or Iberia for the winter, and there are indeed ringing recoveries there of Somerset-bred birds. However, it seems likely that more of our breeders have recently remained to winter with us, partly because of the provision of suitable seed at feeders. In the western hills, most depart or descend in autumn: all but four of the 79 tetrads of the five Central and Western Exmoor squares have breeding Goldfinches, mostly along the beech hedges, but there are winter records from only 17. Breeders return, already paired, in a palpable surge in mid April. On the slightly more friendly territory of Eastern Exmoor and the Brendons, about half the tetrads are occupied in winter, but in the rest of the county there is very little difference between the summer and the winter range. There is a marked spring passage along the coast.

Goldfinch sponsored by Errol Newman

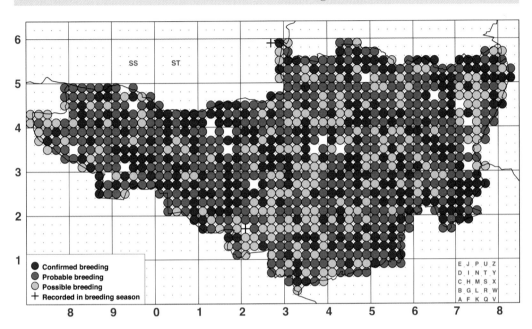

Goldfinch – Breeding

Legend:
- ● Confirmed breeding
- ● Probable breeding
- ○ Possible breeding
- + Recorded in breeding season

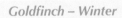

Goldfinch – Winter

Legend:
- ● Recorded in Winter

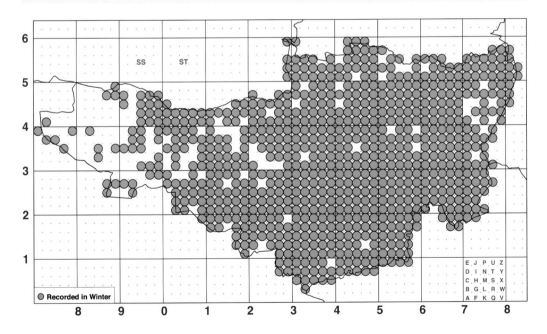

SISKIN *Spinus spinus*

Until the 1960s, Siskins were irregular and no-madic winter visitors, found mainly in the streamside alders of the lowlands. Vast spruce forests were by then maturing in Northern England and Scotland, and wintering flocks in the south were becoming larger and more regular. Breeding was first proved in Somerset in 1979, at Luccombe, but it had probably started some years earlier. In the last 30 years, Siskins have begun to nest in many coniferous woods, from which they bring their young to the nearest available feeders. Most records of confirmed breeding on the maps are based on these sightings, which are likely to be of locally bred birds in late summer, though they may not have been hatched within the actual tetrad.

All the larger tracts of coniferous forest have been colonised. In the west, the densest populations are on the Brendons and their outliers, on North-east Exmoor and on the Quantocks; in five 10-km squares within that area, about half the tetrads hold Siskins. There are others on the Selwood Ridge, on Mendip and on the Blackdowns.

Very large numbers now pass through from October to December, of which some remain to swell the winter population. They occupy a wide range of woodland habitats, including alder and birch woods across the Levels.

Siskin sponsored by Dr Denise Wawman

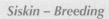

Siskin – Breeding

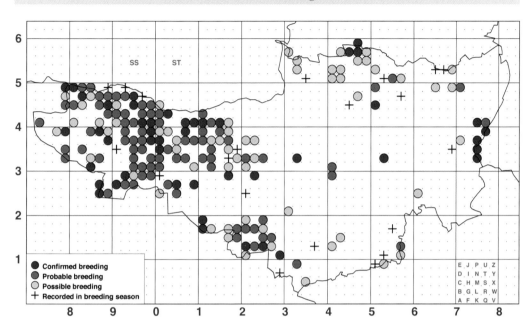

Confirmed breeding
Probable breeding
Possible breeding
+ Recorded in breeding season

Siskin – Winter

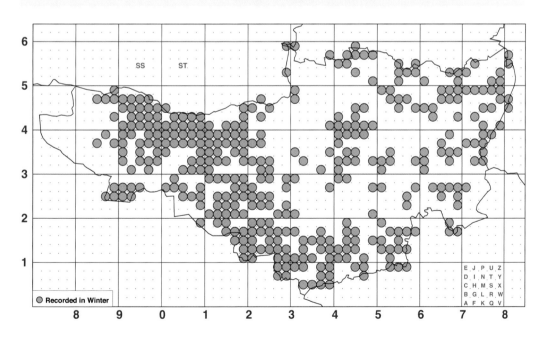

Recorded in Winter

BRAMBLING *Fringilla montifringilla*

Bramblings usually arrive in late October or November, when others pass through. They are nomadic and are heavily dependent on their principal food, which is beechmast. Some now also visit garden feeders. In some winters, few appear at all in Somerset, but in others they are numerous. Numbers usually fall away sharply in February, and there is almost no visible spring passage.

They are not well recorded by Atlas methods, since visits may not coincide with those years and months when they are most numerous. In *WA 1981–84*, which dealt with only three winters, there were entries for 24 10-km squares, but only five of these were at the highest density, and two may have reflected autumn passage rather than wintering. During our five-year Atlas period, they were most widespread in the first winter, 2007/08, which was the only one where counts of over 100 were reported in *SB* and in which unusual numbers visited gardens. Overall, Bramblings appeared in all but one 10-km square, and in 216 tetrads. Records were well scattered, but those submitted to SOS confirm that in lowland areas Bramblings most often occurred in ones and twos, or at most in low double figures. Sizeable flocks were concentrated in Eastern Mendip and in the hilly areas of the south-west and west; as was to be expected, there was a high correlation with the distribution of mature beeches.

There was one summer record, of a singing but unmated male in Long Wood, Mendip, 18 June–4 July 2010. This is almost unprecedented, the only other previous summer record being of a singing male near Culbone in 1957.

CORN BUNTING *Emberiza calandra*

As Somerset residents Corn Buntings have probably been extinct since 2001. Only four were recorded within the Atlas period: two in winter on Cary Moor and singles in summer on Somerton Moor and at Nether Adber, north of Yeovil.

There are still populations not far away across the Dorset border and in Wiltshire, but a species largely dependent on weeds found in arable can have little future in a farming system dependent on herbicides. Somerset was always on the western boundary of the Corn Bunting's range, apart from an isolated population in Cornwall.

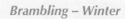

Brambling – Winter

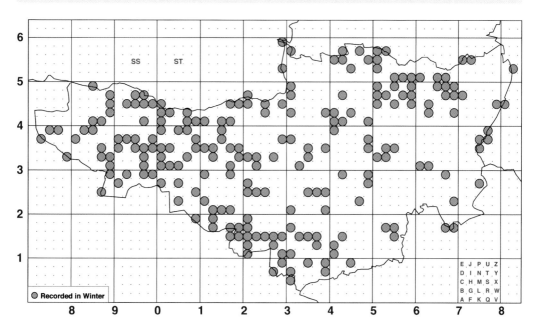

SS   ST

```
E J P U Z
D I N T Y
C H M S X
B G L R W
A F K Q V
```

⬤ Recorded in Winter

8   9   0   1   2   3   4   5   6   7   8

Corn Bunting – Combined Winter & Breeding

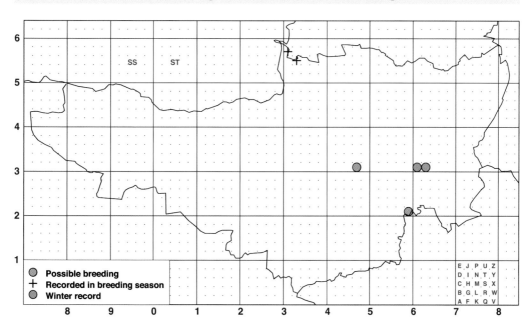

SS   ST

```
E J P U Z
D I N T Y
C H M S X
B G L R W
A F K Q V
```

⬤ Possible breeding
✛ Recorded in breeding season
⬤ Winter record

8   9   0   1   2   3   4   5   6   7   8

YELLOWHAMMER *Emberiza citrinella*

Yellowhammers occupy two distinct habitats in Somerset: arable farmland and heath. They are sedentary, but they may move widely (though still locally) in winter to congregate at food sources, a habit which presumably accounts for the difference between results from summer tetrads and from winter flocking areas; they desert heathland altogether in winter, except perhaps for roosting. The disappearance of good sources of winter grain, and now of setaside, can have a disastrous effect on local distribution. The farmland population may well have halved since the 1970s, but there has been a recent January count of 175, at Stratton-on-the-Fosse on Mendip. Overall, summering birds were present in 52% of all tetrads; the general impression of most older observers is that even in the best areas there has been a very slow but perceptible decline, probably caused by the difficulty of finding enough food to survive the winter; for example, the ten singing males found in 2006 between Williton and Watchet were reduced to two in 2012. The highest numbers are found in areas of largely unbroken arable, especially in the North and East Brendons, where the long breeding season, from April to August, ensured that few were missed during tetrad visits; this area was clearly shown on the abundance map in *NBA 1988–91*. There are other good areas on the Quantock heaths, where the 2012 survey found 115 singing males; and in the coastal farmland from Hinkley Point to Quantoxhead. There are noticeable concentrations also on East Mendip, and in a swathe of mostly lowland farmland running west from Wincanton very nearly to Taunton. In some areas the retention of thick elm hedges has helped to maintain local populations.

Yellowhammers are largely absent from the Levels, from Exmoor except for a few regular breeders on Winsford Hill, and from urban areas. The winter range in the county as a whole contracts by about 15%, as birds congregate at a few good feeding spots, of which some will be outside the breeding range. Almost all upland breeders are only summer visitors.

Yellowhammer sponsored by Nigel Case

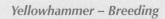

Yellowhammer – Breeding

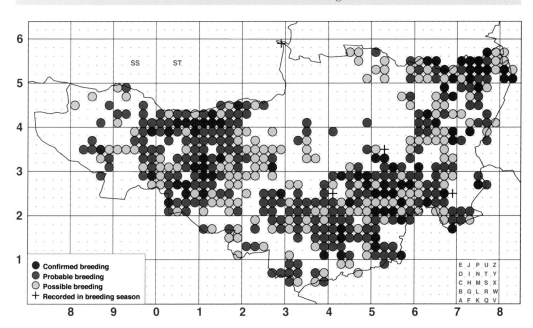

Yellowhammer – Winter

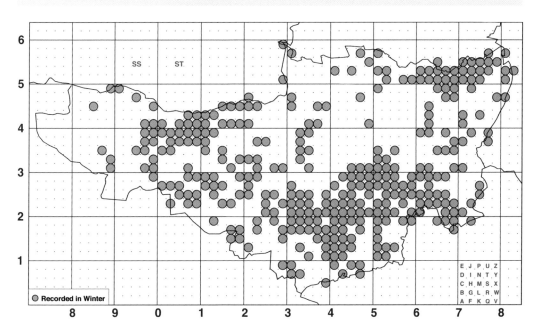

REED BUNTING *Emberiza schoeniclus*

Reed Buntings are widely distributed over lowland Somerset. They frequent rhynes with dense bankside vegetation, reedbeds, brick- and borrow-pits and the edges of reservoirs; the Avalon Marshes alone probably hold at least 250 pairs, and in 2011 West Sedge Moor had 214. They are particularly abundant on the rougher and wetter Levels, with extensive rush cover, where they are not restricted to the field edges. They sometimes use drier sites, such as the bracken on Black Down or the Quantocks. As yet, few have colonised oilseed rape, as they have in some other counties, but there are records from this crop in the south-east.

Since about 1950 they have also spread to Exmoor mires, which in 2008 held 206 territories; they were present in 53 of the 75 tetrads of the Western and Central Moor. The origins of this moorland breeding are something of a mystery; they seem to have colonised Dartmoor at about the same time (Smaldon 2005). The upward expansion may have been connected with the loss of farmland weeds due to the use of herbicides, since it occurred at a time when some lowland populations were shrinking, and Reed Buntings may have been exploring new areas.

In winter, they are still found on the Levels, but they now also sometimes enter gardens and visit feeders. East of the Quantocks, this habit has helped to extend the winter range by 30 tetrads compared to the summer map. Most Exmoor birds desert the highest ground, but they can sometimes be found with Meadow Pipits in sheltered corners of heather moorland; they probably do not go far.

Small numbers are recorded on coastal passage in autumn, and there are presumably also winter visitors, since a Finnish-bred bird was once recovered at Steart. Winter flocks of up to 100 have been recorded in recent years, notably at Cary Moor, where birdseed crops have been planted.

Reed Bunting – Breeding

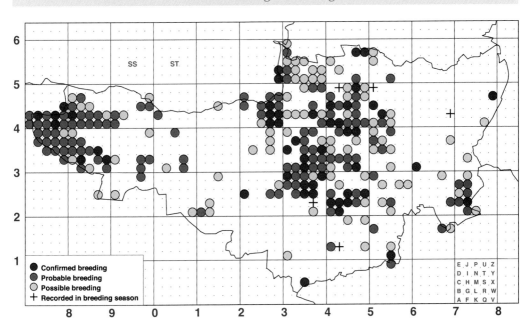

Reed Bunting – Winter

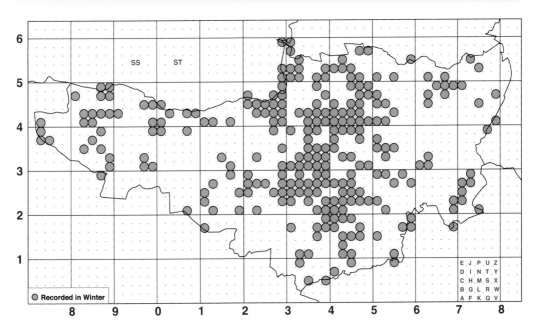

SNOW BUNTING
Plectrophenax nivalis

During the Atlas period about 55 were recorded: 15 on Mendip and Exmoor, and the rest on coasts from Brean Down to Lilstock and from Blue Anchor to Porlock Weir. A few coastal birds made long stays for periods between October and February, but November is the peak month, and most, including all the upland birds, should probably be regarded as late-autumn passage migrants.

LAPLAND BUNTING
Calcarius lapponicus

Always scarcer visitors than Snow Buntings, Lapland Buntings are often found in the same areas, though almost exclusively coastal; the two species are mapped together here. During the Atlas period there were 12 'winter' birds, of which eight were in November and four in December. All were in the Stolford to Hinkley Point area, which is the most favoured, but other coastal sites have also been used in previous years.

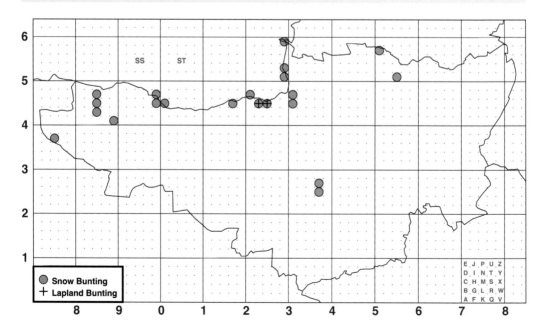

Snow Bunting & Lapland Bunting – Winter

● Snow Bunting
+ Lapland Bunting

Other species recorded

The following species were recorded on at least one occasion during the period 1 November 2007 to 31 July 2012, but without any level of breeding evidence being recorded; as might be expected the majority of these species are scarce migrants or rare vagrants in Somerset. The list of years includes records which fell outside the months of Atlas recording (that is, in March, August, September or October); in the case of those where the English name is in italics all records were in those months. Full details of these records can be found in the relevant years' *Somerset Birds*.

Egyptian Goose	*Alopochen aegyptiaca*	2007/08/09/10/11/12
Ruddy Shelduck	*Tadorna ferruginea*	2008 [Of doubtful origin.]
Lesser Scaup	*Aythya affinis*	2007/08/10/11
Green-winged Teal	*Anas carolinensis*	2009/10/11
Blue-winged Teal	*Anas discors*	2012
Eider	*Somateria mollissima*	2008/09/10/11
Cory's Shearwater	*Calonectris borealis*	2008
Sooty Shearwater	*Puffinus griseus*	2011/12
Balearic Shearwater	*Puffinus mauretanicus*	2008/10/11
Leach's Petrel	*Oceanodroma leucorhoa*	2008/09/10/11
Night-heron	*Nycticorax nycticorax*	2011
Squacco Heron	*Ardeola ralloides*	2008/11
Purple Heron	*Ardea purpurea*	2008/09/10
Black Stork	*Ciconia nigra*	2010/11
Honey-buzzard	*Pernis apivorus*	2008/10/11
Black Kite	*Milvus migrans*	2008/09
Pallid Harrier	*Circus macrourus*	2011
Montagu's Harrier	*Circus pygargus*	2009
Osprey	*Pandion haliaetus*	2008/09/10/11/12
Red-footed Falcon	*Falco vespertinus*	2008/11/12
Corncrake	*Crex crex*	2009
Stone-curlew	*Burhinus oedicnemus*	2010
Dotterel	*Charadrius morinellus*	2009/10
Whimbrel	*Numenius phaeopus*	2008/09/10/11/12
Curlew Sandpiper	*Calidris ferruginea*	2008/09/10/11/12
Temminck's Stint	*Calidris temminckii*	2012
Baird's Sandpiper	*Calidris bairdii*	2008
Little Stint	*Calidris minuta*	2007/08/09/10/11
White-rumped Sandpiper	*Calidris fuscicollis*	2007
Pectoral Sandpiper	*Calidris melanotos*	2008/09/10/11
Grey Phalarope	*Phalaropus fulicarius*	2007/08/09/10/11
Spotted Sandpiper	*Actitis macularius*	2010
Lesser Yellowlegs	*Tringa flavipes*	2011
Wood Sandpiper	*Tringa glareola*	2008/09/10/11/12
Long-billed Dowitcher	*Limnodromus scolopaceus*	2011/12

Great Snipe	*Gallinago media*	2012
Little Tern	*Sternula albifrons*	2008/09/10/11/12
Gull-billed Tern	*Gelochelidon nilotica*	2011
Whiskered Tern	*Chlidonias hybrida*	2008
Black Tern	*Chlidonias niger*	2008/09/10/11/12
Sandwich Tern	*Sterna sandvicensis*	2008/09/10/11/12
Roseate Tern	*Sterna dougallii*	2008
Arctic Tern	*Sterna paradisaea*	2007/08/09/10/11/12
Sabine's Gull	*Xema sabini*	2010/11
Bonaparte's Gull	*Chroicocephalus philadelphia*	2008/11/12
Franklin's Gull	*Larus pipixcan*	2008
Ring-billed Gull	*Larus delawarensis*	2007/08/09
Ring-necked Parakeet	*Psittacula krameri*	2009/10/11/12 [Of doubtful origin.]
Alpine Swift	*Apus melba*	2009/11
Bee-eater	*Merops apiaster*	2008/10/11
Hoopoe	*Upupa epops*	2008/09/10/11/12
Wryneck	*Jynx torquilla*	2008/09/10/11
Golden Oriole	*Oriolus oriolus*	2009/10/11/12
Red-backed Shrike	*Lanius collurio*	2008/09/10
Woodchat Shrike	*Lanius senator*	2008/09/10
Hooded Crow	*Corvus cornix*	2008/11
Woodlark	*Lullula arborea*	2007/08/10/12
Iberian Chiffchaff	*Phylloscopus ibericus*	2012
Barred Warbler	*Sylvia nisoria*	2008
Aquatic Warbler	*Acrocephalus paludicola*	2010
Marsh Warbler	*Acrocephalus palustris*	2009
Great Reed Warbler	*Acrocephalus arundinaceus*	2011
Rose-coloured Starling	*Pastor roseus*	2008
Richard's Pipit	*Anthus richardi*	2008
Tawny Pipit	*Anthus campestris*	2011
Twite	*Linaria flavirostris*	2010
Serin	*Serinus serinus*	2008
Dark-eyed Junco	*Junco hyemalis*	2008

List of observers

Special thanks are extended to the following people, who all volunteered to act as 'Collectors', performing and coordinating fieldwork within one or more 10-km squares, and providing descriptions of their areas used in the 'Somerset and its habitats' section. This Atlas would be the poorer without their considerable efforts.

David Ballance, Dick Best, Richard Bland (Avon Atlas Coordinator), Roger Butcher, Keith Davies, Roger Dickey, Roger Fox, Rob Grimmond, Andy Grinter, Ken Hall, John Hansford, Brian Hill, Paul Madgett, Nigel Milbourne, Stephen Moss, Tony Parsons, Martin Sage, Nigel Smith, Geoff Suter, Julian Thomas, Eve Tigwell, and Barrie Widden.

A

Sheila Ablitt, John Adams, Sean Adams, Tracy Adams, John & Penny Adie, David Agombar, Ginny Ailing, Avriel Allen, Jamie Allen, Michael Allen, A L Allsop, P Allwright, G P Anderson, Kevin Anderson, Susan Anderson, Christopher Andrews, John Arnfield, Janet Atkinson, John Austin, Chris Avanti, M I Avery.

B

Clare Backman, David Bagott, Louise Bailey, Mike Bailey, S & M Bainbridge, Chris Ball, John Ball, Melinda Anne Ball, David Ballance, Dawn Balmer, Nigel Banks, Jeremy Barker, S R J Barker, Henry Barlow, P Barlow, Janet Barnes, Neil Barrett, Jennifer Batten, Mr & Mrs D. Bawden, V R Beaney, Archibald Beattie, Richard Belson, Paul Benham, Bruce Bennett, Jackie Bennett, Val Bentley, Dick Best, John Best, Martin Bevan, Michael Bickerton, Robert Billingsley, Alastair Binham, Richard Birch, Samantha Birch, Gavin Bird, Steven Bird, Birdguides, John Birkett, Liz Biron, A D Blackmore, Richard Bland, D W Bodley, Margaret Bodley, Chris Bollen, P Boobyer, Helen Booker, Jackie Bosley, Coral Botteley, Carl Bovis, Nigel Bowie, Paul Bowyer, D Boyce, Jane Brookhouse, David Brabban, Iain Bray, Peter Bright, C A Bringloe, Dru Brooke-Taylor, Charles Brown, F E Brown, Martin Brown, Stephanie Brown, Brue Monitoring Group, Mary Brunning, BTO Ringers, Neil Buchanan, Frances Buckel, David Buckingham, N Burgum, Craig Burrows, Ken Bussell, Roger Butcher, N J Buxton.

C

Mike Caiden, Chris Caldwell, Peter Cameron, Andrew Camp, Geoff Campbell, Guy Campbell, Susan Caola, Steven Carey, V Carnell, Brett Carter, Brian Carter, Helena Carter, Jimmy Carter, Trevor Carter, Nigel Case, P E Castle, Gordon Caw, Jean Cawthorne, Rob Chace, Alan Chambers, Peter Chapman, R A Chapman, Rob Chapman, Sandra Chapman, Christopher Chappell, T M Cheek, John Chidgey, Dave Chown, Frank Clark, Jon Clark, Peter Clark, Christopher Clarke, John Clements, Maurice Clements, Aaron Clements-Partridge, Andrew Cobley, Joe Cockram, Suzie Coe, Celia Cole, Phillip & Lucinda Colebatch, Hugh Collings, Peter Conachie, John Connolly, Henry Cook, Paul Cook, Andrew Cooper, Michael Cooper, Nigel Cooper, Philip Cooper, Carol Cottle, Nigel Cottle, R Cox, Simon Cox, Helen Crabtree, Nicholas Crabtree, Brian Cracknell, Ann Crawford, Richard Crawford, Nigel Crocker, Robert Crompton, A L Crossman, Neil Croton, Andrew Cudmore, David Culverhouse, Jane Cumming, Stuart Cumming, Michael Curry, Rob Curtis.

D

Chris Dale, Mike Dannatt, C M Dare, Lee Dark, Anne Davage, Stuart Davey, Keith Davies, Steve Davies, Steven Davies, Bea Davis, Tim Davis, Sarah Day, Andrew De Mora, Rod Dean, John Dellow, Jill Denham, Bob Dennison, Matthew Derrington, R H Devitt, Devon Bird Watching & Preservation Society, Roger Dickey, Brenda Dickson, Carol Dimmock, Tom Dingwall, Clare Diprose, Paul Douch, Robert Doughty, Graeme Down, John Down, Ian Draycott, Ed Drewitt, Peter Driver, Jane Druett, Nicola Duckworth, Barry Dunn, P. Durbin.

E

Ray Eades, Alun Edwards, Eirwen Edwards, Keith Edwards, Maureen Edwards, D R Eele, Andrew Ellard, Greg Elliott-Moustache, Brian Ellis, Ian Ellis, Louise Ellis, Paul Ellis, I M Elphick, Kevin Elsmore, Carol Embury, Hugh Evans, Bryn Evans, Jessica Evans, Michael Evans, Alison Everett, James Evry.

F

Malcolm Fairley, the late Mark Farmer, Paul Fawcett, Roy Feltham, Jonathan Fenton, Robin Fenton, D M Ferguson, Roger Ferguson, Maria Fernandes, Sue Ferris, Matthew Field, John Fish, Rosie Fitzgerald, Sheila Flenk, Gillian Flinn, Phil Flynn, Jennifer Ford, T D Ford, Sam Forest, Roger Fox, John Franklin, Christopher Furley.

G

Adam Gale, Neil Galton, Game & Wildlife Conservation Trust, N. Garnsworthy, John Gascoyne, Lady Elizabeth Gass, Rodney Gayer, David Gayton, Robert Gaze, Brian Gibbs, Maureen Gibson, Trevor Gibson-Poole, Derek Gilby, Jonathan Gilder, Chris Gladman, Ron Gleadle, Colin Goatcher, Phillip Goble, Faye Goldsmith, Oriole Goldsmith, Jacqui Goodey, Di Gorringe, S J Gough, Clio Graham, Gabriel Grant, Kevin Grant, Nick Gray, Martin Greene, Colin Greenfield, Ron Greenwood, Sheila Gregory, Chris Griffin, Robin Griffiths, Rob Grimmond, Andy Grinter, William Grant, Bill Gulliford, Chris Gunn, Roger Gurowich, Anthony Gutteridge.

H

Peter Hack, Graham Hall, Ken Hall, Rosamund Hall, R M Halliwell, Dr D.A. Harbour, Roger Halsey, Sheelagh Halsey, Christopher Hancock, Kiff Hancock, Peter Hancocks, Deborah Hanlon, John Hansford, Richard Harbird, Toria Hare, Andrew Harris, Duncan Harris, Kevin Harris, Roger Harris, Sophie Harrison, Robin Hart, Scott Harwood, Richard Hastings, Alison Hawkins, Clive Hawkins, Victoria Hawtin, John Hawtree, Boyd Hay, Margaret Hayter, Jeff Hazell, Sue Healey, Richard Hearn, Dave Helliar, Martin Henderson, Jane Herbert, Russ Heselden, Nigel Hester, Rupert Higgins, Stephen Higgs, Brian Hill, Pamela Hill, Robert Hill, Stuart Hill, Tim Hinder, Ben Hoare, Tim Hodge, Alan Hold, Chris Holdsworth, the late Stuart Holdsworth, Jeff Holmes, Philip Holyday, Nick Hook, Gordon Hopkins, W D Hopkins, Daniel Horsey-Elson, Christine Horsley, Tim Hounsome, Alan Hubbard, James Hudson, Patricia Humphrey, Richard Humphreys, D J Humphries, Belinda Hunter, Gaz Hutchinson, Adrian Huxley, Colin Hyde.

I

Christopher Iles.

J

Kenneth Jarratt, J E Jarvis, Kevin Jarvis, M Jeeves, Paul Jennings, Trevor Jennings, Mike Jewell, Christine Johnson, Mike Johnson, Harold Johnstone, Glenn Jones, Helen Jones, John Jones, Rosy Jones, Steve Jones, Tim Jones.

K

Peter Kauth, Ged Keele, Roy Kelly, Robert Kelsh, Kelly Kelson, David Kennett, Lynne Kett, David King, Paul King, Wilfred King, Melvyn Kirby, G R Kirk, Stephen Kitchen, David Knight, Rex Knight.

L

Penny Ladd, Mrs G. Lamble, P D Latham, John Laws, Kenneth Lee, John Leece, Simon Leech, Jonathon Lees, J Legg, Diana Leighton, Colin Lever, Robin Levien, Gareth Lewis, J C Lidgate, Peter Lineham, Will Lishman, Lorraine Little, David Lloyd, Nicole Lloyd-Jones, J M Lock, George Lodge, Paul Lott, Ian Loudon, M A Lowe, Roger Lucken, Hugh Luttrell, Clare Lyddon, The Earl & Countess of Lytton.

M

Christine McDonald, Kevin McGowan, Graeme McLaren, Jon McLeod, Ben Macdonald, Matthew Macfadyen, R N Macklin, Paul Madgett, Gary Manning, Trevor Mansfield, Robert Marchant, Philip Marlow, Nick Marriner, Eileen Marsh, Mark Marsh, H Marshall, John Marshall, Stephen Marshall, John Martin, Donald Mash, Paul Masters, Cyril Matthews, Anthony Meads, Gina Mear, Andy Mears, Simon Metcalfe, Nigel Milbourne, Andrew Millar, Alastair Miller, David Miller, Doug Miller, Barrie Mills, Jill Mills, John Milner, Charles Minall, Brian Mitchell, Lindy Mitchell, Paul Montgomery, Karen Moore, Sally Morgan, Colin Morris, Robin Morris, Terry Morrissey, Robert Moss, Stephen Moss, Catherine Mowat, C M Mulholland, D A Murdoch, Susan Murphy, Karen Murray, Roger Musgrove, Steven Musgrove, Steve Mynard.

N

Alice Naish, C J Newman, David & Julia Newman, Errol Newman, S P Newman, Peter Newmark, Lesley Nickell, Marion Nieuwenhuizen, Tom Noall, Alison Norris, David Northover, Bruce Nottrodt.

O

Tim O'Rourke, John Oakley, Darren Oakley-Martin, Tara Okon, J C C Oliver, Sue Oliver, Rupert Ormerod, Duncan Orr-Ewing, Eric Osbaldeston, Alan Osborne, J Osborne, Barrie Ottery, Edric Ovens, Doreen Overy, Martin Overy, Pat Owen.

P

Harry Paget-Wilkes, Andrew Palmer, Eric Palmer, N Panayides, Andrew Parker, S J Parker, David Parkin, Paul Parmenter, Tony Parsons, Kath Patrick, Roger Peart, Linda Pemble, David Perriman, Anthony Perry, Jacky Pett, Christine Phelps, Annette Phillips, Margaret Phillips, N J Phillips, Nigel Phillips, Roy Phillips, the late Lou Pickersgill, Michael Pittaway, Roger Poland, Martin Polley, Vic Polley, Mark Ponsford, Geoffrey Pople, Christopher Porter, John Porter, Tony Powell, J Prideaux, John Prince, Elizabeth Prior, Richard Prior, David Pritchard, Brian Prudden, Andrew Pugsley, John Pullen, Maxine Putnam.

Q

William Quantrill, Charles Quinn.

R

Douglas Radford, Dr Philip Radford, Ian Ralphs, D J Ramsden, Graham Rankin, Tom Raven, Neil Rawlings, Paul Reddish, David Renham, Pamela Reynolds, Alex Rhodes, James Riall, M W Richards, C J Richardson, Mary Richardson, Les Rickman, Trevor Riddle, Michael Ridgard, Tim Ridgers-Steer, M J Ridley, John Rivoire, Arwel Roberts, Julian Roberts, Brian Roberts-Wray, James Robinson, Peter Robinson, Rosina Robinson, Steven Robinson, Stuart & Janet Robinson, Sarah Rodger, A S Rosney, Chris Ross, Jim Rosser, Nick Rossiter, Elspeth Rowe, June Roy, Jonathan Ruscoe, Colin Ryall, Kevin Rylands, Alison Rymell.

S

Michael Saffery, Colin Sage, Martin Sage, Alan Salter, Nick Salter, Shelley Saltman, Colin Sampson, M G Sampson, J R Samuel, S P Satterthwaite, E L Saunders, Clive Sawyer, Kevin Sayer, James Scott, John Sealey, Paul Seligman, Gillian Service, Paul Seymour, Mrs M Shapland, Jill Sharland, Alasdair Shaw, Ed Shephard, Hugh Shepherd, Robin Shrubsole, Mike Shurmer, Stephen Shutt, Peter Sim, Karen Sims, Beryl Simmonds, Alick Simmons, Jonathan Simons, Dennis Simpkin, John Simpson, Karen Sims, Andrew Slade, Brian Slade, Michael Smart, Ed Smith, Marcus Smith, Michael Smith, Nigel Smith, P A Smith, Rosalind Smith, Tim Smith, Tony Smith, Wilfred L Smith, Zoe Smith, Anne-marie Smout, C P Sperring, Henry Squire, John Squire, Graham Stacey, I A Stachnicki, D E Stainer, Andrew Stanbury, Frank Stanford, Lesley Staves, Mark Steer, C Stefanino, Liz Stephens, Rodney Stephens, Ann Sterry, Alastair Stevenson, D J Stevenson, Dave Stoddard, Gavin Stoddart, G W Stone, T J Stowe, David Street, Peter Stronach, Bede Strong, Paul Stubbs, Ray Summers, G Suter, M P Sutherland, Robert Swift.

List of observers, continued

T

Angela Talintyre, A Taylor, Bruce Taylor, Howard Taylor, Richard Taylor, Simon Taylor, John Tayton, William Theed, R M Thewlis, Mark Thole, Julian Thomas, Paul Thomas, David Thompson, Max Thompson, P Thompson, Kirsty Thorne, Rebecca Thorne, Simon Tidswell, Eve Tigwell, A B Tomczynski, David Tomlinson, Mike Toms, Mike Tout, John Towers, James Towill, Chris Townend, Paul Treen, Charles Trollope, Rona Troman, Mike Trubridge, Robin Trundle, David Tucker, Christopher Tudge, Ian Turnell, Kate Turner, Malcolm Turner, R Turner, Ruth Turner, Mike Turton, Sash Tusa, Gordon Twinberrow.

U

Jo Unsworth, Geoff Upton, Bill Urwin.

V

James Vale, Adam Vasey, Margaret Vaughan, the late Dr Richard Vaughan, Tim Vaughan, Nicola Venning, Jenny Vickers, Graham Vine.

W

Christopher Walford, Andrew Walker, David Wall, Nick Wall, Julia Ward, Kevin Waterfall, Michael Watson, Nigel Watson, Peter Watson, Ashley Watts, Denise Wawman, Gayle Webb, John Webber, Michael Webster, Dr Chris Weedon, D J Wedd, Anne Wheatcroft, Peter Whitcomb, Tony Whitcombe, Jon White, Richard White, Janet Whitfield, Barrie Widden, Alan Williams, Robert Williams, Wayne Williams, Giles Wilson, Ian Wilson, Peter Wilson, Vivien Wilson, Mark Wingrove, Bob Winn, John Winter, Malcolm Wood, Heather Woodland, A E L Woods, Paul Wren, Tara Wright.

Y

Allison Yellowley, S F Young.

> **Many thanks to all who contributed, and apologies for any errors in or omissions from this list.**

330

Bibliography

This is a complete list of publications used in the preparation of the text of this book and in many cases cited within the relevant species accounts.

References and abbreviations used for publications cited frequently in the text are given on page 34.

Anderson, K., Clarke, S., and Lucken, R. (2013). Nesting behaviour of the first breeding Great White Egrets in Britain. *Brit. Birds* 106: 258–263.

Archer, R. (2008). *Mendip Hills AONB Farmland Birds Survey 2007.* Exeter. RSPB.

Archer, R. (2013). Farewell to the silver meadows? The story of breeding waders on the Somerset Levels. *British Wildlife* Dec 2013: 77–84.

Archer, R. and Forecast, P. (2001). *Somerset Coastal Levels Farmland Bird Survey 2000.* Exeter. RSPB.

Avon Ornithological Group (2010). *Avon Bird Report 2009.* Bristol.

Avon Ornithological Group (2012). *Avon Bird Report 2011.* Bristol.

Baillie, S.R. *et al.* (2010). *Breeding Birds in the Wider Countryside; their conservation status 2009.* Thetford. BTO.

Baillie, S.R. *et al.* (2012). *BirdTrends 2011.* BTO Research Report 609. Thetford. BTO.

Ballance, D.K. (2002). Somerset heronries. *SB 2001*: 132–145.

Ballance, D.K. (2004). *A Bibliography of Somerset Ornithology.* Minehead. Author.

Ballance, D.K. (2006). *A History of the Birds of Somerset.* Penryn. Isabelline Books.

Ballance, D.K. and Gibbs, B.D. (2003). *The Birds of Exmoor and the Quantocks.* Penryn. Isabelline Books.

Balmer, D., Gillings, S., Caffrey, B., Swann, R., Downie, I., and Fuller, R. (2013). *Bird Atlas 2007–11. The Breeding and Wintering Birds of Britain and Ireland.* Thetford. BTO Books.

Banks, A.N., Coombes, R.H., and Crick, H.Q.P. (2003). *The Peregrine Falcon Breeding Population of the U.K. and Isle of Man in 2002.* Thetford. BTO.

Best, J.R. (2013). Avocets breeding at Steart 2012: a 'first' for the county. *SB 2012*: 126.

Blaker, G.B. (1934). *The Barn Owl in England and Wales.* London. RSPB.

Bland, R.L. and Dadds, M. (2012). *Avon Atlas 2007–11.* Bristol. BOC and BNS.

Bland, R.L. and Tully, J. (1992). *Atlas of Breeding Birds in Avon, 1988–91.* Bristol. Bristol Ornithological Club (BOC) and Bristol Naturalists' Society (BNS).

Blathwayt, The Revd F.L. (1906). "Birds" in *VCH Somerset* Vol. I: 140–162.

Booker, H. (2001). *Quantock Hills Moorland Breeding Bird Survey 2000.* Exeter. RSPB.

Booker, H. (2007). *Quantock Hills Heathland Breeding Bird Survey 2006.* Exeter. Quantock Hills AONB Service, National Trust and Somerset Ornithological Society.

Booker, H. (2013). Quantock Hills Heathland Breeding Bird Survey 2012. *SB 2012*: 124–125.

Both, C., Bouwhuis, S., Lessells, C.M., and Visser, M.E. (2006). Climate change and population declines in a long-distance migratory bird. *Nature* 441: 81–83.

Boyce, D.C. (2012). *A Survey of Waders and Other Birds on Mires in Exmoor National Park, 2011–2012.* Exeter. RSPB.

Brenchley, A., Gibbs, G., Pritchard, R., and Spence, I.M. (2013). *The Breeding Birds of North Wales/Adar Nythu Gogledd Cymru.* Liverpool. Liverpool University Press.

British Ornithologists' Union (2013). The British List: a checklist of birds of Britain. 8th edition. *Ibis* 155: 635–676.

Brown, A. and Grice, P. (2005). *Birds in England.* London. T. & A.D. Poyser for Natural England.

Burton, N.H.K. *et al.* (2003). *Low-tide Distributions of Waterbirds on the Severn Estuary SPA: WeBS Low Tide Counts and a Historical Analysis.* Thetford. BTO.

Chown, D.J. (1997). *Avalon Marshes Breeding Bird Survey 1996.* Exeter. RSPB (SW).

Chown, D.J. (2003). *Night-time Use of the Somerset Levels and Moors Floodplain by Waterfowl: Final Report, Winters 2001/02 and 2002/03.* Taunton. English Nature.

Chown, D.J. and Robins, M. (1994). *Exmoor Moorland Bird Survey 1992/93.* Exeter. RSPB.

Cohen, E. (1944). *BTO/EGI Rook Investigation: Draft Report.* Oxford. Unpublished.

Conway, G., Wootton, S., Henderson, I., Langston, R., Drewitt, A., and Currie, F. (2007). Status and distribution of European Nightjars *Caprimulgus europaeus* in the UK in 2004. *Bird Study* 54: 98–111.

Davies, S. and Jarman, R. (1978). *Exmoor Moorland Ornithological Survey 1978.* Exeter and Broomfield. RSPB and Somerset Trust for Nature Conservation.

Davis, A.H. and Vinicombe, K.E. (2011). The probable breeding of Ferruginous Ducks in Avon. *Brit. Birds* 104: 77–83.

Davis, H.H. (1948). *A Revised List of the Birds of the Bristol District. Proc. Bristol Naturalists' Soc.* 4th Series XXVII, Part IV: 225–268; also as separate.

[The Recording Area of BNS extended then over Mendip as far as Cheddar Reservoir.]

Davis, T. and Jones, T. (2007). *The Birds of Lundy.* Berrynarbor. Harpers Mill Publishing for Devon Bird Watching and Preservation Society and Lundy Field Society.

Easterbrook, T. (ed.) (2013). *Birds of the Heart of England.* Liverpool. Liverpool University Press.

D'Urban, W.S.M. and Mathew, the Revd M.A. (1892). *The Birds of Devon.* London. Porter. [The 2nd ed., of 1895, differs only by the addition of a *Supplement*, which is also found separately. Despite the title, many Somerset records were included.]

Eltringham, S.K. (1963). The British population of the Mute Swan. *Bird Study* 10, No. 1: 10–28.

Eltringham, S.K. and Boyd, H. (1960). The Shelduck population in the Bridgwater Bay area. *Wildfowl Trust AR 1958/59:* 107–117.

Eltringham, S.K. and Boyd, H. (1963). The moult migration of the Shelduck to Bridgwater Bay, Somerset. *Brit. Birds* 56: 433–444.

Fraser, P.A. (2013a). Report on scarce migrant birds in Britain in 2004-2007. Part 1: non-passerines. *Brit. Birds* 106: 368–404.

Fraser, P.A. (2013b). Report on scarce migrant birds in Britain in 2004-2007. Part 2: passerines. *Brit. Birds* 106: 448–476.

Freeman, R. *et al.* (2013). Tracking the migration and foraging dynamics of Lundy's Manx Shearwaters. *Devon Birds* 66, No. 2: 18–28.

Geary, S. (2002). *Exmoor Moorland Breeding Bird Survey 1992.* Exeter. RSPB.

Gibbons, D.W., Reid, J.B., and Chapman, R.A. 1993. *The New Atlas of Breeding Birds in Britain and Ireland 1988–1991.* London. T. & A.D. Poyser.

Gibson, M. (2009). *A Breeding Bird Survey of Shapwick Heath SSSI, Westhay Heath and Westhay Moor with Street Heath and Meare Heath.* Taunton. Natural England.

Gladman, C.J. (2004). *Mediterranean Gulls: Blue Anchor Bay, Somerset, with Chapel Cleeve and Old Cleeve.* Old Cleeve. Author.

Gribble, F.C. (1983). Nightjars in Britain and Ireland in 1981. *Bird Study* 30: 165–176.

Guilford, T., Freeman, R., and Maurice, L. (2009). Where the Lundy Shearwaters go. *AR Lundy FS 2009:* 73–75.

Hill, B.J. (2003). The Dartford Warbler in Somerset: an update. *SB 2002:* 152–153.

Hill, B.J. (2013). The Hawfinch in Somerset. *SB 2012:* 132–134.

Holdsworth, S.D. (2004). Swifts in Somerset, 1990–2002. *SB 2003:* 172–174.

Holling, M. *et al.* (2012). Rare breeding birds in the United Kingdom in 2010. *Brit. Birds* 105: 352–416.

Holling, M. *et al.* (2013). Rare breeding birds in the United Kingdom in 2011. *Brit. Birds* 106: 496–554.

Holloway, S. (1996). *The Historical Atlas of Breeding Birds in Great Britain and Ireland.* London. T. & A.D. Poyser.

Holt, C. (2013). The changing status of the Great White Egret in Great Britain. *Brit. Birds* 106: 246–257.

Holt, C.A. *et al.* (2012). *Waterbirds in the UK 2010/11: The Wetland Bird Survey.* Thetford. BTO/RSPB/JNCC.

Hudson, N. and British Birds Rarities Committee (2013). Report on rare birds in Great Britain in 2012. *Brit. Birds* 106: 570–641.

JNCC (2012). *Seabird Population Trends and Causes of Change: 2012 Report.* URL: http://jncc.defra.gov.uk/page-3201.

Kirk, G. and Phillips, J. (2013). *The Birds of Gloucestershire.* Liverpool. Liverpool University Press.

Lack, P. (comp.) 1986. *The Atlas of Wintering Birds in Britain and Ireland.* Calton. T. & A.D. Poyser.

Lawicki, L. (2014). The Great White Egret in Europe: population increase and range expansion since 1980. *Brit. Birds* 107: 8–25.

Leech, S.J. (2013). Breeding Swifts in Taunton: some preliminary observations. *SB 2012:* 127–131.

Lewis, S. (1955). *The Breeding Birds of Somerset and their Eggs.* Ilfracombe. Stockwell. Repr. in facsimile, 2002. Wateringbury. P. Blest.

Mathew, The Revd M.A. (1893). A revised list of the birds of Somerset. *Proc. Somersetshire Arch. & Nat. Hist. Soc.* XXXIX: 102–139.

Mead, C.J. (2000). *The State of the Nations' Birds.* Stowmarket. Whitter Books.

Mead, C.J. and Smith, K. (1982). *The Hertfordshire Breeding Atlas.* Tring. HBBA.

Morgan, G. (2012). The bird populations of Ramsey and Grassholm. *Brit. Birds* 105: 716–732.

Morris, A.J., Burges, D., Fuller, R.J., Evans, A.D., and Smith, K.W. (1994). The status and distribution of Nightjars *Caprimulgus europaeus* in Britain in 1992. *Bird Study* 41: 181–191.

Packer, J.J. and Knight, P. (1997). Colonisation of Somerset by the Dartford Warbler *Sylvia undata*. *SB 1996:* 126–129.

Palmer, E.M. and Ballance, D.K. (1968). *The Birds of Somerset.* London. Longmans.

Parsons, A.J. (1976a). The breeding birds of the parish of Crewkerne, 1975. *SB 1975:* 55–56, 60.

Parsons, A.J. (1976b).The 1975 Rookery Census. *SB 1975:* 57–58; Addenda and Corrigenda. *SB 1976:* 63–64.

Parsons, A.J. (1978). The Carrion Crow in the old county of Somerset. *SB 1977:* 76–81.

Parsons, A.J. (1999). The breeding birds of the parish of Crewkerne, 1998. *SB 1998:* 147–154.

Perrins, C.M. *et al.* (2012). A whole-island census of the Manx Shearwater *Puffinus puffinus* on Skomer Island in 2011. *Seabird* 25: 1–13.

Prytherch, R. (2013). The breeding biology of the Common Buzzard. *Brit. Birds* 106: 264–279.

Risely, K. *et al.* (2012). *The Breeding Bird Survey 2011.* BTO Research Report No. 624. Thetford. BTO.

Ross-Smith, V.H. *et al.* (2013). Population size, ecology and movements of gulls breeding on Flat Holm. *Birds in Wales* 10, No. 1: 7–21.

Round, P.D. (1978). *An Ornithological Survey of the Somerset Levels 1976–77.* Wessex Water Authority and RSPB.

Sangster, G. *et al.* (2013). Taxonomic recommendations for Western Palearctic birds: ninth report. *Ibis* 155: 898–907.

Sharrock, J.T.R. (comp.) (1976). *The Atlas of Breeding Birds in Britain and Ireland.* Berkhamstead. T. & A.D. Poyser.

Shawyer, C.R. (1987). *The Barn Owl in the British Isles: Its Past, Present and Future.* London. The Hawk Trust. [Somerset results in *Bird Notes* 5 (Autumn 1988): 10–11.]

Simms, E. (1985). *British Warblers.* London. Collins New Naturalist.

Smaldon, R. (2005). *The Birds of Dartmoor.* Penryn. Isabelline Books.

Smith, C. (1869). *The Birds of Somersetshire.* London. Van Voorst.

Smith, K.W. (2005). Has the reduction in nest-site competition from Starlings *Sturnus vulgaris* been a factor in the recent increase of Great Spotted Woodpecker *Dendrocopos major* numbers in Britain? *Bird Study* 52: 307–313.

Smith, K.W. and Smith, L. (2013). The effect of supplementary feeding in early spring on the breeding performance of the Great Spotted Woodpecker *Dendrocopos major. Bird Study* 60: 169–175.

Somerset Ornithological Society (1988). *Birds of Somerset.* Gloucester. Alan Sutton.

Spencer, R. *et al.* (1988). Rare breeding birds in the United Kingdom in 1985. *Brit. Birds* 81:99–125.

Sperring, C. (2013). The Community Barn Owl Project. *Somerset Wildlife News* Winter 2013: 24–25.

Stanbury, A., Dark, L., Richardson, R., and Tayton, J. (2008). *Exmoor Moorland Breeding Bird Survey 2008.* Exeter. RSPB.

Street, S. (1992). *Quantock Hills Moorland Bird Survey 1992.* Taunton. Somerset County Council.

Townend, C. (2010). *Exmoor Farmland Bird Survey 2010.* Exeter and Dulverton. RSPB and Exmoor National Park Authority.

Thomas, J. (2012). Two more new breeding species for Somerset. *The Bittern* 3: 1–3.

Trump, D. and Ovenden, G. (1999). *Nocturnal Movements of Wintering Wildfowl and Waders on the Somerset Levels and Moors January to March 1999.* Farming and Rural Conservation Agency (SW).

Tucker, B.W. (1916). *A List of the Wild Birds Found in the Parish of Chewton Mendip, Somerset.* Paulton. Author. Repr. with additions in *AR Wells Nat. Hist. & Arch. Soc. 1918*: 36–52; *1923*: 39–45 and 45–50; *1924*: 31–38.

Tucker, B.W. (1929, 1930). The Heron (*Ardea cinerea*) in Somerset. *Proc. Somersetshire Arch. & Nat. Hist. Soc.* LXXV: 61–90; LXXVI: 63–84.

Tucker, B.W. (1935, 1936). The rookeries of Somerset. *Proc. Somersetshire Arch. & Nat. Hist. Soc.* LXXXI: 149–240; Addenda in LXXXII: 217.

Tully, J. (1993). Population and distribution of winter feeding flocks of Feral Pigeons in the City of Bristol. *Bristol Ornithology* 22: 16–30.

Turner, J.W. (1912). *Notes on Somerset Birds from 1865 to 1912.* Taunton. Ornithological Section of S.A.N.H.S. [Forms the *First Report* of the Section. Deals largely with West Somerset.]

Vaughan, M. and Vaughan, R. (2007). Ten years in a Porlock garden. *SB 2006*: 157–160.

Weaver, D.J. and Chown, D.J. (1983). *Somerset Moors Breeding Birds Survey 1983.* Sandy. RSPB.

Wernham, C., Toms, M., Marchant, J., Clark, J., Siriwardena, G., and Baillie, S. (2002). *The Migration Atlas: Movements of the Birds of Britain and Ireland.* London. T. & A.D. Poyser for BTO.

White, J., Baker, P., and Baker, R. (1987). *A Study of Quantock Streams.* The Friends of Quantock.

White, J. (2012). Nestbox Survey Report, 2011. *Exmoor Naturalist* 38: 34–37.

White, S.J., McCarthy, B., and Jones, M. (eds.) (2008). *The Birds of Lancashire and North Merseyside.* Southport. Hobby Publications for Lancashire and Cheshire Fauna Soc.

Williams, J. (1989). Letter on results of Barn Owl surveys by Shawyer 1987 and 1988 (*v. sup.*). *Bird Notes* 6 (Spring 1989): 7.

Wilson, A.M., Vickery, J.A., and Browne, S.J. (2001). Numbers and distribution of Lapwings *Vanellus vanellus* breeding in England & Wales in 1998. *Bird Study* 48: 2–17.

Wotton, S., Conway, G., Eaton, M., Henderson, I., and Grice, P. (2009). The status of the Dartford Warbler in the UK and the Channel Islands in 2006. *Brit. Birds* 102: 230–246.

Yapp, W.B. 1962. *Birds and Woods.* London. OUP.

Index